Further Studies for Social Care

Sylvia Aslangul ▪ Carolyn Meggitt ▪

SECOND EDITION

Edexcel
Success through qualifications

Keep in Library

Hodder & Stoughton

A MEMBER OF THE HODDER HEADLINE GROUP

Orders: please contact Bookpoint Ltd, 130 Milton Park, Abingdon, Oxon OX14 4SB. Telephone: (44) 01235 827720. Fax: (44) 01235 400454. Lines are open from 9.00 – 6.00, Monday to Saturday, with a 24 hour message answering service.

British Library Cataloguing in Publication Data

A catalogue record for this title is available from the British Library

ISBN 0 340 804246

First Published 1996

Impression number   10 9 8 7 6 5 4 3 2 1

Year   2007 2006 2005 2004 2003 2002

Cover photo from Photo Disc

Typeset by Wyvern 21 Ltd, Bristol

Printed in Great Britain for Hodder & Stoughton Educational, a division of Hodder Headline Plc, 338 Euston Road, London NW1 3BH by **Martins the Printers. Berwick-upon-Tweed.**

Contents

Acknowledgements

Photo Credits: page 100 Wellcome Photo Library; page 224 Wellcome Photo Library; page 264 Science Photo Library.

Extract from Community Care 2–8 August 2001 published by permission of the editor of Community Care; 'Report reveals growing role of pooled budgets' from Community Care 31 May – 6 June 2001 published by permission of the editor of Community Care; extract from Daily Telegraph 3/11/01 © Telegraph Group Limited (2001); 'Minder high on heroin killed baby' © Telegraph Group Limited (2001); 'Jailing Mums puts children at risk' © Observer (1999); 'Parents pain' by Helen Carter © Guardian (2001); 'Ageism: A national disgrace' by Clare Rayner published in the Patients Association journal © Clare Rayner; figure 3.4 courtesy of the Alzheimer's Disease Society; 'Step up to safety' poster reproduced with kind permission of the Department of Trade and Industry; fig 5.5 appears courtesy of Colin Wheeler

Jatinder Bhuhi for research into the needs of asylum seekers and refugees in chapter one.

Crown copyright material is reproduced with the permission of the Controller of HMSO and the Queen's Printer for Scotland.

Chapter 1

Social policy

This chapter relates to Unit 9 and covers the development of social policy and social care provision in Britain. Social policy and welfare provision is developed in response to the perceived needs and problems within a society. These perceptions and needs change over a period of time and are influenced by the social, economic, political and cultural context in which they exist.

This chapter describes:

- The factors affecting social policy in the twentieth century;
- Social policy and social care services today;
- The influences on the development of social policy in the twenty first century.

This unit links to Unit 1 and Unit 5, and while you are studying this chapter it would be useful to keep your main textbook for the course available as you will need to refer to it. This icon ◇ will act as a prompt to refer to *Vocational A Level in Health and Social Care* Thomson, H. *et al* (2000) Hodder and Stoughton.

This chapter covers some of the underpinning knowledge of NVQ level 3 in Early Years and Education.

Assessment

This unit will be assessed externally and the grade you achieve in this assessment will be your grade for the unit. The test paper will include stimulus response material, including basic statistical data such as demographic trends, morbidity or mortality rates. During the chapter you will be asked to complete activities to prepare you for the test.

 Word check

Demography

The study of populations, with particular reference to their size and structure, and how and why these change over time. Demographers study birth, death and marriage rates, patterns of migration and other important factors that affect population growth or decline such as climate, food supply and the availability of employment.

Morbidity rates

Information related to the nature and extent of illness in a population. Morbidity rates can be measured using hospital admission rates, sickness rates and self-reported illness rates.

Mortality rates

The number of deaths per 1000 of the population per year. These rates are often broken down to show differences by age, gender and social class.

In the White Paper (1998) 'Our Healthier Nation', morbidity and mortality rates were the basis for deciding on the national priorities for national and local Health Improvement Programmes (HImPs) These priorities included reducing the death rates from:

- cancer;
- coronary heart disease (CHD);
- accidents;
- suicides.

Health and social care policy was developed in order to achieve these priorities.

As we can see, social policy does not come out of a vacuum. A problem is identified, data is collected and used as evidence to show the extent of the problem, and then a strategy or action plan is developed.

Social policy

What does social policy mean? Social policy covers a range of service provision in Great Britain. Traditionally, five areas have been included in social policy:

- education;
- housing;
- income maintenance (either through benefits or earned income);
- health services;
- social services.

The key legislation affecting the development of the Welfare State is presented in tables in Chapter 5 of the main text book, and it would be useful to look at this now ◇.

Historical factors affecting social policy in the twentieth century

Social policy is dependent on a range of contextual factors. During the twentieth century a variety of historical events, such as wars, changes in legislation, changes in the organisation of work and the role of Britain in the global context, have all had an effect on social policy. Many of these changes were developments of earlier social changes that had occurred in the nineteenth century. We will look at some of these in this section.

Nineteenth-Century Social Policy

The Social Conditions of Nineteenth-Century Britain

During this century the causes of poverty were seen as the result of intemperance and idleness. With the development of factories and towns, poverty became a feature of both urban and rural areas. The development of the Welfare State was a gradual process. The Poor Law Commission of 1834 resulted in the Poor Law Amendment Act of the same year. This Act was based on the belief that people were poor largely through their own fault and that to provide help would only encourage idleness. The Poor Law stated that support would only be given in the workhouse. To receive this support, the family had to leave their home and work in the workhouse for low wages. Poor Law administrators took no account of factors such as large families, old age, irregular employment or low earnings. Various charitable organisations and churches also provided support.

The workhouse test or scheme of 'less eligibility' was imposed on all those seeking help. It attempted to distinguish between the deserving and the undeserving poor. The deserving poor were the sick, the disabled, the elderly and the unintentionally unemployed. The undeserving poor were the feckless, idle and intentionally unemployed. Only those without means were offered help. The workhouses were usually segregated and families were split up, with women and children in one workhouse and men in another. Workhouses were portrayed in the literature of the time, such as Charles Dickens' *Oliver Twist*, and their strict regime meant that people tried to avoid going into them.

Activity

1   Means testing is still done today. Find a copy of the booklet 'MG 1' and identify some examples.

2   Can you think how some groups in today's society could be seen as the deserving and undeserving poor. Look at the following list and think which category these groups would fall into:

• widows;

- teenage unmarried mothers;
- refugees and asylum seekers;
- unemployed school leavers.

The way in which society views these groups can be identified through their treatment

- in the media;
- in the benefit system.

As we have seen in this section, poverty was considered undesirable in the nineteenth century. But the poor were also seen as a threat to the social order. There had been riots against the amended Poor Law after 1834. In spite of the regime in the workhouse, the number of people in workhouses increased from 78,536 in 1838 to 197,179 in 1843 (Thompson E. (1968) *The Making of the English Working Class.* Penguin).

'Outdoor relief' still occurred in many areas as many communities did not want workhouses built in their areas, and by 1850 only 110,000 paupers out of a million were workhouse inmates, many of whom were the old and the sick who had nowhere else to go. Brendon (1994) suggests that the Poor Law Amendment Act succeeded as it brought down public expenditure from £7 million in 1834 to £4.5. million in 1844. It also brought a lasting fear of the workhouse and made poverty seem a disgrace. After the Act, as before it, poor people continued as best as they could, relying on the help of family and neighbourhood rather than on public services.

Activity

Local history groups in your area may have details of workhouses, orphanages and other buildings used to support people in the nineteenth century. Your local library may have a special local history section, or books about local conditions in your area. If you have time, it may be useful to look at these or to ask a member of the local historical society to give a talk to your group. Many libraries keep old maps of the area, which are another useful source of information.

Apart from workhouses other large buildings were developed in the latter part of the century. Charities built hospitals, residential homes (Dr Barnardo's) and hostels. These large institutions reflected the view that certain groups of people should be excluded from living in the community, such as those with mental health problems, learning and physical disabilities, and older people.

Developments in Social Policy in the Early Twentieth Century

The Liberal Government of 1905 laid some of the foundations for the post-1942 welfare state. Lloyd George (who was Chancellor of the Exchequer in 1908 and Prime Minister, 1916–1922) advocated social reforms which included:

- infant welfare clinics;
- school meals for children;
- medical examinations of children in elementary school;
- juvenile employment bureaux to help school leavers find suitable jobs;
- introduction of borstals and probation courts for young offenders;
- old age pensions to the over 70s paid in weekly payments from post offices;
- national insurance schemes against unemployment or sickness.

The main Liberal legislation and administration changes, 1908–1914

- Education Acts of 1907 and 1908;
- Children's Act, 1908;
- Old Age Pensions Act, 1908;
- Trade Boards from 1909 onwards;
- Labour Exchange Act, 1909;
- National Insurance Act, 1911.

These reforms were brought about through the influence of several factors including:

- an ideological belief in the need for reform on the part of the 'New Liberals' such as Churchill and Lloyd George;
- a political need to boost support for the Liberal party, following defeats in by-elections in 1908;
- the threat of the socialist reforms by the Labour Party gaining popular support if the Liberals failed to act.

We can see from the last example that pressures on policy makers can come from both ideological and practical influences.

The impact of the First World War

By 1914, the working class had more support from the state. Many more people were insured, and council housing and a hospital system were being developed. The First World War had stimulated a desire for national efficiency in two ways:

1 There was a concern to maximise output in the war industries. Factory Acts were suspended so that women and young people could work longer hours in factories.

2 There was a concern to preserve 'the national stock' by protecting the health of mothers and children (war officials had been concerned at the poor standard of health and fitness of recruits to the Boer War).

Local councils were encouraged to improve their services for mothers and babies by setting up clinics, home visitors, and hospital treatment and food for the needy. A Ministry of Reconstruction was set up in 1917, which brought together Poor Law provision, public health and education authorities, and insurance commissions. The Ministry focused on four key areas of welfare:

1 *Housing:* "Homes fit for heroes." The 1919 Housing Act authorised local councils to build as many houses as possible. New housing estates were built outside large towns. By 1939, one million new homes had been built by the public sector.

2 *Unemployment:* This was a major problem after the war. By 1921, two million people were out of work. Unemployment insurance was extended to everyone earning less than £5 a week, except for farm labourers, domestic servants and civil service employees. Means testing was still used to determine how much assistance should be given.

3 *Health:* More effective health care provision was developed.

4 *Education:* The Fisher Education Act of 1918 established the principle that all children and young people should have access to education.

During this time, although local government still played a major role in the implementation of social policies, there was more centralised control and new ministries and government departments began to develop. Pressure groups such as the trade unions, and professional groups, such as the British Medical Association (BMA) also exerted pressure on the Government.

 Activity

Look at the 4 key areas. Can you identify key initiatives that are being developed by the Labour government in 2001?

Comment

1 Housing: The need to build more affordable housing, especially for health and care workers is one of the key issues in the twenty-first century.

2 Unemployment: The New Deal initiative is a contemporary example.

3 Health: National Service Frameworks for Coronary Heart Disease and Mental Health.

4 Education: The discussion over loans and grants for university students.

We can see from the above examples that certain key areas are the concerns of government throughout the twentieth and twenty-first centuries. Factors affecting the development of these policies can be:

• economic: the need to reduce state spending;

- demographic changes: the increase in the numbers of people over 75 and a reduced birth rate;
- social: changes in family forms and expectations of certain life styles;
- ideological: ideas about who is responsible for providing support – the state or the individual and family members.

Voting rights

In 1918, the government passed the Representation of the People Act. This gave the vote to all men over 21 if they had been living in the same area for six months (peers, lunatics and criminals were excluded from voting). Women over 30 were also given the vote if they or their husbands owned or occupied any property or land. This meant that out of a total electorate of 21 million, 8.5 million women had the right to vote for the first time. In 1918, women could become MPs; in 1919 they could hold government posts; and in 1928, the right to vote was extended to all women over 21.

The changes affecting the position of women were brought about by a variety of factors:

- the influence of war, when many women worked in munitions factories and assisted the war effort;
- the influence of the Suffragette movement;
- the need to attract women as voters to support the government.

The impact of the Second World War

Just as the First World War had brought about changes in attitudes to the working class and to women, so, too, did the Second World War. Many women contributed to the war effort at home and in the forces. Evacuation of children from the cities into the country brought different groups of people into contact for the first time, and the deprivation of poor urban families could not be ignored. There was a fear that some of the problems experienced after the First World War would occur again, especially with the large-scale bombing of cities that led to a shortage of housing.

The Beveridge Report

In 1941, the government ordered a special commission of inquiry to undertake a survey of the existing national scheme of social insurance to make recommendations for future policy. The chair of the commission was Sir William Beveridge. In 1942, the recommendations were set out in the Beveridge Report. These recommendations proposed measures to deal with the five 'giants' on the road to reconstruction and social progress.

1 *Want:* A complete system of social insurance for all citizens would be set up. In return, if they were sick, unemployed or retired they would receive flat-rate benefits – means testing would be abolished.

2 *Disease:* A New National Health service would be established, free at the point of delivery.

3 *Squalor:* More and better housing would be developed.

4 *Ignorance:* More and better schools, with free secondary education for all up to the age of 15 (to be extended to 16 at a later date).

5 *Idleness*: Unemployment would be reduced by tighter government control of trade and industry.

These recommendations formed the basis for many reforms following the end of the war in 1945. Detailed discussion of these changes are to be found in Chapter 5 of the main text book.

Civil Rights and Civil Liberties

Since the 1970s, the concept of citizenship has had an important influence on social policy in the UK:

- *civil rights* to individual freedom, to free speech and thought, the right to own property and the right to justice;
- *political rights* to vote and to participate in the democratic process;
- *social rights* to economic welfare and security, including the right to education, work and health care.

The early civil rights movements in the USA in the 1960s were concerned with the rights of black Americans and of women, and resulted in Equal Opportunities Legislation outlawing discrimination based on gender, race and age. The Women's Movement of the 1970s in the UK also resulted in legislation, including the Equal Pay Act (1970) and the Sex Discrimination Act (1975). Various Race Relations Acts were passed (1965, 1968, 1976) and the 1976 Act has recently been amended (2000). Other legislation covering the rights of certain groups includes the Disability Discrimination Act and the Human Rights Act, which are covered in the main text book.

Feminism and social policy

The suffragette movement in the early part of the twentieth century was a factor in widening the franchise to all women in 1928. However, women have not benefited from recent welfare development because of their traditional roles as wives and mothers.

1 Child care. Britain is still behind the rest of Europe in relation to the provision of child care. Table 1.1 shows the number of day care places available for children. What level of provision is provided by the state?

2 The 1990 NHS and Community Care Act. Under this Act many large institutions were closed down and people with mental health problems, learning and physical disabilities were to be cared for in the community. Women in the family were seen as their natural carers. Changes in surgery meant that people stayed in hospital for shorter periods and were cared for at home, again by women. As the population becomes increasingly older, women will become the main carers, either unpaid or as low paid workers.

3 Work. Many women would like to return to work once they have had children but there is a lack of child care at an affordable level. Single mothers are being encouraged to return to work to reduce the state benefits they are receiving, through such initiatives as the New Deal, but many women would prefer to stay at home with their children.

Table 1.1   Day care provided for children under the age of 8 (under the age of 12 in N. Ireland)

England, Wales & Northern Ireland					Thousands
	1987	1992	1997	1998	1999
Day nurseries					
Local authority provided[1]	29	24	20	19	16
Registered	32	98	184	216	235
Non-registered[2]	1	1	2	1	12
All day nursery places	62	123	206	236	263
Childminders					
Local authority provided[1]	2	2	4	4	9
Other registered	159	275	398	403	360
All childminder places	161	277	402	407	369
Playgroups					
Local authority provided	4	2	2	2	3
Registered	434	450	424	423	383
Non-registered[1]	7	3	3	1	3
All playgroup places	445	455	429	426	389
Out of school clubs[2]	–	–	–	97	119

1 England and Wales only.
2 England only.
Source: Social Trends 2001, HMSO

 Activity

Look at Figure 1.1 and answer the following questions.

1 What method do you think was used for obtaining these responses?

2 Why do you think you need to be careful when reading the results and the reasons given by women for not working?

Great Britain

Percentages

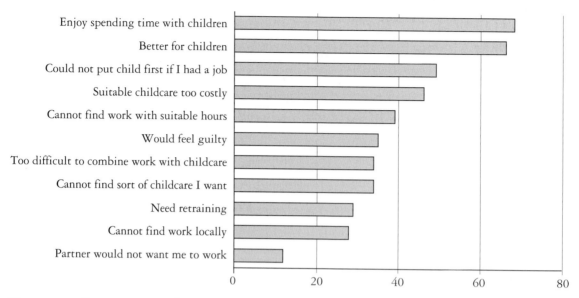

Figure 1.1 Reasons given for mothers not working 1998
Source Social Trends 2001, HMSO

Ethnic minorities and Civil Rights

Minority ethnic groups experience poorer health, more unemployment, lower incomes and poorer housing. Under Section 71 of the Race Relations Act, 1996, local councils were required to take steps to tackle racial discrimination in the provision of services. Black and Asian groups appear to be under-represented as clients of welfare agencies, but higher numbers of children from Afro-Caribbean families are taken into care. More black children are referred to local councils because of family relationships, marital breakdown and financial problems.

Age discrimination

Civil rights affecting older people are being promoted, although there is no legislation in the UK protecting people from discrimination based on age. Under the National Service Frameworks (NSFs) for Older People, health and social care agencies have to check their policies and criteria for care, in order to ensure that there is no age bias.

Disability Rights

Disability Rights groups have been very active since the 1970s. The Disability Discrimination Act, 1995, covers aspects of health and care, particularly with regard to access to services. From 1999, service providers were required to make reasonable adjustments to policies, procedures and practices that exclude disabled people such as excluding guide dogs from restaurants or shops. Service providers had to provide auxiliary aids and services, such as providing information on a cassette or installing an induction loop, to enable it to make it easier to use a service. Where a physical feature is a barrier to a service, providers have to find an alternative method of delivering the service such as low level taxi cabs that have access for wheelchairs.

From 2004, service providers will have to take reasonable steps to remove, alter or avoid physical features that make it difficult or impossible to access a service. Public transport is one of the key areas that disabled action groups have been demonstrating about, and we are now seeing the influence of this in the provision of low access public vehicles in some trains and buses. Various allowances for disabled people have been developed, allowing people to remain independent. Apart from the Disability Living Allowance for people under 66, there are other benefits such as the Direct Payments Scheme, which allows people to organise and pay for their own care. New Deal projects that encourage disabled people into the work force are another initiative that is part of the process of recognising the needs of disabled people and assisting them to take an active and independent part in society.

In this historical overview we have seen examples of policies that have been developed as a reaction to social, economic and political factors. However, another factor affecting the development of policy is related to ideology. An ideology is a set of structured ideas that form a particular perspective or view. The post-World War II legislation and style of government was based on principles of universal provision of public services, free at the point of delivery. Means testing was seen as divisive and time-wasting to administer. The role of the state was to support all its citizens and to reduce inequalities. Bevan talked about the role of the state as supporting people 'from the cradle to the grave'.

Development of Social Policy from 1945 to the present time

The terms 'Right', 'Left' or 'Centre' are used to identify the ideology of a particular political party. Different parties can be described as right-wing or left-wing. The type of social policy that is developed by a political party is affected by ideas about:

- the role and function of the State;
- the model of social welfare provision that is seen as appropriate;
- what criteria are used to identify those who are in need.

Terms related to Models of Welfare

Residual Model of Welfare: The State should provide welfare if the individual, family or private sector is unable to do so. The State should provide a safety net for those most in need.

Institutional Model of Welfare: Mixed economy of welfare that sees welfare provision as an important aspect of society, but this will be provided by a range of agencies. A combination of private, voluntary and statutory services will provide cost-effective care.

Universal Model of Welfare: Welfare services should be available to all by right. The state is responsible for all its citizens.

Table 1.2 The Key Ideologies related to Social Policy and Welfare Provision

	New right/Anti-collectivist/individualist/ market models	Collectivist Old Labour	Reluctant collectivist New Labour	Feminist critique	Anti-racist critique
Core values	• Family values • Market economy • Law and order • Residual welfare	• Equality • State provision and control of services • Universal welfare model	• Family • Equal opportunities • Consultation • Mixed economy	Equality and redistribution of power between men and women needed	Equality and redistribution of power between cultures and races needed
Role of the State	State intervention must be limited	State needs to intervene to ensure stability in society	Two pillar approach; mixed economy; state and private sector	Acts in interests of men; male dominated patriarchal	Acts in interest of white majority; discriminatory
Provision of welfare services	A range of providers would ensure effective delivery of services	State should provide services and support, voluntary and self-help groups	Mixed economy approach using a range of providers	Needs to reflect needs of women and be anti-discriminatory	Welfare services reflect institutionalised racism
Means testing	Efficient way to target those most in need	Stigmatising, bureaucratic, inefficient; universal provision supported	Used to provide services for those most in need	May adversely affect women who are not married	Stigmatising and degrading
Universal provision of services by the State	Inefficient; encourages increased demand and dependence	Committed to universal access and equality	Residual model used; target those most in need	Reflects traditional views of women as wives and mothers dependent on men	Services do not reflect needs of minority groups
Voluntary agencies	One of the providers of services	Supported by State but their main role should be to act as pressure groups	An important provider of services	Useful resource to help women; need to be led by women	Useful resource to help minority groups but need to be *led* by minority groups
Private sector	Encourages choice and competition, leading to efficient services	Choice for well-off; leads to divisions between rich and poor	One of the two pillars in Welfare State	Increases inequality because of women's economic position	Another example of divisions in society
Self-help	Should be encouraged; people should be independent and responsible for their own care	State still takes major role but provides support for self-help groups	Personal responsibility encouraged	Collective work by women useful	Collective approach useful

State intervention in the UK

1945 to the 1970s

The main approach during this time followed social reformist or collectivist views that maintained the State should control and provide welfare provision, using the Universal Model of Welfare.

1979 to 1997

The Conservatives came to power in 1979, and one of their key aims was to reduce government spending on welfare provision. It followed the Residual Model of Welfare and encouraged a mixed economy of welfare provision using State, private and voluntary agencies.

1997 onwards

Since the Labour government took office in 1997, there has been a development of the approach called the 'Third Way', in which State intervention has increased in some instances, such as setting NHS Targets, and has been reduced in others through the involvement of the private and voluntary sector working in partnership. This fits in more closely with the Institutional Model of Welfare. Table 1.2 identifies the key ideologies related to social policy and welfare.

 ## Activity

Look at the following quotations and choose the ideology which fits each one best (in some cases two ideologies could be relevant).

1 'People have a responsibility to look after themselves.'

2 'Instead of having a second holiday, use the money to have your varicose veins done privately.'

3 'Filling in forms is wasteful of time. It costs more in the end to the government.'

4 'Child benefit should be given to everyone, no matter what their level of income is.'

5 'The Partnership approach is important if we are to provide services that are relevant to local communities.'

6 'Giving young people housing support encourages them to leave home and depend on State handouts.'

7 'In this area we make sure that the antenatal clinics are staffed by female doctors.'

8 'It is important to support an interpreting service for our clients and provide information for them in their first language.'

Criticisms of the organisation of welfare provision

The feminist critique

Feminists suggest that welfare policies tend to reflect the patriarchal attitudes in society. Until recently, the caring role of women as mothers and as carers for the disabled or older family members meant that these women were not financially supported by the state. Instead they were used as unpaid workers. Recently, there has been additional legislation and support for carers ◇ but many carers feel the payments do not reflect the true cost of caring.

The anti-racist critique

This perspective identifies the welfare state as part of institutionalised racism in society which denies black and minority ethnic groups access to welfare provision in all aspects, including health care, benefits, housing and access to employment. The welfare state is used to control immigrants and refugees, and the police are seen as racist, failing to protect people who are from minority ethnic groups.

Table 1.3 Public choices for extra government spending in order of importance

Great Britain				Percentages
	1986	1991	1996	1999
Health	47	48	54	47
Education	27	29	28	34
Housing	7	8	4	4
Public transport	–	1	2	4
Help for industry	8	4	4	3
Police and prisons	3	2	3	3
Roads	1	1	1	3
Social security benefits	5	5	3	2
Overseas aid	1	1	–	1
Defence	1	2	1	1
All	100	100	100	100

Source Social Trends 2001, HMSO

Table 1.4 Government spending 1987–1999

United Kingdom					£ billion at 1999 prices	
	1987	1991	1996	1997	1998	1999
Social protection	102	115	140	140	137	137
Health	35	39	47	46	48	50
Education	33	35	39	39	39	40
Defence	32	32	25	25	26	26
Public order and safety	12	16	17	18	18	20
General public services	10	14	16	16	17	18
Housing and community amenities	11	12	7	7	5	5
Recreation, culture and religion	4	5	5	4	5	3
Other economic affairs and environmental protection*	26	27	29	24	23	25
Gross debt interest	32	23	30	32	31	26
All expenditure	297	318	355	351	349	350

*Includes expenditure on transport and communication, agriculture, forestry and fishing, mining, manufacture, construction, fuel and energy services.

Source Social Trends 2001, HMSO

Social expectations

During the twentieth century, the standard of living has increased, people are living longer and health care has advanced so that many illnesses are now treated successfully. The general health of the population has increased, the level of home ownership has increased and working hours have decreased. Leisure activities have expanded, and many people can retire early and look forward to an active retirement with enough money to support them as they get older. Many older people have contributed to the State National Insurance scheme since they began working and they expect to be cared for by the State as they get older.

Expectations for free long-term care for older people were raised by the recommendations made by the Royal Commission on Long Term Care (1998). The government in England and Wales has been slow to respond. In Scotland the recommendations were accepted and the Scottish parliament pledged its support. However, the costs of free long-term care would increase the social protection budget significantly, so there is a concern about how this money would be raised. Table 1.3 shows the areas in which people feel the government should increase its spending, but the government is wary about raising this extra money by increased taxation. Table 1.4 shows the expenditure of central government in 1999.

Word check

Social protection

Refers to the range of benefits, pensions and other payments made by the state.

Activity

Look at Tables 1.3 and 1.4 in turn and answer the following questions:

1 What is the source of the data for each table?

2 How was the data collected?

3 What years does the data cover?

4 What is the difference between the terms 'Great Britain' and 'United Kingdom'?

5 How are the figures in the tables shown (percentages, £s, millions, etc.)?

6 How much difference is there between the priorities given in Tables 1.3 and 1.4?

Can we infer from the information that public opinions and public expectations have an influence on policy decisions?

Public opinion

Public opinion can be assessed by using surveys such as the British Attitudes Survey or other surveys administered by a range of agencies such as Gallop Poll. Importance is given to public consultation about proposed changes to service provision, and the organisation and delivery of care services. Results from consultations are fed back to the relevant national or regional department. Telephone surveys, group meetings, patient participation groups and other focus groups are all being used to generate a response from the public. Some newspapers and TV programmes also offer people an opportunity to express their views. Websites have been set up by local and national government departments on which people can express their opinions.

Examples of how the pressure of public opinion can influence policy include:

- The poll tax riots that led to the reorganisation of collecting community rates in 1993.
- The murder of Jonathan Zito, led to changes in the support of people in the community with severe mental illness. All people with severe mental illness now have to be recorded on a SMI (Severe Mental Illness Register), available to Health and Social Care Services.
- The deaths of babies undergoing heart surgery at a Bristol hospital led to tighter controls over specialist consultants, and their clinical expertise has to be updated on a regular basis.

In many instances, public opinion may be more effective if it is focused through developing a pressure group or using an established pressure group to raise issues of concern such as Age Concern, who raised awareness of age discrimination taking place in the NHS through lobbying Parliament and the Department of Health. As a result, the new NSF for Older People contains a specific reference to removing age as a criteria for health care.

Major pressure groups in the UK

Trade unions

The membership of trade unions has fallen in recent years from 57% of all workers in 1979 to 30% in 1999. The main reason for the decline in membership is the legislation passed during the Conservative term of government that reduced union powers and limited their activities such as balloting members and secondary picketing.

UNISON is one of the largest unions and was formed in 1993 by the amalgamation of NALGO (union for local government officers) NUPE and COHSE (unions for health workers and other public employees). The major unions are affiliated to the Trades Union Congress (TUC). Trade unions exert pressure on the government especially on policy that relates to health and employment. For example, unions influenced the implementation of the national minimum wage.

Business

The CBI (Confederation of British Industry) is another important influence on government social policy. Eleven thousand individual businesses belong to the CBI, as well as 200 representative organisations, including trade associations and employers' associations. Issues that concern the CBI include the privatisation of services and state control. At the 2001 CBI conference in Birmingham, the Transport Secretary, Stephen Byers, was criticised for his department's approach to state involvement in the railway service – Railtrack.

Media

Britain has the highest number of newspaper readers in Europe – 66% of the population read a national daily paper regularly, although this number is declining because of television and the Internet. Most newspapers follow a particular political stance:

- *The Sun*, *The Times*, *The Sunday Times* and the *News of the World* are owned by the Murdoch organisation and tend to have a right-wing approach.

- *The Mirror, the Sunday Mirror, The People* and the *Daily Record* (Scotland) are owned by *The Mirror* group and tend to have a left-wing approach.

In 2000, *The Sun* had the largest circulation figures of 3.7 million whereas *The Mirror* had 2.3 million and the Mail 2.4 million. Newspapers can raise important issues, exerting pressure on the government; some carry out surveys of their readers' views.

Television

With the development of cable TV, many channels are available to viewers. However, the main terrestrial channels of BBC 1 and 2, ITV and Channel 4, all cover social policy issues through national news items, discussion programmes such as *Question Time*, and viewers can also send their views by letter or e-mail. Although there has been a great deal of research into the influence of the media on public opinion, it has been difficult to establish a causal link. In the same way, it is difficult to establish how far the government has an influence on media output. The Prime Minister's Press Secretary, Alistair Campbell, holds regular briefing sessions with the press on government matters, but some newspaper editors maintain they have an influence on government decisions.

Power of the professionals

In the last 25 years the power of professionals has been eroded. Professional groups who could be expected to have an influence on social policy such as teachers, doctors, social workers and lawyers, have all been affected by government legislation and state control, which has reduced their influence. Since 1979 centralised control by the government over these occupational groups has increased. Examples of this increased control include:

- Contracts for GPs (in 2001 these contracts were redesigned by central government). Although the British Medical Association (BMA) was seen as an effective pressure group in the past, various scandals (such as the Shipman Murders, and the Bristol baby deaths) have affected the status of the profession.
- The National Curriculum in Education, whereby teachers have to follow set guidelines and prepare children for SATs.
- The development of Ofsted, which inspects schools. It can put poorly-run schools on special measures and private agencies can be brought in to run a failing school.
- The Social Service Inspectorate (SSI) audits and inspects local government services and has the power to put departments on 'special measures'.

Social policy and social care services today

Care workers need to have a good understanding of the general nature of social care provision and factors that influence its development.

Population changes

One of the key factors affecting social policy and the provision of care services is related to the demography of the UK. The speed of population change depends on the net natural change – the difference between the numbers of births and deaths, and the net effect of people migrating

Table 1.5 Population change in the UK 1901–2021

United Kingdom						Thousands
		Average annual change				
	Population at start of period	Live births	Deaths	Net natural change	Net migration and other	Overall change
Census enumerated						
1901–1911	38,237	1,091	624	467	–82	385
1911–1921	42,082	975	689	286	–92	194
1921–1931	44,027	824	555	268	–67	201
1931–1951	46,038	785	598	188	25	213
Mid-year estimates						
1951–1961	50,287	839	593	246	6	252
1961–1971	52,807	963	639	324	–12	312
1971–1981	55,928	736	666	69	–27	42
1981–1991	56,352	757	655	103	43	146
1991–1997	57,808	754	640	113	87	200
Mid-year projections						
1997–2001	59,009	719	634	85	69	154
2001–2011	59,618	690	624	66	65	131
2011–2021	60,929	694	628	66	65	131

Source Social Trends 2001, HMSO

to and from the country. Most of the population growth in the UK during the 20th century can be attributed to these changes. See Table 1.5. However in recent years, net inward migration has become an increasingly important determinant of population growth, and is now matching the net natural change.

Figure 1.2 shows the rates for births and deaths from 1901 to the predicted figures for 2021. When birth rates and death rates remain the same, the population is said to be stable. However,

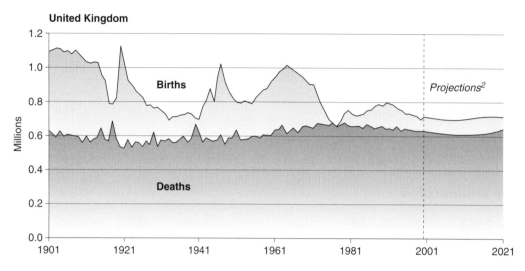

Source Social Trends 2001, HMSO

Figure 1.2 Births and deaths from 1901 to 2021 (predicted.)

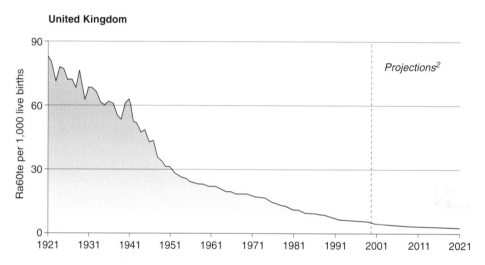

Source Social Trends 2001, HMSO

Figure 1.3 Infant mortallity rates

if the death rate remains the same and the birth rate increases, as during the birth bulge years of the post World War II period and again in the 1960s, this can also have implications for the planning of organisation of health and care services for children and mothers. More maternity services, primary schools and other health and social care services will be needed for this increase. Thus, an awareness of changes in the population is very significant when planning services.

Death rates also include infant mortality rates – deaths in children under one year old per 1000 live births. Figure 1.3 shows how infant mortality rates have fallen since 1921, with projections for the twenty-first century.

Activity

Look at Figure 1.3 and discuss factors that may have reduced infant mortality.

Infant mortality rates are an indicator of the standard of living in a country. If you look at some global statistics you will see that there are many countries in Africa, Asia and South America that have a very high rate of infant mortality. Although immunisations may play a part, many analysts believe that general standards of hygiene and the provision of a clean water supply are key factors, and that many childhood illnesses are the result of poverty.

The health of the population

The White Paper, *Our Healthier Nation* (1998), gave many statistics on the differences in health in certain groups and in different areas. As a result of the White Paper, Health Improvement Programmes (HImPs) have been set up nationally and locally to improve the nation's health.

The statistics on mortality and morbidity in the UK are discussed at length in Chapter 5 of the main text book so we will cover this briefly in this chapter.

Activity

Figure 1.4 shows the death rates for people aged under 65 in the UK between 1971 and 1997. Look at the statistics and answer the following questions:

1   What was the main cause of death for men and women in 1997?

2   Do the tables show any increase or decline in different causes of death?

Comment

The number of premature adult deaths has reduced considerably over the last 25 years. The most common cause of death for men is coronary heart disease, although the death rate has dropped by more than half since the 1970s. Cancer is the most common cause of death for women below the age of 65, with breast and lung cancer being the main cancers that affect women of this age. Suicide rates have generally fallen across the UK over the last 15 years, except among men aged 15 to 44. For both men and women aged 15 to 44, and 45 and over, suicide rates in Scotland were higher than the rest of the UK. In England and Wales, in all age groups, suicides are more common among men than women. Men aged 15 to 44 are almost four times as likely to commit suicide as women of the same age.

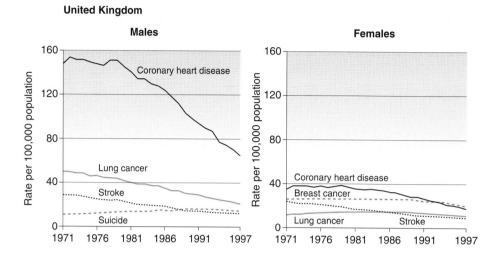

United Kingdom

Figure 1.4 Death rates for people under 65 by gender and selected cause of death

Table 1.6 Suicide rates by region, gender, and age 1992–96

Rate per million population

	Males		Females	
	15–44	45 and over	15–44	45 and over
England & Wales	195	178	50	69
North East	198	192	55	65
North West (GOR)	233	176	64	69
Merseyside	208	164	52	53
Yorkshire & the Humber	201	178	53	71
East Midlands	192	171	45	64
West Midlands	181	170	45	63
Eastern	171	175	39	60
London	182	178	56	74
South East (GOR)	181	181	48	81
South West	196	187	50	76
Wales	247	186	42	62

Source Social Trends 2001, HMSO

Activity

1 Look at Table 1.6 (suicide rates) and describe the regional variations.

2 Read the following statistic: "A person's social class affects their likelihood of committing suicide. In 1991–93 the suicide rate among unskilled men aged 20 to 64 was more than three times higher than among professional men."

Can you think of any reasons for these variations?

Infant mortality rates

Birth weights vary by social class and low birth weight has a strong association with infant mortality. Since 1981 the infant mortality rate has nearly halved, from 11.2 deaths per 1000 live births to 5.9. deaths per 1000 live births in 1997. However, differences still occur between different groups.

Activity

Look at Table 1.7, showing infant mortality rates by social class and answer the following questions:

1 What general patterns do you notice:

• between 1981 and 1996;

• between social class groups;

• inside and outside of marriage;

2 What type of health programme might you develop if you were working as a health worker in an area where the infant mortality rate was high?

As the result of studying morbidity and mortality statistics, the Department of Health has agreed national targets to reduce deaths from cancer, coronary heart disease (CHD) and stroke, suicide and accidents. Local health authorities and primary care organisations have had to draw up plans outlining how these targets will be met. National Service Frameworks (NSFs) for CHD and mental health have also been produced to improve the quality of service to these groups.

By 2010 the following targets in reducing the annual death rate should be achieved:

Cancer: In people under 75 by a fifth (from 69,000 in 1997 to 55,000) in 2010.

Coronary heart disease and stroke: In people under 75 by at least two-fifths (from 69,000 in 1997 to 41,000 in 2010).

Accidents: By at least one-fifth (from 10,000 in 1997 to 8,000 in 2001) and to reduce the rate of serious injury by at least one-tenth.

Suicide: By at least one-fifth (from 4,500 in 1997 to 3,600 in 2010).

Table 1.7 Infant mortality by social class 1981–1996

United Kingdom	Rates per 1,000 live births		
	1981	1991	1996
Inside marriage			
Professional	7.8	5.0	3.6
Managerial and technical	8.2	5.3	4.4
Skilled non-manual	9.0	6.2	5.4
Skilled manual	10.5	6.3	5.8
Semi-skilled	12.7	7.2	5.9
Unskilled	15.7	8.4	7.8
Other	15.6	11.8	8.3
All inside marriage	10.4	6.3	5.4
Outside marriage			
Joint registration	14.1	8.7	6.9
Sole registration	16.2	10.8	7.2
All outside marriage	15.0	9.3	7.0

Source Social Trends 2001, HMSO

Teenage pregnancies

The teenage pregnancy rate in the UK is the highest in Europe (see Figure 1.5) and this is another health statistic that is being monitored carefully. Every local health authority is producing programmes to reduce this rate.

Live births per 1,000 women

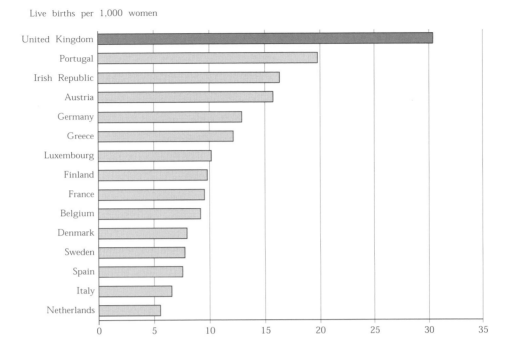

Figure 1.5 Teenage births 1996
Source Social Trends 2001, HMSO

Activity

Can you think of ways in which everyone involved with young people could work in a programme to reduce the pregnancy rate among teenagers? Some authorities have used a 'love bus', touring areas with advice on contraception. The main problem that health workers have encountered is how to involve young men in any programme. What ideas do you have on what could be done?

The role of government and others in the policy-making process

Since 1997 there has been a tremendous increase in legislation affecting health and social care. The key themes underpinning many of the changes have been partnership working, user participation and involvement, and quality of outcomes. For example, prior to the White Paper, 'Our Healthier Nation', there was a Green Paper entitled 'Saving Lives'. The Green Paper was a consultation document that encouraged members of the public, voluntary organisations, and professional health and social care workers to respond. The Health Strategy Unit at the Department of Health studied the responses, and these shaped the final White Paper.

The main piece of legislation that is concerned with the restructuring of the NHS is the Health Act of 1999. This included the White Paper proposals of the 1997 White Paper, 'The New NHS'.

Each piece of legislation has to go through a particular process before becoming law. The process takes a long time.

1 After passing through the Green Paper and the White Paper stage, a Bill is formally introduced in the House of Commons at the 'First Reading'.

2 At the 'Second Reading' the general principles of the Bill are debated and voted upon.

3 At the 'Committee Stage' each clause of the Bill is debated and voted upon.

4 At the 'Report Stage', the Bill is considered as it was reported by the committee and it is decided whether to make further changes in individual clauses.

5 At the 'Third Reading', the Bill as amended is debated and a final vote taken.

6 Next, the Bill then has to pass through the House of Lords, and the same stages are repeated there.

7 Finally, the Queen then gives her Royal Assent to the Bill which then becomes law as an Act of Parliament.

In the run up to the general election in 2001 a new NHS Bill was being debated, which proposed the abolition of the CHCs, as well as other proposals to include patient participation in the health service. Because of the pressures of the election, the Bill did not become law, but further legislation is being developed. Your local Community Health Council (CHC) may be able to advise you about any legislation that is currently being processed.

The European Dimension

The Council of Ministers is the main decision-making body within the European Union, and consists of representatives from each of the member states. The European Social Fund (ESF) provides funding for a wide variety of projects related to supporting people who are disadvantaged. Examples include:

- providing child care for single parents who wish to go back to work;
- offering skills training for people with learning difficulties;
- providing life long learning for socially excluded groups.

The ESF was set up to remove barriers to education, training and employment. There is a web site www.esfnews.org.uk that gives details about the Fund and also gives links to British government departments.

Impact of key inquiries

In recent years there have been several enquiries into health and social care services, which have resulted in changes of practice. These include:

The **Bristol Hospital Enquiry**, which covered the deaths of babies after heart surgery. As a result, surgeons are now more closely scrutinised and have their competence revalidated in performing certain procedures.

The **Waterhouse Inquiry**, which investigated irregularities in child care, is another example that will result in changes in the regulations of practice.

The Waterhouse Inquiry

The Waterhouse Inquiry was set up in 1996 to:

- inquire into the abuse of children in care in Wales since 1974;
- examine whether the agencies and authorities responsible for care could have prevented abuse or detected its occurrence at an earlier stage;
- examine the response of authorities to allegations of abuse made by people, including children formerly in care;
- consider what recommendations should be made for future practice.

Background

Internal investigations of abuse had been carried out in the 1970s and 1990s. One member of staff, Alison Taylor, raised her concerns in 1986 and, through media coverage, a major police investigation started in 1991. As a result, six former care staff were convicted.

Findings

Widespread sexual and physical abuse had occurred in several children's homes and in foster homes. Poor management and the lack of a proper complaints system added to the problems. The local authorities and the police were also criticised for failing to act promptly.

Recommendations

1 An Independent Children's Commissioner for Wales should be appointed to ensure that children's rights are respected, and to publish annual reports on the service.
2 Every social services authority in the UK should appoint an appropriately qualified children's complaints officer.
3 Clear whistle-blowing procedures should be set up.
4 Abuse awareness training for all staff would be implemented.
5 All incidents should be reported and records kept at a local police station with social services having access.
6 Inspection of all homes should be carried out by an independent agency.

Many of these recommendations are also included in the 'Modernising Social Services' White Paper (1998) and in the Consultation Document for Children, 'Working Together to Safeguard Children' (2000). Both Papers are discussed in the main textbook. ◈

Comment

As in the Welsh inquiry, many investigations start off as a result of 'whistle-blowing'. Alison Taylor went to the press to express her concerns. However, whistle-blowing is seen by some people as being disloyal to their colleagues. Because of the recent investigations, all social service and health organisations have a whistle-blowing policy that protects the employee from action against them by the organisation they are criticising. The doctor who was the whistle-blower at Bristol could no longer find work in the UK. He moved to Australia because he was seen to have betrayed his colleagues. By having a whistle-blowing policy in place, it is hoped that workers will feel more able to express their concerns about poor practice in future.

Financial constraints that influence design and delivery of services

Social services

Table 1.8 The proposed government budget 2001–2002

Government income and expenditure, 2001–2			
Income (£bn)		Expenditure (£bn)	
income tax	104	Social Security	109
VAT	61	NHS	59
National Insurance	63	Education	50
Excise duties	37	Debt interest	23
Corporation Tax	38	Defence	24
Business rates	17	Law & order	23
Council tax	15	Industry, Agriculture & employment	16
Other	64	Housing & environment	18
		Transport	10
		Other expenditure	62
Total	**£399 bn.**	**Total**	**£394 bn.**

Source *Guardian* Newspaper 8/3/2001

The government operates a budget that includes the costing of health and social care expenditure. Table 1.8 shows the total government expenditure planned for 2001–2. Organisations have to operate on the principle of 'best value'; services have to reflect efficient use of scarce resources. The local social services budget is partly dependent on a central government grant. Its level depends upon various factors, such as the composition of the local population and the level of deprivation. If a local authority overspends its budget, it will not be 'bailed out' by central government but will have to make cuts in its budget for some services. Every financial year your local council undertakes a spending review, and it has to estimate how savings could be made. In some areas, the council has a public meeting to discuss these issues, and often unpopular decisions have to be made.

Activity

Find a copy of your local council's annual report. This should include details of the annual budget.

Identify the key areas of local government spending.

Health services

Every health authority (HA) has a statutory duty to balance its budget in the local health area. The HAs give money to local hospitals and these hospitals are responsible for keeping within the budget. If a hospital trust overspends, the deficit will pass to the health authority. The HA may be able to transfer the debt to the following year, but neither the HA nor the trust will be able to apply for additional funds. This means that the pressure is on all health organisations, including Primary Care Groups (PCGs) and Primary Care Trusts (PCTs) to keep within their budgets. As with the local councils, cuts may be made in services to keep within budget so hospital managers have to decide the priorities, such as choosing between redecorating the outside of the hospital or closing a ward. Because of these financial pressures, health and social care services are always reviewing services to see how efficiency can be maintained

Regulatory inspection

The Commission for Health Improvement (CHI) is the inspection body for clinical standards of the NHS in England and Wales. CHI started work in April 2000 and is a statutory body under the 1999 Health Act. It will visit every NHS Trust and health authority, including all primary care organisations, every four years and prepares a report. CHI also investigates serious failures in the NHS. CHI's work is based on the following principles. It will:

- put patient's experience at the heart of its work by asking them for their views of the service;
- be independent and fair;
- use a developmental approach to help the NHS improve;
- base its work on evidence not opinion;
- be open and accessible.

A Clinical Standards Board in Scotland provides the same kind of service. CHI has inspected several hospitals since it was set up. It presents a report and the hospital has to respond by drawing up an action plan to show how it will improve those services that are seen to be below standard. The CHI website is www.chi.nhs.uk, if you want further information about inspections in your area.

Inspection and regulation in social care

The Social Services Inspectorate (SSI) is responsible for inspecting services. As a result of the proposals made in the White Paper, 'Modernising Social Services', The Care Standards Act was passed in 2000. This will reform the regulatory system for England and Wales and will come into effect from April 2002. The National Care Standards Commission will inspect all residential and nursing homes, domiciliary care agencies, and private and voluntary care services. At present, inspection units are attached to local councils, which means that the council could be inspecting its own services. By developing a totally independent inspection regime, it is hoped that the quality of services will improve and reach a high national standard.

The main features of contemporary social care provision

This is covered in detail in Chapter 5 of the main text book ◇ Since the NHS and Community Care Act (1990), a mixed economy of care has developed. This means that the role of the public (or statutory) sector has decreased, and the role of private and voluntary organisations has increased. Many local authority care homes have been taken over by private or voluntary (non-profit making) agencies. Social services purchase social care from a range of providers – for example, day centre provision for older people, home care, meals on wheels and other services. Social services also purchase beds in residential care. With the development of closer working with the health service some provision – like intermediate care, is purchased through a pooled budget, where both partners contribute funds.

The voluntary sector also provides services for social care, through service level agreements that may be for one year or longer, or for particular projects that are national priorities, such as work with older people. Because voluntary organisations are dependent on contracts with local councils, this may reduce their role as a pressure group. Self-help groups are an important aspect of social care. As local councils' resources become more restricted, many groups form to help themselves. Young mothers and toddler groups, refugee groups and others join together to share a particular problem. The website www.self-help.org.uk lists self help groups in Great Britain.

Constraints of economic and resource factors

Case study

In South London there are two hospitals, both offering kidney transplant services. It is proposed by the Health Authority that the service should be centralised at one centre for the following reasons:

1 There is a national shortage of specialist nephrology (kidney) consultants and clinical staff.

2 Consultants who specialise in this area have to undertake a certain number of operations each year in order to be accredited as competent. By concentrating the service at one hospital this will make it easier for surgeons to be accredited.

As part of the NHS's commitment to involving patients in consultation about possible changes to service provision, the health authority had various meetings with patient groups Patient Action to Retain Transplant Services (PARTS) – at both hospitals. Patients were concerned about travelling longer distances for transplant surgery and relatives would also have a longer journey when visiting. However, the Health Authority has made an interim decision that the transplant service will be retained at one site, but there will be life-long nephrology support on both sites and continuing care on whichever site the patient receives replacement therapy. As we can see from this example, decisions about centralising services have to take account of using scarce resources in a cost effective way, even if this means longer journeys for patients.

Other examples of this kind include centralising cleft lip and palate services in London as hospitals offering this service will be reduced in future, and rationalising ambulance service provision. In Wiltshire the three emergency services, Fire, Police and Ambulances will be based in a joint headquarters. In Cleveland a joint control centre for the three emergency services is already in operation.

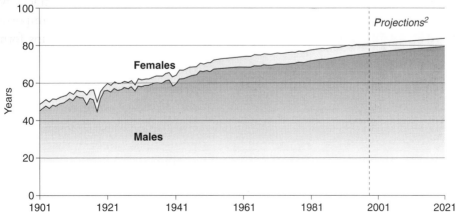

Figure 1.6 Expectations of life at birth 1901–2021

Demographic factors influencing social policy in the next 20 years

Life expectancy is increasing (see Figure 1.6) and we can see from the predicted population figures that the proportion of older people in the UK population is likely to continue to increase. The following is an excerpt from the Office of National Statistics Monthly Digest for October 2001.

Population

Mid-2000 UK population estimates have been released by the ONS. Key findings include:

- The mid-2000 UK population is estimated at 59,755,700, a rise of 3.4 per cent since mid-1991.
- The largest rises were seen in the population of working age of 30 and over (30 to 64/59 for men and women respectively) and the 85 and over age group which increased by 13.6 per cent and

29.5 per cent respectively between 1991 and 2000.

- Although the UK population increased overall, there were decreases in some age groups. The largest decrease occurred in the number of people aged 16 to 29. This group was estimated at 10,645,700 in 2000 which is a fall of 13.9 per cent since 1991.

Source ONS Monthly Digest August 2001, HMSO

Activity

Look at the population changes that are identified and think about the implications of these for welfare policy, especially in the following age groups

- 16–29;
- over 85.

Britain ages as pregnancies fall

Retirement at 72 needed to keep workforce balance

John Carvel
Social affairs editor

The average retirement age would have to rise to 72 to maintain the present balance between the working population and numbers of older dependants, according to demographic forecasts published yesterday by the office for national statistics.

If there is no corresponding increase in the birth rate in the future, there will be fewer economically active adults paying direct taxation and national insurance contributions. Some analysts put forward the view that the retirement age in the future will need to be raised to 72 to pay for the benefits for the older groups (see the excerpt from *The Guardian*). Current predictions suggest that the number of people who are over 75 will increase and this will have an impact on all aspects of welfare.

Housing

More supported housing units will be needed to encourage older people to remain in their own homes. As many of these people will be in single households, which are also predicted to increase in the next century, this may mean a more efficient use of limited housing resources and a greater role taken by local councils in directly providing housing services.

Health

If there is an increase in the over 75s in the twenty-first century, there will be increased demand for those services that are currently provided.

Activity

Look at Table 1.9 and identify the pattern of age to service use.

The additional use of health services will lead to the development of more intermediate care beds, chiropody and other community services, and specific clinical support for diabetes, osteo-arthritis, cardiac problems and ophthalmology. Additional staff will be needed in these areas. The drugs budget will also increase. Recruiting staff to work in health and social care may be a problem if there are fewer young people in the population as a whole.

Education

The predicted fall in 16–29 year-olds will mean fewer places in further and higher education. This may also have an effect on the numbers of people entering teacher training courses.

Employment

Fewer school leavers will be entering employment. Employers may need to recruit older people into work previously done by young people. There may be an increase in older people in their 50s and 60s working full-time or part-time to make up the shortfall.

Benefit system

More benefits will be needed to be paid to older people in order to maintain their independence in the community and also to contribute to the cost of residential care. Because the numbers of economically active people will decrease because of the decline in the younger age groups, indirect taxation may need to increase, as there will be fewer workers paying tax and national insurance on their income.

Table 1.9 Use of health services by gender & age 1998–99

United Kingdom								Percentage
	16–24	25–34	35–44	45–54	55–64	65–74	75 and over	All aged 16 and over
Males								
Consultation with GP[1]	7	9	10	12	16	17	21	12
Outpatient visit[2]	12	14	13	15	20	25	29	17
Casualty visit[2,3]	7	7	5	4	3	3	3	5
Females								
Consultation with GP[1]	15	18	16	19	17	19	21	18
Outpatient visit[2]	13	13	12	17	19	21	26	17
Casualty visit[2,3]	6	4	3	3	3	3	3	4

1 Consultations with an NHS GP in the last two weeks.

2 In the last three months; includes visits to casualty in Great Britain only.

3 The question was only asked of those who said they had an outpatient visit.

Source Social Trends 2001, HMSO

 Word check

Indirect taxation

Taxation that is paid indirectly on goods and services that people buy, such as VAT.

Direct taxation

Taxation that is paid directly out of income, either earned or unearned.

Great Britain

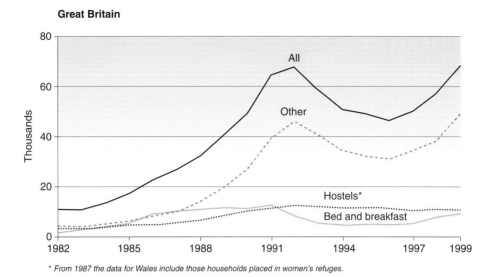

* From 1987 the data for Wales include those households placed in women's refuges.

Figure 1.7 Homeless households in temporary accommodation

Key Issues in the Twenty-First Century

The homeless

Since 1982 there has been an increase in the homeless in Great Britain. In Wales three out of 10 households accepted as homeless in 1999, stated that they were homeless as a result of a breakdown of a relationship with a partner. In Scotland almost a third of homeless households were homeless because they did not wish to remain with friends or family. Figure 1.7 shows the numbers of households in temporary accommodation between 1982 and 1999. When a homeless household makes an application for housing, the local housing authority must decide whether the applicant is eligible for assistance, is unintentionally homeless or is in a priority need group. If these conditions are met in England and Wales, the council must provide sufficient advice and assistance to the applicant. Suitable accommodation should be provided for up to two years. During this time the council may offer a secure council tenancy. In England the main reason for an increase in homelessness is related to the increase in housing costs in London and the south-east and to asylum seekers. Across Great Britain one in seven households in temporary accommodation were housed in hostels (including women's refuges) and one in seven were in bed and breakfast accommodation. The Rough Sleepers Unit (RSU) was established in 1999 as part of the Government's social exclusion policy of 1998. By June 2000, the number of people sleeping rough in England on any one night was estimated to be about 1.2. million

Activity

1   Look at figure 1.7 and describe the main patterns you see.

2   You are a government minister responsible for reducing homelessness. If you were taking a New Right approach whom would you see as responsible for the increase in homelessness and what solutions would you propose? If you were from the Collectivist approach, how would you differ in the causes you would identify and the approach you would use? Use Table 1.2 here.

Refugees and asylum seekers

Britain has had a long tradition of supporting immigrants, from the Huguenots in the seventeeth century to the Jews in the twentieth century. Nationals from the European Economic Area have the right to reside in the UK provided they are working or are able to provide for themselves. Nearly all other overseas nationals wishing to live in the UK require Home Office acceptance for settlement. Immigration controls were set up in 1962. The number of people accepted for settlement in the UK increased by 27,000 to 97,000 between 1998 and 1999. This increase was partly due to people seeking asylum from Yugoslavia and Turkey.

There have also been a high percentage of refugees from Asia and Africa – some are seeking asylum, while others are married to spouses already in the UK. The Home Office required applicants to prove they had not married primarily in order to gain entrance to the UK. The latest asylum figures published by the Home Office in July 2001 show that applicants from Afghan nationals remained the highest applicant nationality for the fifth consecutive month (Figure 1.8).

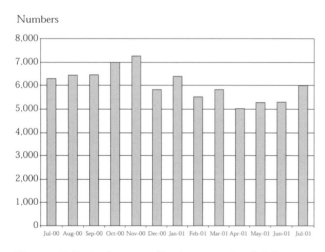

Numbers

Figure 1.8 Asylum applications received July 2000–July 2001
Source Home Office July 2001

Welfare and refugees

The costs of asylum in 2000 are shown in Figure 1.9. Welfare arrangements have been criticised as being degrading and ineffective. Local authorities have had to find accommodation and pay subsistence to refugees. Problems were experienced in arranging benefits for refugees because they did not have a permanent address. A local study into the experience of refugees found the following:

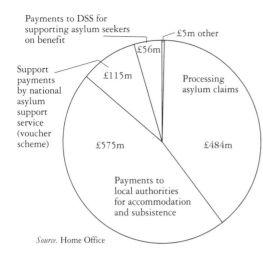

Payments to DSS for supporting asylum seekers on benefit

£5m other

£56m

£115m

Processing asylum claims

Support payments by national asylum support service (voucher scheme)

£575m

£484m

Payments to local authorities for accommodation and subsistence

Source. Home Office

Figure 1.9 The cost of asylum 2000 Source Home Office

- problems for children gaining access to schools;
- lack of support for adults and children with physical and mental difficulties;
- difficulty of access to health and dental services;
- access to housing;
- racist attacks and discrimination;
- little or no interpreting support;
- poverty related to the voucher system, which meant that there was no cash for bus fares or other activities and personal items;
- social exclusion.

Following continued criticism, David Blunkett, Secretary of State for the Home Office, announced the following changes:

- The voucher system will be replaced by Smart ID cards. These cards will include photograph and fingerprint data, and will become cash debit cards to replace vouchers from autumn 2002.
- The value of vouchers will go up in value from £10 to £14 to reflect the overall increase in income support.
- A small network of induction centres near Heathrow and Croydon will replace the use of emergency bed and breakfast accommodation. Asylum seekers will stay at these centres for up to two weeks, and during this time they will be provided with food and accommodation. Centres will not be locked.
- Reporting centres – those refugees who have been dispersed around the UK will be required to report at these centres so that they can be informed of decisions about their application. Those who are told they cannot be accepted will be put in police cells until they are taken to a removal centre.
- Accommodation centres – about four centres will be set up across the UK. They will provide a range of services including basic health care, education for children, leisure activities and access to legal advice and interpreters.
- Appeals – the back log of appeals will be cleared so that 6000 decisions a month can be made by November 2002.
- Removal centres – the network of detention centres across the UK will be enlarged to provide 4000 places by November 2002. The use of prisons for asylum seekers will cease in 2002.
- Refugee resettlement – a new programme that will arrange safe transport to Britain for those groups that are recognised by the United Nations as being in danger in their country of origin.

Activity

1 Look at Figure 1.9 and describe what you see.

2 Look carefully at David Blunkett's proposals. Can you think of possible problems with:

- their implementation;
- their effects on local communities in the UK;
- additional provision that may be needed for children and families;
- employment and integration issues?

3 Traditionally, right-wing theorists discouraged immigration and initiated tight controls. What type of ideology do you think is influencing this current policy towards refugees and asylum seekers?

Poverty

Table 1.10 Examples of recent government welfare policy related to poverty

Health	Low income	Education/employment	Support and community regeneration
NHS plan reform of NHS	Working Families Tax Credit To support families	Extra funding for education and Life Long Learning	Sure Start programmes increased
National Service Frameworks (NSFs) For Mental Health, CHD, older people	Sure Start maternity grant For pregnant and nursing mothers	New Deal Programme extended for disabled people	Neighbourhood Renewal Programmes in poor communities
Improving local services with the development of primary care trusts	Income support Increased for families	Securing Health Together Reducing occupational ill-health and disability	New Deal for Communities Covering poor neighbourhoods
Health action zones Improving health of disadvantaged groups	Minimum income guarantee For pensioners		The UK Fuel Poverty Strategy Helping pensioners and other vulnerable groups
	Increasing the National Minimum Wage		Network of Healthy Living Centres to strengthen community initiatives in health, education and environment
	Children's tax credit Baby credit for a child in the first year of life		Rough Sleepers Unit Developing programmes to reduce the number of people sleeping rough

Source. Tackling Health Inequalities. Consultation Paper (2001), DOH

Another key issue related to social welfare is the need to reduce the numbers of people in poverty. Table 1.10 shows the various welfare programmes that were running in 2001 and many of these will be extended in the future. Poverty is still seen as a major issue, especially when related to children and older people. 'Tackling Health Inequalities' (DoH 2001) identifies six priority themes for future social policy.

1 Providing a sure foundation for life through a healthy pregnancy and childhood.

2 Improving opportunities for children and young people.

3 Improving the NHS Primary Care services.

4 Tackling the major killers – Coronary Heart Disease and Cancer.

5 Strengthening disadvantaged communities.

6 Tackling the wider causes of health inequalities.

The identified national policies are directed to reducing health inequalities and to tackling the root causes of poverty and material disadvantage. They aim to:

- improve the income and material conditions of the poorest by continuing reform of the tax and benefit system;

- continue to improve the position of poorest families by increasing the National Minimum Wage;

- address inequalities in the most disadvantaged communities through implementing the National Strategy for Neighbourhood Renewal;

- reduce the risk of ill health and cut the numbers of excess winter deaths among the most vulnerable groups by implementing the UK Fuel Poverty Strategy;

- address the housing needs of deprived areas by bringing all social housing up to set standards by 2010;

- provide targeted help for those without work, and to find and retain jobs through the New Deal programmes, employment zones and Action Teams for jobs;

- help people of working age by introducing Jobcentre Plus to deliver an efficient labour market and benefit service;

- reduce work-related ill-health, and increase opportunities for rehabilitation through the occupational health strategy, 'Securing Health Together'.

There are a number of websites that are relevant to this section. They include:

http://www.inlandrevenue.gov.uk/nwm/index.htm

http://www.defra.gov.uk/environment/consult/fuelpov/index.htm

http://www.doh.gov.uk/healthinequalities

 Activity

There are many leaflets outlining some of these policies available at post offices and public libraries. See what you can find out. It may also be useful to collect a file of newspaper articles and headlines related to current policy.

Technological developments in the delivery of health and social care

The development of Information technology means that many people will have access to medical help and advice via the Internet in the future. With direct booking of hospital out-patient appointments and day surgery by the GP, waiting lists should be reduced. Continued development of surgical techniques for operations such as cataracts, kidney stones, gallstones and cardiac surgery, means that patients can be treated as day cases. Telemedicine is another example of changes to delivery of care, with the transfer of information via an Internet or video link. These approaches speed up diagnosis and treatment of cardiac conditions. There have been recent examples of operations being undertaken by robots, so perhaps this will be another development in the future. Specialist training is needed to use these developing techniques.

Some GPs are being trained to perform scans and other procedures so that the patient can be treated locally. Blood pressure machines and ECG machines that patients can wear as they go about their daily routine is another way of diagnosing conditions without the need to go to hospital (these machines are used for 24 hours and can be useful for detecting abnormalities that a blood pressure check or ECG carried out in the surgery would not identify). As these different approaches become better known, demand is expected to increase. New technology can cause its own problems as many GPs have been confronted by patients who have diagnosed their condition on the Internet and bring the printout to the surgery!

Scientific developments in Health and Social Care

Transplant services

NHS transplant services started in the UK in the 1960s with kidney grafting. Heart, liver, lung, pancreas, small bowel, cornea, heart valve and bone transplants are now routine, and skin is grafted to treat severe burns. In the last 25 years over one million people have benefited from a transplant.

The UK Transplant Service Authority (UKTSSA) was set up as a Special Health Authority in 1991 and was renamed UK Transplant in 2000. It provides a 24-hour support service for the matching, allocation and distribution of donor organs. It is accountable to the Secretary of State for Health. In 1998 the Government launched an organ donation publicity campaign in order to increase the number of donors and £3 million was put into the plan in 2001 in order to:

- double the number of those on the organ donation register from 8 million to 16 million by 2010;
- develop a National Service Framework for patients with kidney failure to establish national standards and improve services;
- increase the kidney transplant rate by almost 100% by 2005;
- increase heart, lung and liver transplant by 10% by 2005.

In July 2000, Boots the Chemists launched a scheme for Advantage card customers (their loyalty card) to join the NHS organ donor register. Boots invested £500,000 in the scheme and promotes it by using leaflets in their stores.Other credit card companies are also inviting card holders to join the NHS Organ Donor Register from January 2001.

Activity

Visit your local Boots store to find the leaflets. Use the websites related to organ donation to access up to date information on the statistics related to organ donation and for general information.

www.uktransplant.org.uk provides information on the work of the UK Transplant and other general information.

The NHS organ donor website – www.nhs.uk/organdonor provides statistics.

Transplant surgery is seen as a specialist area and one of the key issues related to ensuring the continued quality of its provision is the development of specialist centres of excellence.

Potential scientific developments and their influence on social care services

There has been a great deal of discussion in the media and among the medical profession about many of the developments in this area because of the ethical issues that are raised.

Cloning of body parts

Although human cloning is banned in Britain at the moment, scientists are looking at ways of replacing diseased or failing organs with cloned cells acceptable to the immune system. In 1998, scientists in Scotland identified and managed to grow in laboratory dishes the stem cells or master cells that make all the other cells in the body – such as for skin, blood and bone. This development could mean that damaged tissues could be repaired, whether it is neurons for Parkinson's disease, damaged cartilage cells, heart muscle cells or white blood cells.

Scientists answered MPs' questions about these new developments at a meeting in November 2000. Stem cell therapy is one area that could be developed to treat a range of conditions but concern was raised that these cells would be obtained from week-old foetuses. This research would be controlled by the 1990 Human Fertilisation and Embryology Act, which prevents human embryos beyond 14 days being used. In August 2001, bone marrow stem cells were taken from a 46-year-old man's pelvis and injected into arteries near his heart. The cells migrated to areas in the heart that had been damaged by a heart attack and turned into healthy muscle cells that began to beat. Using a person's own stem cells may be suitable as they will have the same DNA and will not be rejected. However, research into cloning will continue in spite of ethical problems that will need to be resolved, as there could be real benefits to disorders that affect nerves and muscles, such as Parkinson's Disease and Multiple Sclerosis.

Improvements in transplant surgery

As transplant surgery becomes more routine and acceptable, the demands for the service will continue to increase. However, the current shortage of donors could continue. Donors from black and minority ethnic groups are less likely to come forward. Research has shown that this is because of cultural and religious beliefs about the body needing to be maintained in its whole state after death. Transplant surgery is expensive, not just because of the procedure itself, but because of the medication that patients need to take for the rest of their lives to guard against tissue rejection. Demand for transplants will always out strip supply.

Genetic engineering

This is another controversial development in health care. Genetic screening is developing, especially when there is a family history of disease, such as breast cancer or ovarian cancer. In the field of cancer research inherited genetic factors seem to regulate some aspects of risk that an individual faces. Certain genes such as (BRCA–1) which increases some women's susceptibility to breast cancer, have been identified; others, such as hMSH2 on chromosome 2p, have been identified as a potential cause of colo-rectal cancer. In genetic screening, harmful genes such as these can be looked for in a person's DNA. There are ethical and practical considerations. The knowledge that a potential health risk is present could affect a person's chances of employment or insurance. It would also be a cause of anxiety, especially if there is no effective treatment to prevent the disease developing. Certain genetic conditions are more common among certain ethnic groups, for example, Ashkenazi Jews carry a higher incidence of genetic mutations associated with certain cancers. Genotypic prevention involves the diagnosis of a genetic disorder before birth, with the implication of offering the parents a choice of termination. Many disabled people have criticised this type of screening as they feel that people with genetic conditions are being discriminated against.

In October 2000 the Government announced that Britain will be the first country to allow insurers to use the results of genetic tests to identify people with hereditary illnesses. Approval would first be given for Huntingtons Chorea. Hereditary breast cancer and Alzheimer's disease are also expected to be approved. Critics of the decision feel that vulnerable groups would find it difficult to get life insurance or a mortgage as people would be asked to disclose the results of any genetic testing they had undergone. However, this is still under discussion and although insurance companies may request results of genetic testing in the future, clients may be allowed to refuse to divulge the information.

Activity

Mary is expecting her first baby. Her husband has achondroplasia (a condition that used to be called dwarfism). She has been told that male children are more likely to have this condition and she has been offered a pre-natal screening test to identify if the baby is a boy. If the baby is a boy, the foetus could be genetically screened to find out if it has the condition. Her husband, Brian, has mixed feelings about this. His father had the condition and had a successful career in paediatric medicine. He is a teacher. He feels that the condition has not affected his life chances and that by offering genetic screening it encourages a form of selection of the fittest, by assuming that people with disabilities are a drain on society. If you were the health worker involved in this case how would you approach this situation?

In this chapter we have covered a range of issues that affect workers in health and social care. We have seen how present-day social policy has its links with the past. If you wish to study social policy in more detail, you may find the following book useful: *Social Policy for Health and Social Care* by Tina Lovell and Claire Cordeaux (1999) Hodder and Stoughton.

References and resources

Community Care is a weekly publication that contains useful articles relevant to this area.

Brendon, V. (1994) *The Age of Reform 1820–1850.* Hodder and Stoughton

Holden, C. *et al.* (1996) *Further Studies for Social Care*, First Edition. Hodder and Stoughton.*

Lawson, T. and Garrod, J. (1996) *The Complete A–Z Sociology Handbook.* Hodder and Stoughton.*

Lovell, T. and Cordeaux, C. (1999) *Social Policy for Health and Social Care.* Hodder and Stoughton.*

Meggitt, C. (1997) *Special Needs Handbook for Health and Social Care.* Hodder and Stoughton.*

'Our Healthier Nation: Saving Lives' – White Paper (1999) HMSO.

Richards, J. (1999) The Complete *A–Z Health and Social Care Handbook.* Hodder and Stoughton.*

'Social Trends' (2001) HMSO.

'Tackling Health Inequalities' (2001) DOH.

Thomson, H. *et al* (2000) *Vocational A Level for Health and Social Care.* Hodder and Stoughton.*

Items marked with an asterisk are recommended reading for students.

Useful websites

Department of Health
  www.doh.gov.uk

Department of Social Security
  www.dss.gov.uk

Department of Trade and Industry
  www.dti.gov.uk

Government Actuary Department
  www.gad.gov.uk

Health Inequalities report
  www.official-documents.co.uk/doh/ih/contents.htm

Immigration and Asylum Statistics
  www.homeoffice.gov.uk/rds/index.htm

Institute for Social and Economic Affairs
  www.iser.essex.ac.uk

National Assembly for Wales
  www.wales.gov.uk

National Insurance Statistics and Research Agency
  www.nisra.gov.uk

National Statistics
  www.statistics.gov.uk

NHS in Scotland
  www.show.nhs.uk/isd

NHS Plan
  www.doh.gov.uk/nhsplan

'Our Healthier Nation' White Paper
  www.doh.gov.uk./ohn.htm

Sure Start Programme
  www.surestart.gov.uk

Teenage Pregnancy Unit
  www.teenagepregnancyunit.go.uk

Glossary

Ageing population   A population in which the proportion of people over 65 is increasing.

Ageism   Negative feelings towards, and discriminatory behaviour against, a person on the basis of age.

Birth rate   The number of live births per 1000 of the population.

Black Report   A report on the inequalities of health, which shows there is a marked social class difference in health and health chances of the British population.

Care in the community   Policy of deinstitutionalisation introduced during the 1990s, when large-scale hospitals for the long-term care of people with mental health problems, learning disabilities, physical disabilities and older people, were closed and provision of care was placed in the community.

Census   Full-scale national survey taken every 10 years since 1801 (apart from 1941). Statistics from the census form the basis for planning welfare services.

Child Support Agency   Established 1993 by the Conservative government to reduce the cost to the taxpayer of financial support to one-parent families. Absent parents (usually fathers) were traced by the CSA and required to pay an appropriate amount of support.

Council housing   Homes built for, and rented out by, the local council as a low-cost alternative to buying. Public housing stocks have reduced following the selling-off of council homes to tenants.

Death rate   The crude death rate is expressed as the number of deaths per 1000 of the live population.

Demography   The study of population, with particular reference to its size and structure, and how and why it changes over time, through changes in the birth and death rates, marriage rates, patterns of migration and other factors.

Dependency Culture   New Right view that universal welfare provision has led people to expect the state to provide for them.

Direct taxation   Taxes – income tax or inheritance tax – directly levied on a person's income or wealth.

DNA (deoxyribonucleic acid)   A nucleic acid mainly found in the chromosomes of cells. It is the hereditary material of all organisms except for some viruses.

Epidemiology   The study of the nature, amount and spread of disease, in order to develop an appropriate approach to prevention and cure.

Family credit   A social benefit in the UK which tops up the income of low-paid workers with children.

Feminism   The ideological perspective that examines society and events within society from the viewpoint of women.

Genetics   The study of biological inheritance and the extent to which individuals are the product of their parental DNA.

Gross National Product (GNP)   A measure of the value of the productivity of a country, and therefore its wealth.

Ideology   A systematic set of beliefs which explains society and its policies.

Income support   A means tested benefit for unemployed people, single parents and disabled people whose income has been assessed as inadequate.

Indirect taxation   Taxes that are levied on goods and services (VAT). This form of taxation takes a greater proportion of the income of poorer groups.

Infant mortality rate   The number of deaths of infants under one year old per 1000 live births. It is an indicator of general prosperity.

Liberal Democratic Party   Formed from the amalgamation of the Liberal Party and the Social Democratic Party (SDP – a splinter group from the Labour Party).

Life expectancy   The average number of years a new-born baby can expect to live. Male babies born in 1994 in the UK can expect to live until about 74 years of age, and female babies until 79 years of age.

Local authorities   Local political bodies that control towns, cities and rural areas.

Marketisation   The process by which market principles and practices are introduced into areas that were not markets before, for example, health, schools and social services. In the view of the New Right, this approach is more likely to respond to service users' needs.

Means tested benefits   Social benefits that are delivered only when the claimant is able to show need. Many older people in need tend not to apply for these benefits.

Mixed economy   The public, private and voluntary sectors provide goods and services for service users, for example, day centres and nursing homes.

New Deal   Government programmes assisting unemployed people to enter work. Special advisors offer support to women, young people and people with disabilities.

New Right   Traditionally a Conservative approach, which has links to the *laissez-faire* policies of the nineteenth century, in which a free market with little intervention by the State is seen as effective, by encouraging competition and individual responsibility.

Official Statistics   Statistical data provided by central and local government and government agencies on unemployment rates, crime rates, etc.

Ofsted (Office of Standards in Education)   Set up by the Conservative government to inspect, monitor and report on the performance of schools.

Patriarchy   Term used by feminists to describe society as organised by men for the benefit of men and the oppression of women.

Poverty   A lack of sufficient resources to achieve a standard of living considered to be acceptable in a particular society. The benefit system in the UK is based on the idea of an absolute poverty line – if the person's income falls below that line they are said to be in poverty. In the European Union, the poverty line is usually drawn at 50% of the average income in that particular society.

Privatisation   Government policy in which the public sector influence is reduced and services are transferred to private agencies, for example, gas, water and electricity.

Progressive taxation   Direct taxation which increases depending on the amount of income received. This measure is to achieve a greater equality of distribution of income and wealth in a society.

Racism   Ideas about race are translated into negative feelings and discriminatory action against a particular racial group.

Recession   Deteriorating economic conditions when unemployment increases and productivity declines.

Redistribution   In which income and wealth are taken from the rich by progressive taxation and given to the poor in the form of benefits.

Social engineering   Planned social change brought about by the implementation of particular social policies, for example, the development of comprehensive schools.

Social Fund   Budget made available under the Department of Work and Pensions to provide loans to the recipients of social security benefits.

Social Security   The system of welfare support provided by the State for its citizens. Unemployment and sickness benefits and pensions are contributory through National Insurance contributions; non-contributory benefits provide a safety net for those most in need.

Social Trends   Annual digest of statistics produced by the Central Statistical Office.

Universalism   An approach to welfare that maintains that all citizens have an equal right to free and accessible services provided by the State.

Voluntary Sector   Non-profit making organisations that provide services and/or act as pressure groups.

Welfare pluralism   Provision of services from many different sources: private, public and voluntary.

Welfare state Areas of service provision in which the government has a role in funding, planning and regulating. The key areas are health, education, income maintenance, housing and personal social services.

Chapter 2

Planning health and social care provision

This chapter is about planning health and social care services and relates to Unit 10 and builds on Chapter 5 of the *Vocational A Level in Health and Social Care* text book (Thomson, H., *et al.* (2000) Hodder and Stoughton). While you are working on this chapter it would be useful to have the textbook covering the Mandatory Units available.

This chapter describes:

- how services are planned to meet the needs of communities;
- how health and social care and early years services are planned in partnership with other agencies, such as the voluntary sector;
- how stakeholders are involved in planning services;
- how allocation of limited resources can cause conflict;
- how standards of service are monitored.

Assessment

Unit 10 is assessed through your portfolio work. You will be asked to complete an investigation into how services for two client groups are planned and implemented. In order to prepare for this assessment, you will need to collect information about the services in your area. This can be done by contacting organisations such as Community Health Councils, local voluntary organisations, local Hospital and Primary Care Trusts, and the Local Health Authority. At the moment there are continuous changes taking place in the provision of services. Local newspapers may give information about some of these changes. Your local Health Authority and Health Trusts all have to produce annual reports, and these are another source of information. Local councils and voluntary organisations also produce annual reviews. Many organisations now have their own websites, which are another source of information. It may be helpful to keep a project file during the course.

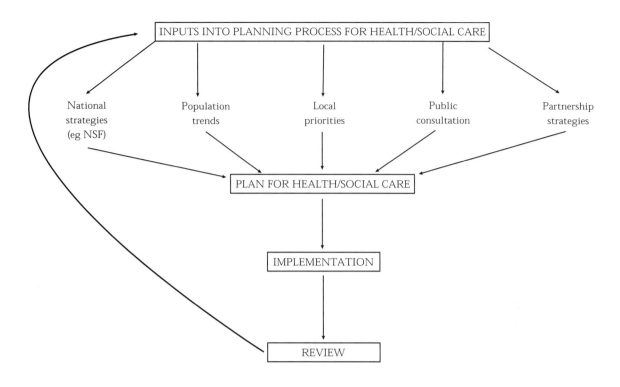

Figure 2.1 Cycle of planning for health and social care

Planning services to meet the needs of communities

Planning health and social care provision is a complex process. As you can see in Figure 2.1, there is a cycle of planning. Before any planning can take place, demographic statistics have to be examined as different areas have different population profiles. An urban area that has a high proportion of ethnic minorities and older people will have different priorities from a rural community with a scattered population and a high proportion of children. National policies such as the Health Improvement Programmes will have an impact on how services are developed locally and all planning has to take account of the resources available.

An example of a national initiative affecting local planning is the National Service Framework for Mental Health. Planning these services has to take account of the population involved and factors such as unemployment, poverty and poor housing, which have an impact on health. Figure 2.2 shows the population distribution in London boroughs and identifies those areas that are most in need of mental health support. However, it is pointless if services supporting mental health are implemented without addressing the problems of poor housing, poverty and unemployment; the government recognises that social issues need to be addressed as well as health problems. In this chapter you will see examples of various projects that try to plan services to support a range of health and social needs.

Mental illness needs index (MINI)

The MINI calculates the relative mental health service needs between populations, and is based on 1991 census data. An area with a greater score has a greater need for mental health service provision than one with a smaller value. The scores are based on variables chosen on the basis of an established association with mental illness rates, covering areas such as social isolation, poverty, unemployment, sickness and quality of housing. The variables are:

- Single, widowed, divorced
- No car
- Permanently sick
- Unemployed
- Household not self-contained
- Hostel, lodging houses etc

Mental illness needs index score 1991
England = 100

1	Hillingdon	94.1
2	Harrow	95.6
3	Brent	111.2
4	Ealing	106.8
5	Hounslow	102.2
6	Hammersmith & Fulham	119.0
7	Richmond upon Thames	98.9
8	Kingston upon Thames	97.3
9	Barnet	100.0
10	Wandsworth	113.3
11	Merton	101.3
12	Sutton	96.1
13	Kensington and Chelsea	118.0
14	Westminster, City of	121.1
15	Camden	120.9
16	Islington	122.4
17	Enfield	99.8
18	Haringey	116.5
19	City of London	106.5
20	Lambeth	119.9
21	Southwark	117.2
22	Lewisham	112.4
23	Hackney	122.2
24	Tower Hamlets	117.5
25	Newham	113.6
26	Croydon	100.1
27	Waltham Forest	107.2
28	Redbridge	99.5
29	Greenwich	106.5
30	Bexley	93.2
31	Bromley	95.0
32	Barking & Dagenham	103.4
33	Havering	93.3

Source: GR Glover, 1996

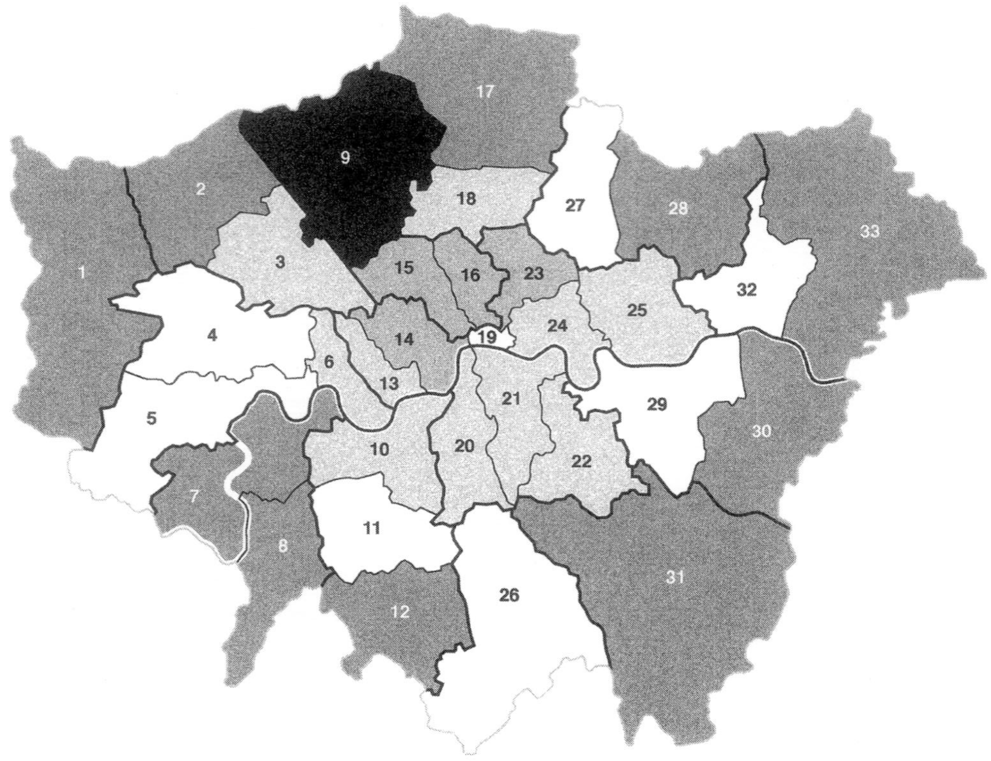

Better than England average 0-9
Equal to England average
Worse than England average 0-9, 10-19, 20-29
Health Authority boundary
London Borough boundary

Figure 2.2 Mental Illness Needs Index (MINI) for London

Planning services to reduce inequalities

Since 1990, there have been many government initiatives to try to reduce health inequalities by providing services targeted at certain groups or areas.

Examples of planning services to reduce inequalities

Recent legislation

1 Following the **White Paper 'the New NHS' (1997)**, the Health Act came into force in 1999. This Act abolished GP fundholding and set up Primary Care Groups to develop services that reflected the needs of the community (see Unit 5). Under fundholding, patients could receive different types of care, depending on whether their GP was a fundholder or not, and this led to local inequalities. Primary Care Groups represent local GPs in an area. They also include nurses and a member of the social services on the Board, so decisions made about planning and providing services reflect the needs of the community, and all patients should have equal access to services.

   (**NB** PCGs will become PCTs (Primary Care Trusts) by 2004, when they will employ staff as well as commission services.)

2 Following the **'Healthier Nation' White Paper** (1999) Health Improvement Programmes (HImPs) were developed jointly by PCGs and Local Authorities to address local issues such as access to services, screening for cancer, reduction in teenage pregnancies, and smoking cessation clinics.

3 **Modernising Social Services White Paper** (1998) focused on the needs of children through a programme called **Quality Protects**. Sure Start programmes are another example of providing services to reduce inequalities. With Sure Start, a new mother is visited by a health visitor and offered support and information, supported by a grant. In May 2001 the Department of Health announced there would be a National Service Framework for Children and Maternity Services. Standards will be drawn up to ensure that all women and children would have equal access to an improved midwifery and neo-natal (newborn) service in all parts of the country. The **Acheson Report** (1998) recommended that a high priority should be given to reducing health inequalities in women of childbearing age, expectant mothers and young children. In all these programmes health and social care services work together.

National Service Frameworks

Since 1999 National Service Frameworks (NSFs) have been developed by the government to reduce inequalities and to standardise services. NSFs have been drawn up by groups of specialists including health and social care managers, partner agencies and service users. NSFs give clear guidelines on the services that should be provided by all agencies, and the standards that should be achieved. NSFs that have been developed so far are:

- Mental Health Services, 1999
- Coronary Heart Disease (CHD) 2000
- Services for Older People 2001

NSFs for children and maternity services are being developed. These NSFs can be accessed on the Department of Health website: http://www.doh.gov.uk

Social Services and local Trusts work together to produce guidelines for their staff, and plans to show how they will implement the NSF locally.

Example The NSF for Older People

Standard 1: Rooting Out Age Discrimination

NHS and social care services will be based on need, and age will not be used to restrict access to services (e.g., surgical operations or drug treatment to older people).

Standard 2: Person-Centred Care

NHS and social care services will treat older people as individuals and help them make choices on their care. 'There will be a single assessment of health and social care needs.

Standard 3: Intermediate Care

Older people will have access to a range of intermediate care services (see page 54) at home or in designated care settings. Unnecessary hospital admission will be prevented and rehabilitation services will be provided.

Standard 4: General Hospital Care

Older people's care in hospital will be delivered by appropriately trained staff.

Standard 5: Strokes

The NHS will work with other agencies to prevent strokes. People who have a stroke will be treated by a specialist stroke service and will have a programme of rehabilitation.

Standard 6: Falls

The NHS will work with other agencies to take action to reduce falls.

Standard 7: Mental Health in Older People

Older people who have mental health problems will have access to mental health services provided by health and social services.

Standard 8: Promoting an Active Healthy Life in Older Age

Health and well-being of older people will be promoted through co-ordinated programmes led by the NHS and the local councils.

Activity

Taking each Standard in turn discuss, possible answers to the following:

1 What type of services will be needed? Where will they be based?

2 Who will provide them? For example, one way of preventing falls is to give exercises to older people to improve their balance; another way would be to check the person's home for hazards that could lead to falls.

3 How could the voluntary sector or leisure services be involved?

4 What are the resource implications for the NSF in terms of staff needed and other expenses?

As you can see, NSFs rely on close working between NHS, social services and voluntary services. Private agencies may also be involved in the provision of residential care or rehabilitation. Carers and users of services will also be involved in planning the services.

Example of inter-agency work

As part of the NSF for Older People, local Age Concern groups have developed a programme called Ageing Well, when volunteers visit an older person to check their home for safety and advise them on keeping well. This is paid for by the local council, which has agreed a one-year contract for the service. The voluntary sector is an important agency in providing services in the community.

Activity

Visit your local library or contact your local centre for voluntary services and find out what services are provided for older people in your area.

Integrated Care

As we have seen, one of the key issues in the provision of health and social care services relates to the provision of care for older people. As the proportion of people aged 75 and over in the population increases, services need to be developed for this age group. The proportion of older women living on their own has increased, and many of these clients have no family close by. Social changes mean that many of these people are isolated in the community, with little contact with neighbours.

Intermediate Care

The National Beds Enquiry (2000) found that many acute beds in hospitals were blocked by older people who had nowhere to go; they needed support and rehabilitation, but did not need acute clinical care.

The NHS Plan (2000) claims that intermediate care will solve many of these problems. A new approach to caring for older people will be developed and this will:

- increase efficient discharge of older people from hospital
- enable older people to be treated effectively outside hospital
- reduce hospital admission
- release acute hospital beds for other patients

Case study

Sally is an Intermediate Placement Officer based in a busy acute hospital. Her responsibility is to arrange for older people to be discharged as soon as possible. She can arrange for patients to go to a statutory rehabilitation centre that is jointly funded by health and social services, or she can arrange for the patient to go to a local private home for additional care. Once patients have recovered sufficiently, they will be transferred to their own homes. The key message with intermediate care is that it promotes the independence of older people, so that they can stay in their own homes for as long as possible, supported by health and social services. In order to achieve this, Sally works with a care manager who arranges for a discharge plan to be developed for the patient, when they have received their initial treatment in the hospital. The discharge plan is drawn up at a multi-disciplinary team meeting attended by the care manager, occupational therapist, physiotherapist, nurses and doctors who decide on the future care of the patient and plan the discharge in advance. The patient could be discharged to:

- *further care in a nursing home;*
- *a residential home;*
- *a rehabilitation unit for a limited time;*
- *or to their own home*

Sally's post is funded by the NHS and the care manager's post is funded by social services; this is another example of the close collaboration between health and social care workers.

Case study

Vanessa is the co-ordinator of an intermediate care team that offers a 24-hour service. Her aim is to prevent hospital admissions for older people by providing alternative services in the community, although she also works with the local hospital to plan the discharge support. As part of the process of preventing hospital admission, Vanessa and her team have devised an alert register. This register identifies and registers patients who have a greater than average risk of requiring emergency admission. If these patients are admitted to hospital, this information is used to develop a discharge plan. Vulnerable patients would include those who have a previous history of falls or strokes. The information on the register is available to social services and the hospital. When the alert register has been fully developed, it will be used for individual patient care planning as well as for identifying any gaps in provision of the service.

How will these changes to intermediate care work in practice?

Case study

Beatrice was 87 and living in Prioryville; she was widowed when she was 72. She had lived in her home for 60 years, a large Victorian house with no central heating, an outside lavatory and a small downstairs bathroom. Beatrice had problems getting up and downstairs because of arthritis, and she rarely left her house. Most of the people she knew who had lived nearby, had died or moved away. Her family lived far away and phoned occasionally and visited once or twice a year. Beatrice was independent and didn't like strangers coming into the house; she was suspicious of 'welfare' and she was not in touch with social services.

One night Beatrice needed to get out of bed and go downstairs to the toilet. The bulb in the landing light had gone out and she was unable to put a new one in herself. Beatrice lost her footing and fell downstairs, and she was not found until the following morning. An ambulance was called and Beatrice was taken to hospital where she had surgery for a broken hip. A social worker visited her and told her they were going to move her to a nursing home to recover. Beatrice did not like the nursing home, she wanted to go home. She became confused and withdrawn and stopped eating. Four weeks after her fall, Beatrice died in the nursing home. No one was with her.

(Adapted from case study provided by Merton, Sutton and Wandsworth Health Authority.)

Activity

How could intermediate care make a difference to Beatrice's story?

Look at the earlier part of this chapter on the NSF for older people and the provision of services for older people. Rewrite Beatrice's story so that it has a happy ending.

Joint Planning of Services

We have seen that in initiatives such as Health Improvement Programmes (HImPs), and NSFs, local councils, health services and the voluntary sector are working more closely than before.

Joint Investment Plans (JIPs)

These are usually Three-Year Plans agreed by partnerships. An example of a JIP would be an agreed plan to implement the NSF for older people. The local council, Primary Care Group (or Trust), Community Trust, Health Authority and the voluntary sector would all agree to the plan.

The plan would include:

- a statement of the resources invested by each group;
- an analysis of possible cost pressures (these could be the increased cost of staff);
- an analysis of the possible demand for services and the extra resources needed.

Case study

A London borough and its partner organisations from health and the voluntary sector have devised a JIP to implement the NSF for older people. The JIP is drawn up like an action plan, stating the target to be met, the action to be taken, the lead agency responsible, and the date of completion (see Table 2.1).

- **Target:** to implement alert registers in primary care and link with local A&E (Accident and Emergency), social services, hospital and district teams.
- **Action:** research to be done into the use of alert registers in primary care and links with A&E and social services.
- **Lead Agency:** Primary Care Group/Trust working with the local hospital, Community Trust and local council.

Table 2.1 A London borough's Joint Investment Plan to implement the NSF of the elderly

Target	Action	Lead Agency	Date for Completion
To implement Alert Registers in Primary Care and provide links between services	Research and data collection of current Alert Register Systems	Primary Care Group	December 2001

Joint working: partnership in action

We have seen examples of joint working in this chapter, we now need to look in more detail at some of the methods used by health and social services to work together.

Pooled budgets

This is where health and social services put a proportion of their funds into a mutually accessible joint budget to enable more integrated care. Pooled budgets need careful administration and audit but they are seen as having many advantages. Look at the extract from *Community Care*.

Report reveals growing role of pooled budgets

Pooled budgets are the most popular way of using flexibilities brought in under the Health Act 1999 in NHS and local authority partnerships, an interim report revealed last week.

The Act introduced three flexibilities in April 2000 – pooling budgets, lead commissioning and integrated provision.

By November 2000, 32 localities had notified the Department of Health that they would be using these flexibilities; 22 were the subject of an evaluation by the National Primary Care Research and Development Centre and the Nuffield Institute for Health.

Typical partners were a health authority, a local authority social service department and NHS Trusts. Fourteen partnerships used mainstream budgets, often supplemented with ringfenced grants including the partnership, prevention, carers or mental illness specific grants.

Half were going to charge users for the social services elements of the partnership. Two said that the NHS – as well as social services – staff would carry out user financial assessments.

Older people's services, particularly intermediate care and winter pressure schemes, and adults with learning difficulties were the most common user groups covered by the partnerships.

Budgets for these schemes ranged from under £25,000 to more than £60 million. Overall, NHS and local authority partners made equal financial contributions.

Community Care, 31 May–6 June 2001

Lead commissioning

This is where one authority transfers funds to another, which will then take responsibility for purchasing both health and social care. The legislation allows the local authority or health authority to delegate their functions and money.

Integrated provision

This is where one organisation provides both health and social care. It is often integrated provision (for example, of health and social care for people with learning disabilities) that brings most benefit to users. This flexibility allows NHS Trusts and Primary Care Trusts greater freedom to provide social care, and social services in-house providers to provide some community health services on behalf of the NHS.

Pooled budgets

Look at the following case study. This illustrates the differences that could be made by the use of pooled budgets.

 Case study

Asha, who is seven, is a child with complex medical and social needs dealt with by a range of health care specialists from the local hospital paediatric unit and from the Community Trust, supporting primary care at home and in school. The social services are involved as she is a 'child in need' under the Children Act and because she needs respite care. She also has special educational needs.

Health and social services have agreed a pathway of care for Asha which includes: respite care, home-based medical and nursing care, social care at home in support of her parents (especially her mother) and family; nursery care for her younger sister and support at a local special school that she attends three days a week.

'Old' system

The care package takes a long time to devise. There is an overlap between the health and care workers, and a duplication of tasks. The package is complicated, involves a lot of different people and is not flexible enough to be adapted to meet changes in Asha's condition.

'New' system

Asha's needs are assessed and a flexible package of services are put together. Most aspects of Asha's needs are met from a pooled budget, and the key worker can implement changes without consulting other professionals. The family feels happier that the process is quick and that they only deal with the key worker.

Lead commissioning

The following case study illustrates the advantage of this process.

Case study

John is 14 and has been looked after by the local authority in a foster home for two years. He has learning difficulties His literary skills are behind his chronological age and he has difficulty concentrating in class. Over the last year his school attendance has declined and he has become increasingly defiant and aggressive. Recently, an incident in the playground has led to a time-limited exclusion from school. This, in turn, has led his foster carers to contact the local authority saying that they cannot cope and that if things do not improve they will no longer be able to have John.

'Old' system

John's social worker decides that he needs a psychiatric assessment and refers him to the local child Mental Health Service. There is a three-month waiting list. The school refuses to take John back and the foster parents feel they cannot wait until the assessment. John is placed in a children's home and becomes increasingly difficult. He refuses to attend the assessment. When he is finally seen, he is diagnosed with dyslexia, attention deficit disorder and depression. He has medication but his progress is slow. After eight months he is ready for another foster care placement and after one year he returns to normal school.

'New' system

The Social Services is lead commissioner for all community-based mental health services for looked-after children. A specialist mental health social worker assesses John quickly, his needs are further assessed at the next weekly meeting of the mental health team who decides John needs urgent treatment. The specialist mental health worker provides immediate support to John's foster family. John is introduced to the psychiatrist at a later stage when the initial period of stress and anxiety is over and the child psychologist plans the next step in John's care. He is diagnosed as having mild attention deficit disorder, dyslexia and low self esteem with a tendency to depression.

The response is quick. The combination of support to John's foster parents, cognitive behaviour therapy and extra help given in school show the advantages of lead commissioning in this case.

Integrated provision

Users and carers want reliable, integrated services. The integration of some health and social services within a single provider brings great benefits.

The following case study shows how health and social services can be provided in a more efficient and helpful way if a local authority-run day centre can operate as an integrated provider.

Case study

Ramesh is 45, a quiet and retiring man who lives with his elderly mother in their family home. He enjoys being at home but wants to do more than watch TV every evening. He has severe learning disabilities and a mild heart condition. His mother is worried that he is very overweight but she feels food is one of his few pleasures. Only people who know Ramesh well can understand what he needs and wants.

'Old' system

Ramesh attends a day centre run by the local authority who also provide transport. Ramesh has to pay a small charge for these services but he enjoys going to the centre and it gives his mother a break. He receives speech therapy at the centre and is finding this helps him to communicate with others. Ramesh prefers sedentary activities at the centre rather than going out, and the day centre staff are reluctant to insist on his being more active because of his heart condition.

'New' system

Ramesh attends a day centre run by the local authority, which also provides transport. Ramesh has to pay a small charge for these services. The community disability team is involved in assessing those using the centre and in helping staff prepare individual programmes for each client. As an integrated provider, the day centre is able to provide community health services as well as social services. Ramesh receives some speech therapy at the centre, which helps with his communication. A physiotherapist also liaises with a further education college to provide more opportunities for physical activity. Ramesh has tried and now enjoys a keep fit class for people with health problems that meets one evening a week. The physiotherapist liaises with his GP and the keep fit instructor to make sure the programme is suitable for him. He enjoys being with people who do not have a learning disability, and his mother is pleased that he is losing weight and she is able to plan some evenings out for herself.

(The case studies in this section have been adapted from 'Partnership in Action, A Discussion Document', DoH 1998.)

Health services for black and ethnic minority groups

Significant health inequalities exist in the health and health experience of black and minority ethnic communities. The government has acknowledged that these groups need additional support. The Department of Health has set up various programmes to ensure that black and minority ethnic groups are not disadvantaged in terms of access to services. Example of initiatives taken includes Health Action Zones (HAZs) where particular problems have been identified and services put in place. One HAZ in the Midlands has been set up specifically to address the needs of Asian groups with diabetes. Some genetically-determined conditions such as sickle-cell anaemia and thalassaemia affect certain ethnic groups and the government is committed to develop adequate services for these groups. Certain diseases that have been given priority in the National Health Improvement Programmes are of specific concern to minority ethnic groups.

- Coronary heart disease is more likely to occur among people from the Indian Sub-continent.
- Stroke and hypertension are more common among people from the Caribbean and African countries.
- Cervical cancer is increasing among Caribbean women, but the use of screening services is low among black and minority ethnic groups.
- Diagnostic rates for schizophrenia are high for Afro–Caribbean males.
- Suicide rates are high among young Asian women.
- Poverty among some minority ethnic groups means that children from these families are more at risk of accidents.
- The incidence of diabetes is four to five times higher in Asian people than in non-Asians.
- Minority ethnic populations are at greater risk of kidney disease related to diabetes.
- Infant mortality is higher in Afro-Caribbean and Asian babies than in the population as a whole.

Health Authorities are developing action plans to develop services to meet the needs of minority ethnic groups in their areas.

After April 2002 many of the responsibilities of the HA's will be taken over by the PCT's.

Ethnic monitoring

Before developing appropriate services, HAs need to collect information about the population profile of their area. This is done through ethnic monitoring of patients in both primary and secondary care. Most HAs depend on the figures from the 1991 census. As the census is only done every 10 years, the data tends to be out of date. As part of the Race Relations (Amendment) Act 2000, ethnic minority systems must be in place by May 2002.

Ethnic minority needs assessment

Once the profile of the area is established, the next step is to identify the services and support required, using an ethnic minority needs assessment. In one London area the following needs were identified through working with the local community:

- language support;
- social support;
- greater awareness among health professionals of cultural issues;
- support for refugees and asylum seekers.

Action planning

This is the next stage in the process. The key health areas that were identified in the London area were as follows:

- CHD support;

- diabetes detection;
- eye health – including glaucoma;
- HIV issues;
- interpreting services;
- access to GPs and NHS dentists;
- health screening, cervical, breast, TB, etc.;
- blood disorders, such as sickle cell anaemia.

Health Promotion was also a key issue.

Activity

In your groups, devise a strategy that a HA could use to increase the use of health screening services for minority ethnic groups – in particular breast and cervical screening. You need to think about how you would publicise the service, and how you could ensure that the service is culturally sensitive.

Partnerships in health and social care

Partnerships in health and social care can be described as links between a range of different agencies. So far in this chapter we have looked at the links between the NHS and social services with the development of pooled budgets, lead commissioning and integrated provision. However, partnerships in health and social care can include a range of other agencies as we can see in Figure 2.3.

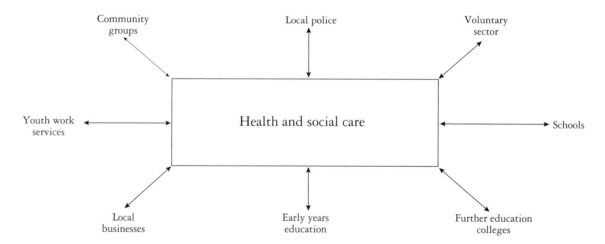

Figure 2.3 Partnerships in health and social care

Examples of partnerships

Health Action Zones (HAZs)

Health Action Zones were initiated in 1998 in order to develop new approaches to improving the health of certain community groups through multi-agency partnership.

Lambeth, Southwark and Lewisham HAZ

This is a Safe Kids project that brings together emergency services, police, schools and other groups to reduce accidents inside and outside the home.

Health Living Centres (HLCs)

A network of HLCs is being developed in the UK. The aim is to promote health by helping people of all ages to maximise their health and well-being. HLCs involve a range of partnerships at local level.

 Case study

A HLC has been set up in a deprived area in South London. A steering group has been formed to plan and provide a range of activities.

Membership of the steering group includes:

- *members of the local council;*
- *members of the local church;*
- *a worker from the local Health Promotion Unit;*
- *local residents;*
- *representatives of the voluntary sector;*
- *a community nurse.*

This HLC is partly funded by the national lottery and by the local council. Certain activities were identified as meeting the needs of the community, and the current programme includes provision for the children, parents and older people. These include:

- *a toy library;*
- *a play centre;*
- *a mother and toddler group;*
- *numeracy and literacy workshops for adults;*
- *parenting skills courses;*
- *behaviour management sessions for parents with hyperactive children;*
- *healthy eating courses;*
- *exercise classes for older people.*

Healthy School Scheme

This is an example of a partnership between primary schools and community-based health care professionals.

Case study

Lavender Fields is an area in South London that has been identified as an area of ill health and social deprivation. The teenage pregnancy rate is one of the highest in the London boroughs. When population and health statistics are analysed, the evidence shows the following:

- *a high proportion of children under five – many of whom are on the 'at risk' register;*
- *a high proportion of lone teenage mothers;*
- *a high rate of chronic long-term illness related to respiratory problems;*
- *a high hospital admission rate for a range of reasons, including accidents;*
- *a long standing drug problem in the area;*
- *148 children are in foster care.*

The Healthy Schools Team includes a local GP, teachers, a senior school nurse, a health visitor and a practice nurse. The team is led by the Healthy Schools Team co-ordinator. Figure 2.4 shows the programme that has been developed for three primary schools.

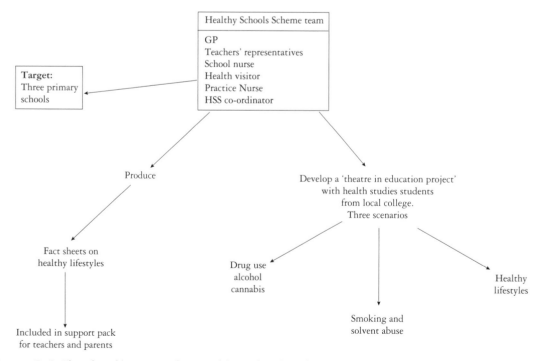

Figure 2.4 The development of a Healthy Schools Scheme

Activity

Imagine you are part of the Healthy Schools Team. In your groups, produce and perform a short dramatic piece on one of the topics identified in the programme suitable for seven- to nine-year-olds.

1 What messages are you trying to put across?

2 What do you need to be aware of if you are approaching a sensitive subject in a primary school?

Regeneration Programmes

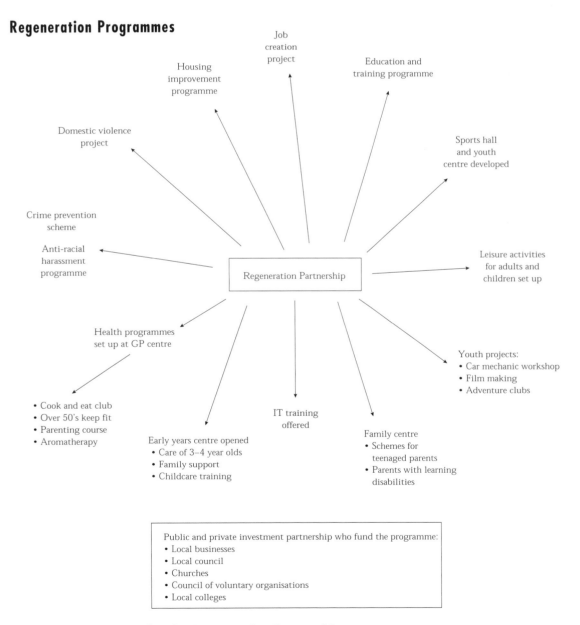

Figure 2.5 An example of a Regeneration Partnership

Regeneration programmes

These are a further example of partnerships in a community. The Single Regeneration Project (SRP) was introduced in 1994 and combined a number of previously separate government programmes. The partnership is formed between public and private investment. Partners would include local businesses, local councils, churches, the voluntary sector, local colleges and other community groups. The purpose of the project is to provide sustainable regeneration, economic development and industrial competitiveness in a way that meets the need of the local community. Figure 2.5 shows the range of activities provided by a regeneration project in a London borough.

Early Years Development and Childcare Partnership

Child care and Early Years Services play an important role in the delivery of the Government's overall aims which are to:

- increase opportunities for all;
- build responsible and secure communities;
- raise productivity and sustainable growth.

The Government requires all local authority areas to set up partnerships, the Early Years Development and Childcare Partnership (EYDCP), must produce and implement a plan. This explains how nursery education and child care places for all children will be organised and created. There are numerous new targets on the creation of early education and new childcare places, recruiting more childcare workers, raising quality standards, training, equalities and the Children's Information Service.

National targets of the EYDCP

1 To create new child care places for 1.6 million children by March 2004, allowing an extra 1 million children to benefit from child care.

2 By March 2004 there will be child care places in the most disadvantaged areas for every lone parent entering employment.

3 To put in place universal nursery education for three-year-olds by September 2004. Figure 2.6 shows the people who would be involved in a local partnership group. We can see that child care could be provided by private, statutory and voluntary organisations, as well as individuals who will give child care such as childminders

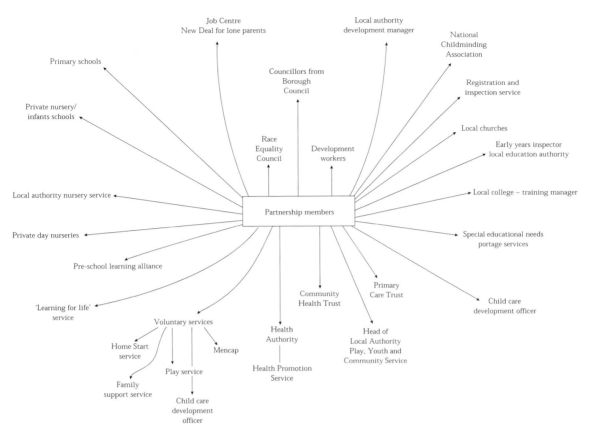

Figure 2.6 Participants in a local EYDCP

Activity

In order to ensure good-quality child care, it is important that providers of services are trained and monitored. Ofsted is taking on the role of inspecting nurseries, playgroups and childminders, but you need to think about the training required for child care workers. Does your college offer child care courses? What is the content of the courses?

One of the key issues in the new arrangements is to ensure that children with Special Educational Needs (SEN) are included in the planning. A SEN officer would be responsible for the provision of specialist services in each area. Equal opportunities is another target and the plan in each area must show that all sections of the community have equal access to child care and Early Years Services, regardless of their gender, age, special educational needs, disability, background, religion, ethnicity or competence in spoken English.

Activity

Approach your local council (perhaps your teacher will do so for you) and obtain a copy of their local Early Years Development and Childcare Plan.

If you are interested in training and employment in child care, contact your local Children's Information Centre.

Involving stakeholders in planning services

A stakeholder is anyone who has an interest in the service being provided or proposed.

Case study

A long stay hospital for people with learning disabilities is being closed and alternative accommodation and support will be provided in the community in small homes in local residential areas. Medical care will be given by the GPs and the community health teams, including therapists. As this is a change in service provision, the health authority has to consult stakeholders. Figure 2.7 shows the consultation process. Consultation usually takes three months to complete.

Activity

1   Who are the stakeholders involved in the hospital closure and what may their concerns be?

    You could think of many people who could be affected by the proposed changes – parents, carers, local residents, staff who are currently employed in the hospital, GPs who may feel they lack the skills to care for this group, and so on.

2   Every year consultation takes place on changes to service provision. See if you can find out about a consultation that is taking place in your area. One group that is involved in preparing a response to proposed changes of service is the local Community Health Council. Perhaps your teacher could arrange for someone from the CHC to visit your school or college and to explain the process.

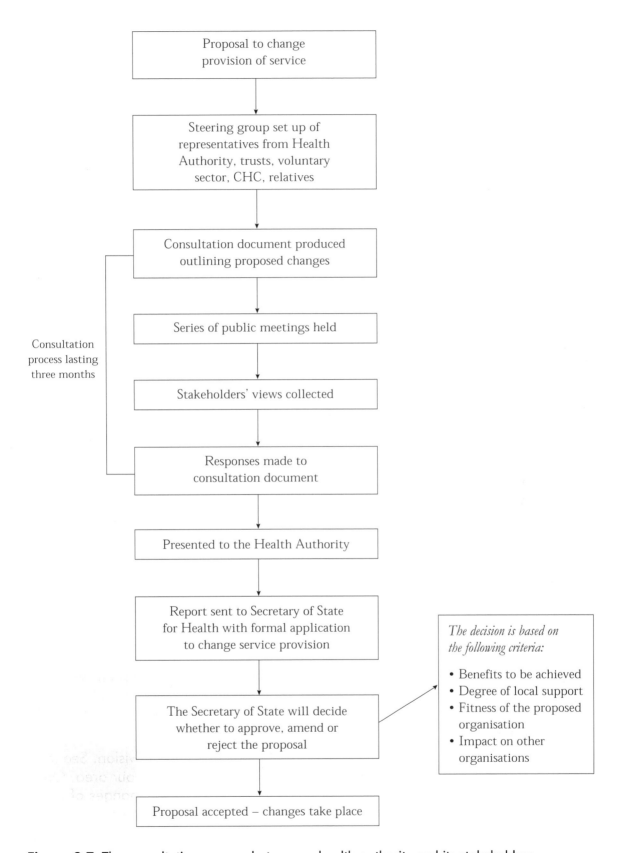

Figure 2.7 The consultation process between a health authority and its stakeholders

Public and patient involvement

One of the key features of health and social care policy since 1997 has been the importance of public and patient involvement in the planning of services. Examples of this approach include:

- a lay member on the Boards of PCGs;
- users and carers involved in planning and reviewing services;
- patient satisfaction questionnaires administered in both primary and secondary care provision.

In July 2000 the NHS Plan was published by the government setting out a 10-year plan to modernise the health service. Chapter 10 of the plan sets out the ways in which the public will be involved in the future. A key point in Chapter 10 is that by April 2002, every NHS and Primary Care Trust will establish a Patient Advice and Liaison Service (PALS) managed by Trust staff. The staff will be easily accessible to patients, their carers and families and provide three critical roles:

1 To help to resolve patients' concerns quickly and efficiently, and improve the outcome of care in the process.

2 To provide information to patients to make contact with the NHS as easy as possible.

3 To act as the visible contact point to enable patients and the public to access the new system of patient and public involvement.

While PALS will provide support to individual patients, the new system will also provide new ways of ensuring that patients' views are taken into account when important decisions about the NHS are being made. The whole of the NHS – Health Authorities, Primary Care Trusts and NHS Trusts – must consult patients and the public on the planning of services and proposals to change and develop services.

In 2001, several PALS were established as pilot schemes, funded by the Department of Health. In one hospital, the PALS was set up in an office by the entrance to the hospital so that patients were able to make contact easily.

Activity

Certain groups may have difficulty making complaints or comments. Can you think of ways PALS could help people who have learning difficulties, hearing or other disabilities or English as a second language? If you were the co-ordinator for a PALS, how would you ensure that the patients knew about the service?

Clients and users' groups

It is now recognised that clients and users can make a useful contribution to the planing of services.

Case study

A health authority decides to change the provision of services for a group of elderly people with mental health problems. At the moment they are cared for in a range of settings:

- *a day hospital attached to a community hospital;*

- *a day centre in another part of the area;*

- *a long-stay ward in the community hospital;*

- *respite care beds in a variety of placements.*

It has been decided that in order to rationalise the services, all provision should be based in a purpose-built centre at one end of the borough. There is no public transport to the proposed site. After discussion and consultation with the HA, representatives of relatives and carers joined the steering group for the new centre. Based on their personal experiences as carers, the representatives were able to advise on a range of issues concerning the type of care and support needed. Transport issues were discussed and a local bus company was approached to provide a service to the site. It was agreed by the HA that having relatives in the group had been very helpful in planning the services.

Activity

Can you think of possible problems that could arise in a group that contains professionals and users of services?

Often there can be a conflict of interest as the HA has to work within a fixed budget which may affect the level of staffing and service provided.

Carers

A carer is anyone who is helping to look after a partner, friend or relative who, because of illness, old age or disability may not be able to manage at home without help. There are 6 million carers in the UK. Carers save the government an estimated £34 billion every year by caring for people at home. Without this care many people would have to live in residential care.

Research by the Princess Royal Trust (1998) has estimated that most carers are aged over 45, but there are also younger carers who are balancing being a carer and work. Another group of carers are young carers – aged under 16 – who have to cope with the demands of growing up, education and caring. Recent legislation has given carers more rights and financial help: The Carers' (Recognition and Services) Act (1995), and the Carers' and Disabled Children's Act,

(2000). Carers have an input into planning services by attending case conferences and discussing their own needs and that of the cared-for person. Although many carers use local carers' centres for advice and help, some carers find they need additional support and advocacy when trying to agree the services that should be provided.

Case study

Rosemary is a 48-year-old Jamaican woman who cares for her 19-year-old son, Martin, who suffered severe head injuries at the age of five. Martin has multiple caring needs but Rosemary has decided she wants to keep him at home. The community care package that has been devised for him is very complicated and requires a large team of care workers. The care package worked well but when Martin was transferred to adult services, Rosemary felt that 'the care disappeared and I was faced with agency staff coming and going with no one worker getting to know Martin'.

Rosemary lost confidence in the workers and she became very frustrated. Because of cultural and language differences, she found it difficult to communicate with the care workers and they saw her as difficult and aggressive. Finally, Rosemary had an argument with one of the workers over the standard of care for her son. The care agency refused to send staff to the house and complained to social services. At the same time, the house was being adapted, with a new bathroom being built, and Rosemary was in a dispute with the builder about changes he had made to the original plans. The house was in a mess, and the final straw for Rosemary was when she lost Martin's benefit payment book, so she could not get any money.

Rosemary approached the local carers' centre and the carers' support worker attended a social services team meeting to explore how the situation could be resolved. The worker suggested that Martin's care should be arranged through direct payments. This would resolve the current fragmented care and allow Rosemary to employ her own care team. This was refused as it was thought that Rosemary could not cope with such an arrangement, and as Martin was unable to make a decision it would not be legally possible.

The carers' centre arranged an advocate each for Martin and Rosemary to ensure that their rights under equal opportunities were met. As a result of this support, a care plan for services has been devised and will be provided by a voluntary agency and be paid for by direct payments.

(Case study supplied by E. Parsons of the Princess Royal Trust Care Centre.

This case study shows how changes in approaches to planning care, supported by legislation and additional funding, can help users and carers have more say in how services are provided.)

Involving the local community, schools and community groups

One of the initiatives in recent years has been the **National Strategy for Neighbourhood Renewal.** Government research over the past 20 years has demonstrated that:

- poverty is more concentrated within individual neighbourhoods and estates;
- social exclusion on these estates has become more marked.

In comparison with the rest of the country many of these deprived areas have:

- 30% higher mortality rates;
- 25% of the population are likely to have low skills and literacy;
- unemployment rates are six times as high as elsewhere;
- there is three times as much burglary.

Activity

Can you think of reasons why these areas are more likely to experience these problems?

Aims of the strategy

- to narrow the gap between Britain's most deprived neighbourhoods and the rest of the country;
- to form a foundation for a future regeneration and social exclusion policy.

We have already seen an example of a regeneration project on page 66 of this chapter.

Key principles for Neighbourhood Renewal

- to revive local economies;
- to revive local communities;
- to provide good public services;
- to provide leadership and joint working between the different agencies.

Measures of success for the strategy

- more jobs;
- better educational achievement;
- less crime;
- better health.

Case study

Brambledown has been identified as a community that reflects the problems described in the research. It is a large estate built in the 1930s. There is a high level of:

- unemployment;
- truancy;
- single parent families;
- teenage pregnancies;
- drug related crime;
- deaths from cancer and respiratory disease.

In Brambledown, the voluntary services with representatives from the local PCG and the council, held a series of meetings to ask the community what they wanted to see happen on the estate. These were the issues raised by the residents:

- they wanted the strategy to be led by the community not dictated by professionals;
- they wanted adequate funding to be given directly to residents, community and voluntary groups;
- they wanted the funding to be long term – 5 or 10 years – rather than short term funding for one year;
- they wanted excluded groups to participate – refugees, unemployed, older people;
- they wanted people to be helped into work;
- they wanted IT skills training.

As a result of the consultation with the community the following services have been put into place or are planned for the future:

- IT skills training at the local community centre;
- close working with the police to reduce anti-social behaviour;
- a neighbourhood warden has been introduced;
- house-letting procedures have been reviewed and improved;
- arts and sports programmes have been implemented for all age groups in the area;
- a local community project has been set up based on a co-operative where community members buy fresh fruit and vegetables and sell it at a reduced price;
- a drop-in service has been set up at the local community centre to advise residents on benefits;
- a local community nurse holds a surgery three times a week to advise on aspects of child care, health and contraception;

- a local chiropody service has been set up;
- refugees and asylum seekers have access to English classes.

The main lesson to be learned from Brambledown is the importance of involving the community in developing services that are relevant to their needs.

Health Needs Assessment

This is another example of a community initiative, usually developed by the local Health Promotion Unit, when a certain area is identified as having specific needs. The purpose of the HNA is to involve the different local groups in identifying the health needs they may have and the service provision that could be developed. This approach has been used in socially deprived areas (see Figure 2.8).

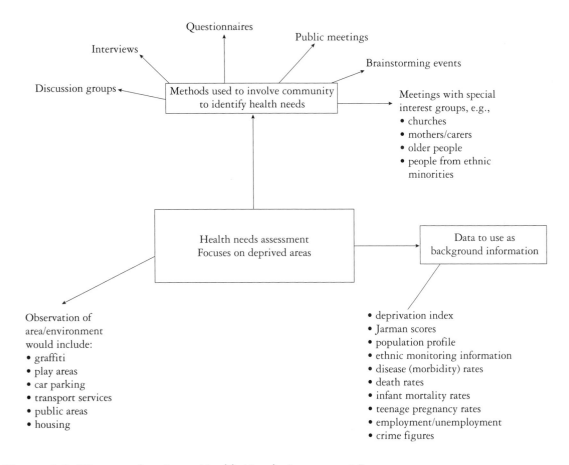

Figure 2.8 Diagram showing a Health Needs Assessment Programme

The role of the current administrative services

Community services, whether they are based at the local council, the PCG or PCT, or in the voluntary sector have certain priorities.

One of the key issues in local government at the moment is Best Value, a concept that was introduced in the 1990s. Each year the council has to review one or two of its services to see if they are offering cost-efficient services, while at the same time ensuring that quality is maintained. All areas of services are reviewed in turn. Local councils are dependent on central funding from government; they also raise funds from the rates levied for business and private home owners. Local councils have a duty to ensure that public money is spent as effectively as possible.

PCGs and PCTs are also working under constraints. They receive their funding from the health authority and have certain allocations for different budgets. The PCG/PCT allocates budgets to all the GP practices in its area, and also commissions services from local hospitals. One of the key problems at the moment for PCGs is to control spending on prescriptions. Drug prices have increased and patients' expectations of services, have led to spiralling costs. Most prescriptions are for older people who do not pay, but have repeat prescriptions on a regular basis.

Case study

In one PCG the pharmacy advisor worked with local community pharmacists to see how the costs of repeat prescriptions could be reduced. In their research they found the following:

- *Many people had repeat prescriptions for several items and requested a repeat for all of them, although they only needed one.*

- *Cupboard checks made by the nursing staff found that many prescribed drugs were never taken but hoarded by patients.*

- *One patient had 22 items that had not been used but had been prescribed and dispensed.*

Activity

If you were the pharmacy advisor what measures could you take to:

- reduce unnecessary repeat prescribing;

- prevent hoarding of medicines.

It is a difficult ethical problem as you cannot simply march into people's homes and check their cupboards!

Voluntary organisations

Voluntary organisations were originally set up to advise and support certain groups in society and act as pressure groups on national and local government. In the last 15 years their role has changed. They still use unpaid volunteers to provide certain services, but they increasingly employ staff to administer the organisation, raise money and agree contracts for the provision of services to a variety of agencies. The voluntary services are now more like local businesses that compete for contracts, but at the same time they still maintain their role in the community in giving advice and support. They are dependent on local and national government for funding (as well as the Lottery), and they still receive donations.

Tensions in planning and providing services

Many of the tensions in planning and providing services are related to the limited resources available in both health and social care.

Examples of recent stories in the press relate to:

Adviser rules against MS drug on NHS over cost

PATIENTS with multiple sclerosis should not be given beta interferon on the NHS because of the high cost, a Government advisory body has decided.

The decision by the National Institute of Clinical Excellence (Nice) was immediately condemned by doctors, patient groups and drug companies.

Three out of the four companies said they would appeal and the fourth company is considering doing so.

The drug costs between £6,660 and £10,000 per patient per year. The MS Society estimates that about 10,000 patients would benefit. The society, which will also appeal against the decision, accused Nice of turning its back on people with MS and saying they were not worth treating.

The Daily Telegraph 3 November 2001

- the prescribing of expensive drugs (see the extract from an article in *The Daily Telegraph*);
- the provision of certain services.

One of the major issues is the provision of long term care. In the Royal Commission on Long Term Care (1999) recommendations were made that long-term care should be provided free of charge. In the Government's response, it was agreed that nursing care should be provided free of charge but that social care should be supplied subject to means testing. The next debate that took place was what was meant by 'nursing care'. The Health and Social Care Act 2001 defined nursing care as 'any services provided by a registered nurse and (a) involving the provision of care or (b) the planning, supervision or delegation of care, other than any services which do not need to be given by a registered nurse'. However, many nurses are confused by what this means. The extract from *Community Care* shows the proposed implementation of free nursing care. With closer working between the health and social services sector, single assessments and the development of care trusts, the confusion is likely to continue.

Categories of eligible groups for free nursing care

From 1 October 2001

■ Existing self-funding residents, or those admitted after October following an assessment, who pay the full cost of their care, except those with preserved rights to higher rates of income support.

■ Those who, after October, are assessed as needing registered nursing care and placed by social services departments, where departments pay the full standard rate: but where the individuals chargeable income exceeds the cost.

■ Those placed by social services before and after October where social services pay only a very small part of the cost.

From 1 April 2002

■ Those placed by social services departments which currently pay the full care costs of those people placed under Mental Health Act 1983 section 117(2).

■ Those in a nursing home with preserved rights to higher rates of income support whose care management is transferred to local councils.

Community Care, 2–8 August 2001

Another example of conflict is related to charging for social care. At the moment social services can charge a 'reasonable amount' for the provision of services. These charges vary across the UK and this has been seen as very unfair to clients. Proposals have been put forward that charging policies should be developed nationally, so that wherever people lived in the UK, they would be charged the same amount. Social Services may not charge for services provided under the Mental Health Act. Social Services provide assessments of caring needs free of charge.

Conflicts with mental health provision

With the recent media coverage of murders and attacks in the community by people with mental health problems, the NSF for Mental Health proposes the development of additional secure units for detaining those people who are seen to be potentially violent. At the same time, GPs are required to keep a register of their patients who have severe mental illness (SMI). With the introduction of the Human Rights Act (1998) continued detention of people with severe mental illness will only be lawful if a mental disorder is continuing. Mental Disorder Tribunals will be set up to ensure that all decisions made are compatible with Human Rights.

Conflicts with early years provision

We have discussed the Government's proposal for early years childcare provision in relation to working mothers, but some single parents may feel that they want to stay at home with their child and not return to work. Some parents feel that children are too young to start school full time at four years old, so we can see that there are possible conflicts between government policy and plans, and individuals' choices.

Another example of conflict can be with the statementing process. Statementing is a formal process of negotiation between the education authority and the parents of the child. The aims of the process are to identify the areas of need and define the treatment and/or educational support required. The Statement of Special Education Needs is a legal document that must describe the child's needs precisely. The statement must be updated regularly – generally once a year.

Case study

Anna is five-years-old. She has been diagnosed as having dyspraxia, which means she has manual dexterity problems that affect her ability to write. She was statemented when she started school, and the local education authority decided to supply a classroom assistant for six hours a week as the result of the Statement process. Her parents did not think this was adequate support and appealed to the local education authority to reconsider the support they could give Anna. To support their claim, they paid for a private psychologist to prepare a report on Anna's needs, but the education authority refused to increase the support given. Anna's parents have considered appealing to a tribunal but they feel that it will increase the stress on their daughter. Because of their experiences of the lack of support for their daughter in a mainstream school, they have decided to move her to a school for children with special needs.

The statementing procedure can be seen in a positive way as it identifies any additional educational needs the child may have at an early age. However, some people feel that statementing is another way of labelling certain groups as inferior, and there can be a conflict between the parents and the education authority over the level of support that is appropriate.

Promoting quality in the NHS

The Government has put quality on top of the agenda for the new NHS. The NHS Quality Framework is stated in 'A New First Class Service: Quality in the NHS' (1998). The framework includes the following:

- National Institute for Clinical Excellence (NICE);
- Clinical Governance;
- a system of National Service Frameworks;
- continuing professional development and life-long learning;
- improved professional self regulation;
- Commission for Health Improvement (CHI);
- performance assessment frameworks;
- patient and public involvement.

Figure 2.9 shows the inter-relationship between these different groups and approaches.

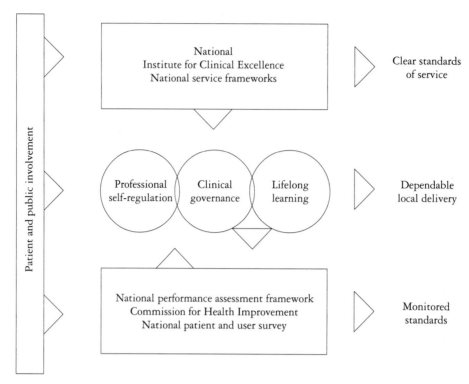

Figure 2.9 Delivering improved quality care
Source: A First-class Service: Quality in the New NHS 1998, DOH

Definitions and explanations

NICE

NICE has three clear functions:

1 To appraise new and existing technologies.
2 To develop clear guidelines for practice.
3 To promote clinical audit and confidential enquiries.

One area of the work of NICE that tends to be reported in the media is the approval or rejection of certain drugs for NHS prescription.

Clinical governance

This is defined as 'a framework through which NHS organisations are accountable for continuously improving the quality of their services and safeguarding high standards of care by creating an environment in which excellence can flourish' (DoH). All PCGs and PCTs have a clinical governance lead on the Board who ensures that standards are maintained in the GP practices. This could be achieved through annual audits of practices to find out if the NSFs are being implemented by the GPs. For example, with the NSF for CHD all patients who are identified as 'at risk' would be on a CHD register and have their blood levels monitored. Audit for excellence would also include how far the targets for cervical smears, flu immunisations and childhood immunisations were being met according to national guidelines.

Lifelong learning and continual professional development

This would be part of the annual education programmes organised by the PCG/PCT. In future years, GPs will have to apply for revalidation in order to stay in practice and they will be expected to show evidence of their professional competence through the development of a portfolio of practice. This will ensure that doctors keep up to date with changes in clinical advances.

CHI

CHI will inspect organisations within the NHS and produce a public report. Any areas of poor practice will be identified and the organisation will have to produce an action plan showing how improvements will be made. During 2001 several hospitals were inspected and shortcomings identified.

Performance assessment framework

Figure 2.10 shows how performance assessment will operate. As you can see, both patient and carer experience are seen as essential.

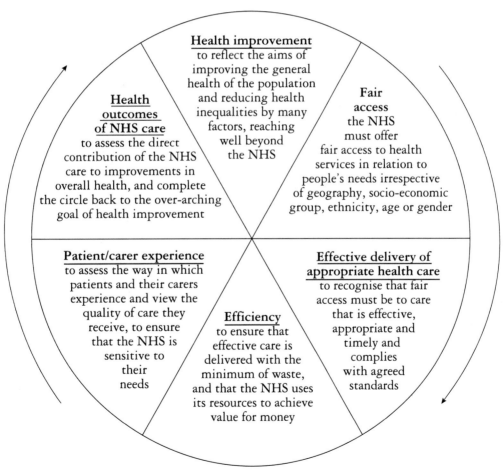

Figure 2.10 The elements of the Performance Assessment Framework
Source: A First-class Service: Quality in the New NHS 1998, DOH

Clinical audit

This is defined as the systematic and regular evaluation by health care professionals of the care they provide.

Performance indicators

When assessing quality of practice, whether in a hospital or in a GP practice, certain statistics are used to monitor performance. In a hospital, clinical indicators would include:

- deaths in hospital within 30 days of surgery;
- emergency readmission to hospital within 28 days of discharge from hospital.

These figures are produced annually and published in the press. See if you can find these during your course.

Developing and maintaining service standards in nursing

The UKCC currently has the responsibility for setting and maintaining standards in nursing. This will be replaced by the Nursing and Midwifery Council in April 2002.

The UKCC protects patients by:

- setting standards for nursing, midwifery and health visiting education, practice and conduct;
- maintaining a register of qualified nurses, midwives and health visitors;
- providing advice for nurses, midwives and health visitors on professional standards;
- considering complaints about professional misconduct or unfitness to practise due to serious ill health, and taking action against those who are found guilty of misconduct or who are not fit to practise.

Patient representatives sit on committees that consider complaints about professional conduct. The UKCC has an annual conference with patients' organisations so that they can listen to the views of patients and can explain to patients how the UKCC protects patients.

There are over 640,000 nurses, midwives and health visitors on the UKCC register. There are around 900 complaints each year from the public, employers and practitioners about possible professional misconduct by registered nurses, midwives and health visitors. The most common complaints are:

- physical, sexual or verbal abuse of patients;
- stealing from patients;
- failing to care for patients properly;
- failing to keep proper records;
- failing to administer medicines properly;
- deliberately concealing unsafe practice;
- committing serious criminal offences.

The most common examples of unfitness to practise for reasons of ill health are:

- alcohol or drug dependency;
- untreated mental disorders;
- serious personality disorders.

The UKCC publishes 'Guidelines for Professional Practice', which covers all areas of practice and gives useful case studies. It can be obtained from their publications department.

Standards in Social Care

As part of the modernising agenda laid down in the White Paper, 'Modernising Social Services' (1998), the Government intends to reform the regulation of social care services and private and voluntary care by establishing a new independent body called The National Care Standards Commission.

The Commission will regulate statutory and independent sector care services in accordance with the new national minimum standards to be set by the Secretary for State for Health. The Commission will carry out regular inspections of services and it will have powers of enforcement to ensure that services meet the required standard. The aim of the Commission is to improve the quality of services and the level of protection for vulnerable people. The commission will register and inspect:

- all residential care homes;
- nursing homes;
- childrens' homes;
- domiciliary care services;
- residential family centres;
- independent fostering agencies;
- voluntary adoption agencies;
- nurses agencies;
- boarding schools;
- local authority adoption and fostering services.

At the moment registration and inspection is carried out by the local council or by the health authority. Concern has been expressed about standards in care homes and a Government Paper, 'Fit for the Future', will finalise standards of care homes for older people. The NCSC:

- will report to the government on the provision and quality of social care services across the UK;
- will advise the government on any changes it thinks should be made to the national minimum standards;
- will have the general duty of encouraging the quality of social care standards.

The NCSC was set up as a result of the Care Standards Act 2000. It will become fully operational in April 2002.

The Act can be accessed on http://www.legislation.hmso.gov.ukacts2000.htm

Early Years Standards

Inspection of Early Years education services will transfer to Ofsted. The first two objectives relate to Early Years Services.

Objective 1. To deliver high-quality inspection of schools, funded nursery education and local education authorities, providing independent assessment to help them raise educational standards.

Objective 2. To provide high-quality advice, based on inspection evidence to the Secretary of State for Education, to assist in the formation and evaluation of government policies.

In Early Years education, 8,000 nurseries were inspected in 2000–01. Ofsted is also responsible for inspecting child care and will implement a national system of regulation by 2002. As part of ensuring high standards, Ofsted will:

- establish a publicly accessible national register of childminders and day care providers by April 2002;
- establish integrated inspections of child care and nursery education by April 2003;
- conduct annual inspections of all registered childminders and day care providers by April 2003;
- set targets for the registration and inspection of child care providers by December 2001.

Sure Start

As part of the Government's spending review in 2001, a revised public service agreement has been drawn up for Sure Start. Sure Start is a cross-departmental programme, which is overseen by the Departments of Education and Skills, Work and Pensions, Health, Environment, Food and Rural Affairs, Transport, and the Home Office. The programme works with parents-to-be, parents and children to promote the physical, intellectual and social development of pre-school children. Sure Start has five objectives:

1 Improving children's social and emotional development.
2 Improving children's health.
3 Improving children's ability to learn.
4 Strengthening families and communities.
5 Increasing productivity (of inspection).

Each objective is measured by a series of targets to:

- provide support and information for all parents;
- reduce by 10% children re-registered on a child protection register;
- ensure that all Sure Start programmes are implemented in a culturally-sensitive way, and include ways of identifying, caring for and treating mothers with post-natal depression;

- achieve a 5% reduction in low birth weight babies;
- achieve a 10% reduction in children admitted to hospitals as an emergency during their first year of life with gastro-enteritis, a respiratory infection or a severe injury;
- ensure that every family will be in contact with the Sure Start programme within the first 2 months of a birth.

Progress will be reviewed. In the past a great deal of concern has been expressed about the standards of parenting and child care, and the Sure Start programme is one way of improving standards for all children.

New developments on technology and expertise

In the last 20 years considerable advances have been made in the detection of disease and in the provision of health care. Sophisticated scanning and imaging techniques assist in the detection of health problems, and staff are trained to use the procedures. GPs are being encouraged to train in scanning procedures so that they can offer the service to their patients in their local practice rather than refer them to hospital. This saves time and the results are available quickly. Telemedicine is another example of ways in which the latest information technology can be used to identify problems and treat them effectively.

Example 1

A PCT and specialist unit in a hospital work together to treat cardiac patients. In the traditional approach, many patients who had a heart attack would be at risk from dying because of the time taken for the ambulance to respond to the call, the assessment of the patient's condition and transfer to the nearest A&E department.

Telemedicine can overcome many of these problems. The paramedics can take an electrocardiogram (ECG) and transmit this electronically to the hospital for diagnosis. Arrangements can then be made for the patient to be treated as soon as they reach hospital. Telemedicine can also be used in the patient's own home. Using the home television and a small video camera, nurses can assess patients in their home and send the results to the hospital.

Telemedicine can reduce unnecessary visits to hospital. As well as cardiac conditions, telemedicine can also be used to send pictures of patients with skin problems to the consultant dermatologist for diagnosis. This is important as the incidence of skin cancer is increasing; with increased outpatients' appointments, consultants are finding it difficult to see everyone with a possible skin cancer within the target of two weeks from referral. (The Cancer Guidelines set by the Government state that all suspected cases of cancer have to be seen in hospital within two weeks of being seen by their GP.)

Other technological developments have also helped in the detection of cardiac conditions. Patients who have palpitations or other unusual heart rhythms do not need to go to the hospital for investigation. They can wear a device called an ambulant ECG machine. Electrodes are attached to their chest and the device is kept in place with a belt. It can be worn under the clothes and the patient does normal everyday activities (apart from swimming or bathing as the device has to be kept dry!). After 24 hours the device is returned to the doctor and the ECG is read via a telemedicine link.

New technology is also used to develop patients records. The Electronic Patient Record (EPR) will include details of the patient's medical history and can be accessed (using a password) by health and social care agencies. Hopefully, this will mean the end to missing records. When the patient attends either the GP or the hospital, the record will be updated. This will give up to date information to all groups involved in the care of the patient.

NHS Direct

Figure 2.11 describes a telephone service available in all parts of the UK (see Unit 5). When a patient calls for advice, the nurse dealing with the call may advise the patient on a number of options (see Figure 2.12).

Figure 2.11 Information leaflet for patients about NHS Direct

England	Percentages
	1999–00
Nurses advice given	
Gave self-care advice	36
Advised on urgent GP visit (within 24 hours)	29
Advised a routine GP visit	12
Advised a visit to accident and emergency	9
Advised patient to contact other professionals	9
Arranged for emergency ambulance	3
Other/call aborted	2
All calls receiving nurse advice (=100%)(millions)	1.2
Other calls (millions)	0.4
All calls (millions)	1.6

Figure 2.12 Breakdown of the outcome of calls to NHS Direct, 1999–2000 Source Social Trends 2001, HMSO

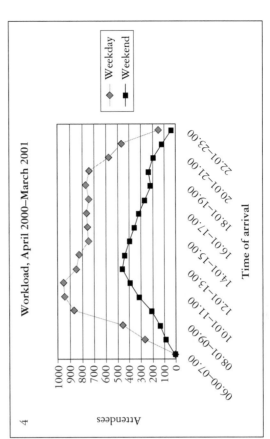

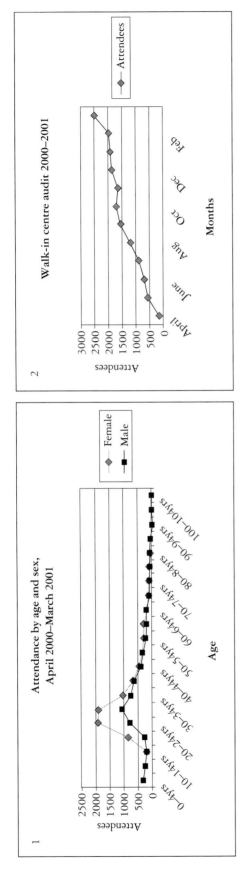

3   Attendance by diagnosis

The majority of patients seen in the walk-in centre have primary care needs, which are managed by the nursing team. It is not uncommon for patients to have multiple health needs that are addressed in one consultation.

The top 10 presenting diagnosis have been (most common first):

- ENT conditions
- emergency contraception
- muscular-skeletal condition
- dermatological
- laceration
- ABCs/infection
- Ophthalmological
- upper respiratory tract infection
- urinary tract infection
- gastro-intestinal condition

Figure 2.13 Walk-in centre audit, 2000–2001 (1)

1. Source of referral

Source of referral	Attendance (%)
Self-referral	76
GP practice	8
Walk-in centre request return	6
A&E Department	5
HS Direct	4
Other Hospital Department	1

2. Outcome for visitors to the walk-in centre, April 2000–March 2001

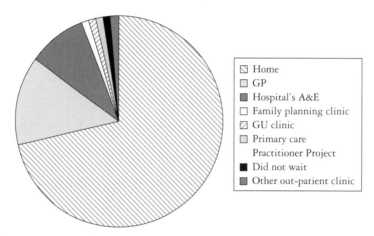

Legend:
- Home
- GP
- Hospital's A&E
- Family planning clinic
- GU clinic
- Primary care Practitioner Project
- Did not wait
- Other out-patient clinic

Figure 2.14 Walk-in centre audit, 2000–2001(2)

NHS walk-in centres

These are another example of new services that are being offered to patients. A walk-in centre in South London was opened in March 2001 and there are several others in the UK. They tend to be placed in busy areas and may be near an A&E department. Most walk-in centres are nurse-led, although a doctor is available for consultations and some prescriptions. The London centre is open from 7am to 11pm. No appointment is necessary.

These centres were set up to try to reduce the pressure on A&E departments by offering an alternative service for less serious problems. They were also seen as helping to provide a service for patients who may find it difficult to get to their GP surgery during surgery times. People who are homeless or not registered with a GP also tend to use the service. Figures 2.13 and 2.14 shows the pattern of use of the service and the outcomes of consultations.

Activity

Study the graphs in Figures 2.13 and 2.14 and describe the patterns you see.

Because of the pressure on the health service, many people are being encouraged to self-care rather than go to the doctor. They are being encouraged to use other services for advice, such as the local pharmacist.

The role of professional bodies in planning services

In spite of the development of numerous government bodies such as CHI and NICE, the colleges and professional bodies still have an important role in planning services, especially related to the provision of appropriately qualified staff. The NHS Modernisation and Health Service reforms are being supported by the Royal College of Nursing (RCN) through leadership programmes for nurses. Nurse-led services are developing, especially in the community. Several primary care practices are nurse-led and employ GPs. Nurses are getting involved with the planning and commissioning of services based on the health care needs of their communities.

The Royal College of General Practitioners has been influential in the education and professional development of GPs, and identifies GP practices that can assist in the training of GPs in the three year programme that has been developed. The General Medical Council is the regulatory body for all doctors and has validated programmes for GPs and doctors in hospitals, so that standards are met in all services.

During this chapter you have seen how health and social care services respond to the changing needs of the community. However, service provision may also reflect national and local initiatives as well as the needs of the community. All organisations work within constraints of resources. Staffing, budgets and premises all affect the level of care provision.

References and resources

Bruce, T. and Meggitt, C. (1997) *Child Care and Education*. Hodder and Stoughton.*

'Modernising Social Services' – White Paper (1998) HMSO.

'The National Beds Enquiry' (2000) (DoH).

'The NHS Health Act' (1999) HMSO.

'The NHS Plan' (2000) DoH.

'National Service Framework for CHD' (1999) DoH.

'National Service Framework for Mental Health' (1999) DoH.

'National Service Framework for Older People' (2000) DoH.

'A New First Class Service. Quality in the NHS' (1998) DoH.

'Our Healthier Nation. Saving Lives' – White Paper (1999) HMSO.

'Partnership in Action, A Discussion Document' (1998) DoH.

'Pocket Guide to the NHS in London 2001/2002'. Department of Health.*

Richards, J. (1999) *The Complete A–Z Health and Social Care Handbook*. Hodder and Stoughton.*

'The New NHS, Modern Dependable' – White Paper (1997) HMSO.

Thomson, H. *et al* (2000) *Health and Social Care Vocational A Level*. Hodder and Stoughton.*

Wellards NHS Handbook 2001/2002 (2001) JMH Publishing.

Community Care is a weekly publication that contains articles relevant to the course.

References helpful for students are marked with an asterisk.*

Useful addresses

If you write to organisations that are charities, please enclose a stamped addressed envelope. Many of these charities and organisations have websites and you may find it quicker to access the information through the internet.

Age Concern England
Astral House
1268, London Road
London SW16 4ER

Carers' National Association
20/25, Glasshouse Yard
London EC1A 4JS

The Princess Royal Trust
Freepost LON 2278
London EC3B 3PS

Useful websites

Department of Health Press Releases
  http://www.doh.gov.uk/newsdesk/index.html
Department of Health Website
  http://www.doh.gov.uk
Health and Social Services Circulars
  http://doh.gov.uk/coinh.htm
Kings Fund
  http://www.kingsfund.org.uk
NHS National
  http://www.nhs.uk
NHS Direct On-line
  http://www.nhsdirect.nhs.uk
NHS Plan
  http://www.nhs.uk.nationalplan
National Institute for Clinical Excellence (NICE)
  http://www.nice.org.uk/nice-web
National Statistics
  www.statistics.gov.uk
Our Healthier Nation
  http://www.ohn.gov.uk

Glossary

Ageism   Discrimination based on age (a person is treated unfairly or differently from others because of their age).
Assessment   The formal method of identifying the health and social needs of a service user in order to set up a care plan.

Audit Commission   Central government agency that audits local authorities and the NHS in terms of finance and quality.

Care plan   The plan of treatment and care decided upon jointly by the service user and the named nurse or key worker.

Carer   The person who takes on the responsibility for the care and support of a person who cannot fully support themselves.

Case conference   The formal meeting of professionals, service users, carers and family to plan future action.

Clinical Governance   Action taken by PCGs and PCTs to ensure that clinical standards are maintained in primary and secondary health services.

Clinician   Any health professional who is directly involved in the treatment and care of patients (e.g., midwife, doctor).

Code of Conduct   Professional code of behaviour and practice drawn up by a professional body to set standards (e.g., UKCC).

Community Health Council   Independent body that reviews the services provided by the NHS.

Demography   Study of population changes, including death and birth rates, and migration rates.

Domiciliary services   Health and social care services that take place in the service user's own home.

Epidemiology   Study of the incidence and spread of disease.

Health Action Zone   A particular area that has been identified as needing additional financial and clinical support through the partnership between health and social care.

Health Improvement Programmes (HImPs)   National, regional and local plans to improve the health of the population, focusing on the particular needs of the area.

Independent Sector   Agencies that provide health and social care services independently of the statutory sector. They can either be private (profit making) or voluntary (non-profit making).

Informal care   Care that is provided by friends, family and neighbours (usually unpaid).

Joint Commissioning   Where the local authority (social services) and the NHS co-ordinate the service and share the costs.

Key worker   A named person who ensures that the care plan is followed and care given to the user. In health, there would be a named nurse who is responsible for the care of certain patients.

NHS Direct   A 24-hour phone advice service staffed by nurses.

NHS Trusts   Hospitals or community services that are independent bodies and employ staff to deliver care.

PCGs   Primary Care Groups – set up in 1999 to deliver primary health care and to develop links with the secondary sector. They will develop to become PCTs (Trusts), which will commission and deliver services in health care.

PCHT   Primary Health Care Team, which includes GPs, nurses, pharmacists and other health workers.

Secondary Service   Medical care that is given in a hospital rather than in the primary health care setting.

Chapter 3

Education for health and social well-being

This chapter describes:

- Definitions of health and social well-being
- Levels of health education
- Areas of health education:
  - 1 Promoting a healthy lifestyle: diet, hygiene, physical activity, mental health and positive personal relationships;
  - 2 Reducing the likelihood of ill-health: immunisation, heart disease, strokes, cancer, Sexually Transmitted Diseases (STDs), substance abuse;
  - 3 Promoting personal safety: safety in the home, road safety
- The origins of health education campaigns
- The roles of organisations and professionals involved in health education
- Planning for health education
- Evaluating health education campaigns

What is health?

The **World Health Organisation** (WHO) defines health as 'a state of complete physical, mental and social well-being and not merely the absence of disease or infirmity.' A more useful definition of health includes three other very important aspects of health: emotional, environmental and spiritual. Health is a resource for everyday life not the object of living. It is a positive concept emphasising social and personal resources as well as physical capabilities, and is regarded by WHO as a fundamental human right.

1 **Physical health** is the easiest aspect of health to measure. It involves the physical functioning of the body and includes the growth and physical development of the baby and child.

2 **Emotional health** involves how we express emotions such as joy, grief, frustration, hurt and fear. This ability to express our own emotions and to react to other people's emotions leads on to coping strategies for anxiety and stress.

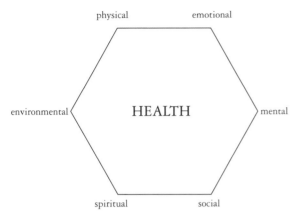

Figure 3.1 The six aspects of health

3 **Mental health** involves our ability to organise our thoughts logically, and is closely linked to emotional and social health.

4 **Social health** involves the way we relate to other people and form relationships.

5 **Spiritual health** involves personal and moral codes of conduct as well as religious beliefs and practices.

6 **Environmental health** refers to the general health of the society in which we live. In areas of famine – where the first priority for health is to obtain enough food – people may be denied access to health. Poverty and overcrowded living conditions are all negative aspects of environmental health.

What is health education?

Health education focuses on the individual and describes any activity that promotes health-related learning. It is also a means of **self-empowerment**. This means that by providing advice and information on health matters, people are able to take more control over their own health and the factors that affect their health. **Health promotion** is the umbrella term given to programmes of health education; it describes the process of enabling people to increase control over, and to improve their health.

It is now recognised that people's lifestyles and behaviour have a great effect on their health and social well-being.

Social influences on health and social well-being

- Ill health is not a matter of chance or bad luck. Some people have a greater or lesser chance of good health than others. There is now a mass of evidence detailing variations in health status according to socio-economic factors, gender, culture ethnicity and age.

- The existence of social inequalities in health is generally accepted. The new government health strategy 'Our Healthier Nation' recognises that there are inequalities in health across society:

    > The poorest in our society are hit harder than the well off by most of the major causes of death. In improving the health of the whole nation, a key priority will be better health for those who are worst off.
    >
    > *(From the summary of 'Our Healthier Nation', Department of Health 1998.)*

- Income is a key factor affecting health. An individual's income can determine access to resources such as a good diet and warmth. It also has an effect on people's psychological health, with those on a low income experiencing stress, depression and social isolation.

- Employment is a key factor affecting health. People who work live longer lives.

Unemployed men and women are more likely to die prematurely from heart disease, cancer (particularly lung cancer) or suicide.

- A social network can protect people against stress. Social exclusion that may arise from unemployment, a low income or isolation can significantly affect health. A social network that offers practical and emotional support has been shown to have a protective effect on health.

Behavioural influences on health and social well-being

- Many major causes of death are preventable and are the result of people's lifestyles:
  - smoking is deemed to be responsible for lung cancer in 90% of all cases;
  - a lack of fibre in the diet is responsible for stomach and colon cancer in up to 30% of all cases;
  - a lack of exercise is a contributory factor in hypertension (or high blood pressure).
- Individual responsibility for health. The government health strategy 'Our Healthier Nation' acknowledges a 'contract' for health between government, communities and individuals. The government and its lead agencies (including the Health Development Agency) have also set up media campaigns to persuade the population to change to healthier ways of living. The role of the health educator has thus been seen to give advice and information to encourage people to change and to equip people with the skills and confidence to make changes.
- Healthy behaviour is not evenly distributed across the population. There are differences in health across society and personal behaviour has a part to play in this. Damaging behaviours such as smoking are far more common in lower socio-economic groups. Forty per cent men in social classes IV and V smoke, compared with 21% in social class I. These groups are also less likely to take up healthier behaviours such as exercise.
- Lifestyles are partly determined by income: For example: a healthy diet has been shown to cost an average £5 more per 'shopping basket'; other factors over which people have little control, such as access to leisure facilities or shops selling fresh produce, may also be affected by income.
- People's behaviour can be a response to social circumstances. Smoking, drinking and illegal drug taking can all be seen as ways of coping with stressful lives.
- There is a danger of 'victim blaming'. If the focus is solely on changing behaviour, people may be blamed for ill health over which they have little control – 'victim blaming'.

Levels of health education

Table 3.1 Three levels of health education

Type of health education	Aim	For whom
Primary health education	Prevention of ill-health	Directed at reducing risks to the entire population in order to prevent ill-health from arising. **Examples:** Children in school learn about healthy eating, road safety and basic hygiene; immunisation.
Secondary health education	Reducing risk of ill-health	Directed at reducing risk factors for people already at risk, i.e., people with a health problem or a reversible condition. **Examples:** Encouraging overweight people to change their eating habits or a smoker to quit smoking; **screening** (routinely examining) apparently healthy people who are likely to develop a particular disease.
Tertiary health education	Promoting rehabilitation and adjustment	Directed at people whose ill-health or disabling condition has not been, or could not be, prevented and who cannot be cured completely. **Examples:** Rehabilitating a person who has undergone major heart surgery, to enable the individual to get the most out of life; educating parents and carers to help a child with brain damage to achieve their own potential.

Areas of health education advice

Table 3.2 Main areas of health education advice

Promoting a healthy lifestyle	Reducing the likelihood of ill-health	Promoting personal safety
Diet, hygiene, physical activity, mental health and positive personal relationships	Immunisation, heart disease, strokes, cancer, STDs (Sexually Transmitted Diseases), substance abuse	Safety in the home, road safety

Promoting a healthy lifestyle

A healthy lifestyle is a combination of a balanced diet, suitable physical activity or exercise and avoidance of harmful lifestyle practices such as smoking or substance misuse.

Healthy eating

No single food contains all the nutrients we need for health. The key to healthy eating, therefore is to enjoy a variety of foods without eating too much of any one kind. Food is energy that we burn constantly, even when we are sitting or sleeping. However, if we take in more energy than we need, the excess is stored as fat. Research shows that too much fat and oil in our diets may lead to obesity, heart disease and some cancers. The Government's 'Health of the Nation' programme recommends a balanced diet as a way of avoiding these problems and gives eight simple guidelines for a healthy diet:

- enjoy your food;
- eat a variety of different foods;
- eat the right amount to be a healthy weight;
- eat plenty of foods rich in starch and fibre;
- don't eat too many foods that contain a lot of fat;
- don't have too many sugary food and drinks;
- don't eat too much salt;
- if you drink alcohol, keep within sensible limits.

You should aim to eat foods from each of the main food groups every day.

The five main food groups are:

1 Starchy foods such as bread, cereals and potatoes.
2 Fruit and vegetables, including fresh, frozen and tinned.
3 Milk and dairy foods, including cheese, yoghurt and fromage frais.
4 Protein-rich foods, including meat, fish, nuts, beans and pulses.
5 Fatty and sugary foods.

Figure 3.2 The balance of good health

Risks to health from poor diet

Risks from a poor diet include:

- **Cancer.** The risk of certain cancers is lower in people who eat diets rich in vegetables, fruit and starchy foods. The risk of certain cancers is higher in people who eat large amounts of red and processed meats, drink too much alcohol or become obese.

- **Heart disease.** Saturated fats are a major part of fat in foods such as milk and milk products (e.g., butter), and in meat and meat products. They are also found in some vegetable oils such as palm and coconut oil, and in some cooking fats, biscuits, cakes and pastries. Increasing intake of saturates increases levels of blood **cholesterol**. Having too high a level of cholesterol in the blood can increase the risk of having a **heart attack**, as it can be deposited on the walls of the blood vessels and cause damage.

Eating disorders

These include obesity, anorexia nervosa and bulimia nervosa. Boys, girls, men and women from all types of background and ethnic groups can suffer from eating disorders. Eating disorders are not just about food and weight, but about feelings. It may be difficult to face up to, and talk about, feelings such as anger, sadness, guilt, loss or fear. An eating disorder is often a sign that a person needs help in coping with life and sorting out personal problems.

Obesity

Obesity literally means fatness, but it is now recognised as an **eating disorder** that results in the person being overweight. Obesity is common in North America, Australasia and Europe. It also occurs, but is less common, in developing countries. In 1996, 45% of men and 34% of women in England were overweight. A further 16% and 18% respectively were obese. It is likely that the incidence is similar in other parts of the UK. Obesity tends to be more common among people aged 40–60 years and those from lower income groups. Today, more people are obese than ever before. Obesity in children is on the increase in the UK. Not only is this a health hazard while they are young, but it also sets a pattern for later life.

Obesity is caused by a mixture of factors, and each will contribute to obesity:

1 Lack of exercise.

- A more sedentary lifestyle: using the car has taken over from walking and using public transport, and watching TV is a popular leisure activity.
- Cycling or even walking to school is not as safe as it was. Parents are now more likely to run their children to school by car.
- Non-physical playing: television and computer games compete with games that involve physical activity.

2 Inappropriate diet.

- We live in a fast-food society: we eat more restaurant food, junk food, instant snacks and pre-cooked foods. These foods are usually very high in the two most fattening ingredients: fat and sugar.
- People eat more sweets and crisps and drink more fizzy drinks, partly because of advertising but also because they are more available.
- Poor fresh fruit consumption: despite it being more readily available, many people do not eat enough fresh fruit, preferring processed varieties that often contain extra sugar and fat products.

Being overweight can lead to problems such as:

- recurrent chest infections;
- diabetes;
- heart disease;
- high blood pressure (hypertension) and stroke;
- some cancers;
- arthritis and gout.

Obese people may also have poor self-esteem; they don't just have a struggle to contain and manage their *physical* problem, they also have to deal with people's *attitudes*. Those attitudes can range from disrespect, through mockery, to bullying and prejudice. Obese children are particularly vulnerable: it is not just other children who hold these attitudes – adults unwittingly pass on their ideas about 'fatness' and personality.

Anorexia nervosa

Anorexia is often, but wrongly, called the 'slimmer's disease'. It is most common in teenage girls, especially at about $14^{1}/_{2}$ years and again at 18. However, it has been diagnosed in children as young as five years of age. It is characterised by severe weight loss, the wilful avoidance of food and an intense fear of being fat. The following signs and symptoms are frequently experienced:

Physical	Psychological	Behavioural
• Severe weight loss • Periods stopping • Difficulty sleeping • Dizziness • Stomach pains • Feeling bloated • Growth of downy hair (lanugo) • Constipation • Feeling cold • Chilblains	• Believing they are fat when underweight • Being irritable • Setting high standards • Wanting to be left alone and losing friends • Increased interest in food, calories and cooking • Difficulty in concentrating	• Excessive exercising • Having ritual behaviours • Lying about eating meals • Lack of interest in normal activities • Cooking cakes and meals for the family

There is no single known cause for anorexia, but theories include:

- Those affected see it as a way of taking control over their lives.
- It may be a result of not wanting to grow up and change their body shape.
- Media obsession with the importance of achieving the 'perfect' (i.e. slim) body.
- It may be a physical illness caused in part by hormonal changes during adolescence.
- It may be caused by depression or a personality disorder.

Hospital treatment is often necessary to help the anorexic person return to a normal weight. Treatment is usually a combination of:

- a controlled re-feeding programme – in severe cases, a naso-gastric tube may be used;
- individual psychotherapy;
- family therapy.

Bulimia nervosa

Bulimia nervosa is characterised by episodes of compulsive overeating (bingeing) usually followed by self-induced vomiting. As with anorexia, those with bulimia nervosa are also obsessed with the fear of gaining weight. The foods eaten tend to be high in carbohydrate and fat. Sufferers may also use large quantities of laxatives, slimming pills or strenuous exercise to control their weight. Many bulimics have poor teeth due to regular vomiting (vomit is acidic and can erode teeth). The following symptoms are commonly experienced:

Physical	Psychological	Behavioural
• Sore throat and mouth infections	• Feeling emotional and depressed	• Eating large quantities of food
• Damaged teeth enamel – caused by the acid present in vomit	• Feeling out of control	
• Irregular periods	• Mood swings	• Being sick after meals
• Dry or poor skin condition	• Obsessions with dieting	• Taking laxatives
• Feeling tired		• Being timid and lying
• Difficulty sleeping		
• Swollen glands		

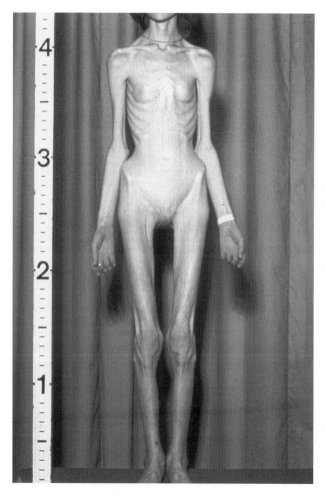

Figure 3.3 Anorexia

Media blamed for rise in eating disorders

Women on television, including news presenters and actresses, are 'abnormally thin' and are causing a rise in the number of young women suffering from eating disorders. A report by the British Medical Association shows that the position has reached an 'unacceptable level' with every family doctor in the country treating two patients suffering from anorexia and 18 with bulimia nervosa.

Doctors called for the media to show 'more realistic body shapes' to reduce the number of deaths caused by eating disorders. The research shows that the gap between the perceived ideal body shape and reality is widening, as women are generally getting larger while models, actresses and women who appear on television are getting smaller. The research showed that more female characters on television are thinner than average. It has been estimated that models and actresses in the 1990s have 10 to 15 per cent body fat, whereas a healthy woman has 22 to 26 per cent.

'We need more Sophie Dahls and fewer Kate Mosses,' said Professor Nathanson. 'Actresses on popular drama and television and news presenters tend to be thin. Whereas male news presenters are all different shapes and sizes, female news presenters are all thin. The pressure on these women to be thin and conform is enormous.'

There are an estimated 60,000 people in Britain with eating disorders. One in 10 is male but the majority are young women. Anorexia nervosa affects 1 to 2 per cent of women, aged 15 to 30 in the UK. Of those who develop the disorder, 15 to 20 per cent will die within 20 years. Dieting is a factor in the development of eating disorders and recent research showed that more young girls are expressing dissatisfaction with their body shapes; one in seven girls aged 11 is on a diet, rising to one in three by the age of 16.

Professor Sir William Asscher, the chairman of the board of science and education at the association, said that although there was no scientific proof of a direct causal link between media images of superthin women and eating disorders in young women, all the research pointed to a direct impact on teenage girls. 'In societies where there is no culture of thinness, eating disorders are very rare,' he said. 'Increasing Westernisation has led to an increase in eating disorders in several cultures.'

The BBC and ITV dismissed the notion that they only represented 'superthin' women on television. 'The BBC seeks to depict real life across the board and shows people of all shapes and sizes,' said a spokesman for the corporation. 'When we do specifically address the issue of body image through campaigns or programmes, we put the emphasis on health and fitness rather than body size.'

A spokesman for ITV said there were a lot of presenters on television, such as Dawn French, Gaby Roslin and Lisa Tarbuck, who were not 'superthin' but were among the most successful.

Rebecca Martin, editor in chief of *Jump*, a monthly magazine for teenage girls, said that it was very difficult to pin down the media as solely responsible for the increase in eating disorders in young girls. 'Editors can help by not putting people who look unhealthily thin in their magazines,' she said. 'We have girls of all shapes and sizes in *Jump* and try to portray normal women but this does not mean we are anti-thin, some girls are naturally thin.'

However, Premier agency, which represents the supermodels Naomi Campbell and Claudia Schiffer, said women who bought fashion magazines featuring thin models were as much to blame as the editors and advertisers. 'Statistics have repeatedly shown that if you stick a beautiful skinny girl on the cover of a magazine you sell more copies,' said a spokesman for the agency.

Adapted from an article in The Independent, *31 May 2000.*

Activity

1 Read the article 'Media blamed for rise in eating disorders'. Discuss the prevalence of slim role models on film and on television. Would it be 'healthier' if such media reflected society more honestly? (40% of adult women in the UK wear size 16 or more clothes).

2 Collect some magazines aimed at young women and young men. How prevalent is the image of the perfect (i.e. thin) body? Discuss the content of 'lifestyle' articles and specific reducing diets. Do you feel that these magazines encourage an unhealthy obsession with physical appearance?

Physical activity

Physical activity is necessary to stimulate the body's own natural maintenance and repair system. Whatever your age physical activity plays an important part in your health and social well-being. Some people think only sportsmen and women need to build physical activity into their lives. However, everyone needs to do some sort of physical activity in order to be healthy. Your bones, joints and muscles – especially your heart – will actually stay younger if you keep them busy. If you are not physically active you increase your health risks in many ways.

The three main components of being physically fit are **stamina**, **strength** and **suppleness**.

Stamina

You need a well-developed circulation to the heart and lungs to give you the ability to keep going without gasping for breath. With stamina you have a slower, more powerful, heartbeat, and are able to cope more easily with prolonged or heavy exercise.

Strength

You need well-toned muscles to give you the ability to do physical work. When your shoulder, trunk and thigh muscles are toned-up, they will work well and you will not experience strains and injuries as often.

Suppleness

Developing good mobility in your neck, spine and joints will prevent you spraining ligaments and pulling muscles and tendons. You will also be less likely to experience aches and pains from stiff joints.

Physical activity is now accepted as a major contributor to good health and an increasingly important focus for health promotion. Evidence from epidemiological studies clearly indicates that morbidity and mortality from a range of chronic diseases are lower in physically active groups compared to sedentary groups. Half-an-hour a day of physical activity, of at least a moderate intensity, helps to prevent and reduce risks to health.

The risks of not taking enough exercise include:

- coronary heart disease;
- stroke;
- high blood pressure;
- non-insulin-dependent diabetes mellitus;
- obesity;
- osteoporosis;
- mild depression;
- cancer of the colon;
- stiff joints.

Most people are aware that they feel better both physically and mentally when they have taken some physical activity. The report below describes the benefits of exercise to people with mental health problems, particularly depression.

Exercise 'helps mental health'

Many people say exercise helps them feel good. Many people with mental health problems use physical exercise to make them feel better, a survey has found. The survey by the charity Mind found that 83% of people with mental health problems looked to exercise to help lift their mood or to reduce stress. Two-thirds said exercise helped to relieve the symptoms of depression and more than half said it helped to reduce stress and anxiety. Some people even thought it had a beneficial effect on manic depression and schizophrenia. Six out of ten said that physical exercise helped to improve their motivation, 50% said it boosted their self-esteem and 24% said it improved their social skills. Mind found that people with mental health problems were more likely to get their exercise from everyday activities like walking, housework and gardening. However, 58% did not know that GPs can sometimes prescribe exercise sessions and activities.

The biggest barriers that prevented people from taking part in physical exercise were motivation problems, the cost of sport and lack of confidence.

One respondent to the survey said: 'I would not have recovered over the last few years without daily exercise, combined with alterations of diet.' Another said: 'I still suffer from depression, anxiety and stress, but doing exercise does give relief and greatly helps me through the days.'

Report author Sue Baker said: 'Our survey proves, beyond any doubt, that physical activity and exercise has a valid place in the "treatment" of mental health problems. As such it deserves far more recognition and should be made more widely available.'

However, she stressed that physical exercise could not prevent all mental health problems from developing, and should not be seen as a replacement for other 'treatments'. Mind is calling for:

- More information about the availability of exercise prescriptions from GPs.
- Greater access to leisure facilities for people with mental health problems.
- Subsidies to leisure centres for people on limited or low incomes.
- Increased provision of exercise in mental health services, for instance as part of care treatment plans.

Source Taken from a survey conducted by the mental health charity, Mind

Promoting positive social relationships

Mental health and social well-being

Mental health problems range from the stresses and worries that all of us experience at some times in our lives, to life-changing conditions which affect our whole personality and our general health and well-being.

The scale of the problem

- Between 7% and 12% of men will suffer diagnosable depression at some point in their lives; for women the figure is as high as 20–25%.
- One in 10 children between the ages of five and 15 have mental health problems.
- One person in 10 is likely to experience a 'disabling anxiety disorder' at some stage in their lives.
- One in 100 people will have schizophrenia at some point.
- Suicide is the second most common cause of death in young people in the UK under the age of 35.
- Since 1985 suicide attempts have risen by more than 170%.
- In Scotland, the number of young male suicides is more than double that of England.

Who has mental health problems?

Mental health problems can result from the range of adverse factors associated with **social exclusion** and can also be a *cause* of **social exclusion**. This is why they have such a profound effect on an individual's health and social well-being. For example:

- Unemployed people are twice as likely to have depression as people in work.
- Children in the poorest households are three times more likely to have mental health problems than children in well-off households.
- Half of all women and a quarter of all men will be affected by depression at some period during their lives.
- People who have been abused or been victims of domestic violence have higher rates of mental health problems.
- People with drug and alcohol problems have higher rates of mental health problems.
- Between a quarter and a half of people using night shelters or sleeping rough may have a serious mental disorder, and up to half may be alcohol dependent.
- Some black and minority ethnic communities are diagnosed as having higher rates of mental health problems than the general population – refugees are especially vulnerable.
- There is a high rate of mental health problems in the prison population.
- People with physical illnesses have twice the rate of mental health problems compared to the general population.

The most common mental health problems in the UK today are:

- depression;
- anxiety disorders;
- alzheimer's disease;
- schizophrenia
- eating disorders (see pages 97–102).

What is depression?

Depression is a common mental illness. It can strike at any age and the feelings of hopelessness and helplessness attached to it can make it difficult for people to carry out their normal activities. It can be more or less severe and symptoms are varied, making it often hard to diagnose. It is thought that some individuals may be more prone to depression, whether because of life experiences, their body chemistry or genetically inherited conditions. Anyone can suffer from depression. The most common symptoms include:

- feelings of helplessness and hopelessness;
- feeling useless, inadequate, bad;
- self hatred, constant questioning of thoughts and actions, a need for reassurance;
- feeling vulnerable and being oversensitive to criticism;
- feelings of guilt;
- loss of energy and the ability to concentrate and be motivated to do even the simplest tasks;
- harming oneself;
- sudden loss or gain in weight;
- sleep disruption or a need to sleep very long hours;
- agitation and restlessness;
- loss of libido;
- physical aches and pains.

Most people only suffer two or three of these symptoms at any one time. People with severe depression may also experience suicidal feelings, stop eating or drinking and suffer from delusions or hallucinations.

Different types of depression

There are many different types of depression, including

- **clinically diagnosed depression**;
- **bi-polar disorder** (or manic depression): marked by extreme mood swings, between highs when a person experiences excessive energy and optimism, and lows when they may feel total despair and lack of energy;
- **post-natal depression** can occur from about two weeks after the birth of a child to two years after and differs from the mood swings suffered by many in the first few days after the child is born (also called 'post-natal blues').

Other forms of depression include **Seasonal Affective Disorder** which is thought to be associated with the approach of winter and may be linked to lack of sunlight.

Causes of depression

Depression can be caused by a combination of factors:

- It often runs in families, suggesting a **genetic** component, but it may be triggered by stressful events.
- Major depressive illness is usually linked to some form of chemical imbalance in the brain.
- It is also thought that people with low self-esteem, a pessimistic outlook on life and difficulty coping with stress are more prone to depression.

- Life events that may trigger depression include bereavement, chronic illness, relationship problems and financial difficulties.

Treatment of depression

- **Anti-depressant drugs**, which include **Prozac** are thought to correct chemical imbalances in the brain.
- Other types of drugs may also be used to treat depression.
- **Psychotherapy**, which aims to uncover the reasons for depression and help the patient to find ways of overcoming them.
- **Self-help groups** may also offer people a forum for talking about their condition and sharing it with others so that they do not feel isolated and alone.

In extreme cases, a person with depression may need to be treated in hospital if, for example, they are threatening or have attempted to commit suicide – or if they pose a threat to others.

Anxiety disorders

Anxiety disorders are among the most common mental illnesses in the UK. They cover everything from **panic disorder**, **phobias** and **obsessive compulsive disorder** to **post-traumatic stress disorder**. Each has its own particular symptoms and differs greatly from normal feelings of nervousness.

Causes of anxiety disorders

There are several possible reasons for anxiety disorders; these include:

- genetic factors;
- biochemical changes in the brain;
- traumatic life events.

Symptoms of anxiety disorders

These vary from person to person but may include:

- panic, fear, apprehension;
- uncontrollable obsessive thoughts;
- repeated flashbacks of traumatic experiences;
- nightmares;
- ritualised behaviour such as repeated hand-washing;
- problems sleeping;
- cold or sweaty hands;
- palpitations;
- shortness of breath;
- inability to be still and calm;
- a dry mouth;
- numbness or tingling in the hands or feet;

- upset stomach;
- tense muscles.

Often there appears to be no particular reason why symptoms occur since the feelings of panic are dissociated from events which are happening or about to occur. People who suffer from anxiety disorders may also have other mental illnesses, such as depression.

Treatment of anxiety disorders

Anxiety disorders often respond well to treatment:

- behavioural therapy;
- counselling to find out the cause of the anxiety;
- relaxation techniques;
- drugs which control the symptoms or correct chemical imbalances.

Alzheimer's disease

Alzheimer's disease is a progressive, degenerative and irreversible brain disorder that causes intellectual impairment, disorientation and eventually death. It is linked to gradual formation of plaques in the brain, particularly in the hippocampus and adjoining cortex. As the disease develops, it destroys chemical messengers used by the cells of the brain to communicate with each other.

Causes of Alzheimer's disease

So far no one single factor has been identified as a cause for Alzheimer's disease. It is likely that a combination of factors is responsible, including:

- age;
- diet;
- overall general health;
- genetic inheritance;
- environmental factors.

Age continues to be the greatest risk factor for dementia. Dementia affects one in 20 over the age of 65 and one in five over the age of 80. But Alzheimer's is not restricted to elderly people: there are 18,500 people under the age of 65 with dementia in the UK.

Symptoms of Alzheimer's disease

- Poor or decreased judgement
- Difficulty in performing difficult tasks
- Problems with language
- Disorientation to time and place
- Problems with abstract thinking
- Problems with memory
- Change in mood and behaviour

- Change in personality
- Loss of initiative
- Listlessness and apathy

The disease is often associated with depression, anxiety and sleep disturbance. The rate of decline varies from person to person. The disease course runs anywhere from three to twenty years, with eight years being the average life span after diagnosis.

Treatment of Alzheimer's disease

- Drug treatment is often used, for example antioxidants designed to limit the impact of free radicals and Cholinesterase Inhibitors including tacrine and donepezil.
- Therapies: art therapy, music therapy, reminiscence therapy.
- Aromatherapy and massage may help alleviate agitation, anxiety, sleep disturbance and may relieve physical discomfort in people with dementia. Also for carers complementary treatments can offer natural ways to relax.

Those caring for a friend or relative with Alzheimer's disease need a great deal of practical help and emotional support.

"Mum always loved shopping.
Then one day
she forgot the way home."

Alzheimer's disease is a physical illness which destroys the mind and memory. If you had Alzheimer's you might one day forget how to dress, where your home is, even your family. The Alzheimer's Society was founded to give advice and help on all forms of dementia. If you need help or information, phone the Alzheimer's Helpline on **0845 300 0336**. Or contact your nearest branch.

www.alzheimers.org.uk
Alzheimer's Society, Gordon House, 10 Greencoat Place, London SW1P 1PH

Alzheimer's
Dementia care & research

Figure 3.4 A poster from the Alzheimer's disease society

Schizophrenia

Schizophrenia is a severe mental illness that is characterised by changes in perception, thoughts and behaviour. The illness has been described in all cultures and its incidence (about 1 in 100) is much the same throughout the world. Schizophrenia can be confused with other mental disorders, such as bi-polar disorder (see page 105) and with physical illnesses. Schizophrenia affects males and females equally and typically starts between the ages of 15 and 30. There are some false ideas about schizophrenia:

- It isn't about having a 'split personality'.
- It doesn't mean a person will automatically be violent, ill, or in hospital for life.

Causes of schizophrenia

The cause of schizophrenia is unknown but it may have a genetic component. If a grand-parent had the illness, the risk rises to three per cent. If one parent was affected, the risk is as high as 10 per cent. This rises to 40 per cent if both parents have schizophrenia. Other predisposing factors include complications during pregnancy or childbirth and difficulties in childhood development. Factors which may trigger an episode of schizophrenia include stressful life events, and the use of illegal drugs such as cannabis. Schizophrenia is not caused by bad parenting.

Symptoms of schizophrenia

The symptoms and severity of schizophrenia vary widely from person to person. But in general, during an episode of schizophrenia, the way someone experiences and interprets the outside world becomes disrupted. A person may:

- Lose touch with reality: have difficulty organising their thoughts or difficulty concentrating.
- Have disturbances of thinking: see or hear things that aren't there, or feel as if thoughts are put into or taken out of their head, or are being broadcast to the world.
- Develop delusions (or 'false beliefs'): for example, that other people can read their thoughts; that somebody is trying to harm them or perhaps actually trying to kill them; that things they see or hear have a special message for them, for example, seeing a red car may mean the world is about to end.
- Experience hallucinations: that is, hearing, seeing or smelling things that are not seen, heard, or smelled by other people.
- Have difficulty expressing their emotions.

During an acute phase the person may deny that they are behaving unusually as their altered perception is very real to them. They will usually behave in unusual ways in response to their experiences. An episode of schizophrenia can last for several weeks, and can be frightening or disturbing for the person themselves and their friends or family. After this acute phase, people can go into a long-term period of 'negative' symptoms, including:

- lack of motivation;
- a feeling of flatness;
- social withdrawal.

Treatment of schizophrenia

- Antipsychotic drugs such as chlorpromazine and haloperidol are used to improve symptoms and to prevent relapse.
- Antipsychotic medication can also be given as an injection that lasts for days or weeks. This is known as a depot injection, and is often used for people with schizophrenia who have recovered from their acute illness and want to prevent a relapse, or who maybe find it easier to have an injection than to remember to take daily medication.
- Psychological and social therapies: Research shows that interventions with the families of people with schizophrenia can reduce relapse rates. These family interventions usually last several weeks and consist of education about the illness and help with problem solving.
- Cognitive behavioural therapy may help to reduce relapse rates.

A review of almost 2000 patients' life histories suggests that 25% of those with schizophrenia achieve full recovery; 50% recover at least partially; and 25% require long-term care.

Case study

Joanne's story

I had quite a wild time as a teenager – truanting, shoplifting, taking drugs – but somehow I still managed to get good marks at school. I went to university, to study sociology and ended up in a house with people who were quite restrained and middle class – very different from me. I don't know what brought it on but things started to feel strange when I became convinced my housemates were thinking bad thoughts about me and whispering all the time behind my back. Slowly I just got more paranoid, until I thought people could read my thoughts just walking down the street. I was hearing voices all the time but I didn't even realise I was ill. I thought maybe it was an after-effect of drugs I'd taken when I was younger.

My friends didn't really know how to treat me – I think friendships and social relationships can really suffer when you've got a mental health problem, either because people are scared, or they don't understand, or sometimes just because they're just thoughtless. I've had friends who have dropped me – they seem to have written me off as a worthwhile person. One friend used to go round 'warning' people about me before they met me, so of course they were pretty suspicious when they actually did meet me.

I became really depressed and even attempted suicide. It took about a year for me to get help, and I went to hospital as a voluntary patient. I was diagnosed with schizophrenia. Things got worse first but then with treatment they slowly got better. Eventually I managed to go back and complete my degree and now I work for a project that helps people with mental health problems get into employment. I feel much better about myself, just knowing that I have come through and that I can do a job that helps others in my situation – it's really rewarding.

I also think the media is very biased and this doesn't help people to understand what mental illness is all about. Schizophrenia only seems to exist in the media whenever a violent crime takes place. Otherwise we're the forgotten people and our stories are not told. People believe what they read in the papers, so what journalists write can have a real impact on the general public's view of schizophrenia and other mental health problems.

Activity

Exploring mental health

1 Find out about the support groups in the field of mental health, for example, the Alzheimer's Society, the Schizophrenia Fellowship, SANE, MIND, etc. How do these charities help those with mental health problems and their families?

2 Using material from the voluntary organisations, mount a display focusing on *one* mental health problem and provide the following information:

- what it is;
- who is likely to have the problem;
- help and support available.

3 Read Joanne's story above. What could have been done to help her when she first started experiencing problems? Find out about the different therapies available for those with schizophrenia.

Stress

Stress affects virtually everyone at some time in his or her life. Stress has physical effects on the body because it is part of the instinct we need to flee from danger quickly. Faced with pressure, challenge or danger, our bodies release hormones such as cortisol and adrenaline. These affect our metabolic rate, heart rate and blood pressure to prepare us for optimum performance. Unless we can compensate with physical activity, this natural reaction to stress reduces our ability to cope.

What causes stress and who is at risk?

Many events (or the anticipation of them) can lead to stress, including:

- pressure to perform at work, at school or in sports;
- threats of physical violence;
- money worries;
- arguments;
- family conflicts;
- divorce;
- bereavement;
- unemployment;
- moving house.

It is important to differentiate between temporary stress, which you know will soon go away, and long-term or **chronic stress**. Temporary stress can often be relieved by relaxing, by taking a walk or by a good night's sleep, but chronic stress is harder to deal with and can be damaging, both psychologically and emotionally.

Chronic stress can lead to:

- irritability or anger;
- apathy or depression;
- constant anxiety;
- irrational behaviour;
- loss of appetite;
- 'comfort eating';
- lack of concentration;
- increased smoking, drinking or drug-taking.

The physical effects can include:

- fatigue;
- skin problems;
- aches and pains resulting from tense muscles, including neckache, backache and tension headaches;
- increased pain from arthritis and other conditions;
- heart palpitations;
- in women, missed periods.

In moments of extreme stress, you may begin to shake uncontrollably, to hyperventilate (to breathe faster and deeper than normal) or even to vomit. If you suffer from asthma, stress can trigger an asthma attack.

Dealing with stress

Strategies to help deal with stress include:

- delegating or sharing your responsibilities at work;
- avoiding confrontation with difficult colleagues;
- learning to be more assertive;
- taking regular exercise;
- looking for humour or absurdity in stressful situations;
- never taking on more than you know you can complete;
- organising your time better to get as much done as possible;
- talking to friends or family, sharing your thoughts and fears;
- listening to music or relaxation tapes;
- breathing can help release tension and stress – learn to breathe deeply from your diaphragm and practise holding your breath for a few seconds before slowly exhaling.

Complementary therapy

There are many stress management techniques in the form of counselling, psychotherapy and hypnotherapy. Aromatherapy and reflexology may provide a quiet, relaxed environment in which to wind down. The Alexander technique may help to relieve muscle pains and help to control breathing in stressful situations.

Stress-related illnesses

As well as the emotional and psychological disruption it causes, **stress-related medical problems** are becoming increasingly common. Various illnesses may be said to be either caused or triggered by stress, including:

- **Stomach ulcers**, which may sometimes be caused by too much acid being produced in the stomach at a time of anxiety or worry.
- **Heart attacks**: it is thought that the fat released into the bloodstream when the body responds to demands gets trapped in the walls of the heart's own vessels. This gradually narrows these tubes, and when increased demand is placed on the heart, the narrowed tubes prevent the flow of oxygen, causing the heart muscle to die.
- **Skin disorders** such as eczema and psoriasis.
- **Myalgic encephalomyelitis (ME)**: the role of stress has been well documented in this very distressing condition.

ME is sometimes called **post-viral fatigue syndrome**. Studies have shown that people in the caring professions make up the largest group affected, with three times as many women as men suffering from ME.

No one definite cause is known, but theories have suggested the following:

- persistent viral infection;
- damage to the immune system following a viral infection;
- a neurotic disorder, for example, hyperventilation.

The main symptoms are:

- muscle fatigue;
- exhaustion;
- headaches;
- dizziness.

Other symptoms common to many people with ME are:

- muscular pains;
- fever;
- depression;
- bowel and digestive problems.

There is no diagnostic test, although entero-viruses can be traced in the colon of more than half of ME sufferers. Diagnosis is by process of elimination of other illnesses and diseases. The medical profession has little to offer in terms of scientific explanation or treatment of ME. The following treatments are among the more common:

- Anti-depressants: these are often prescribed, but the long-term use of these drugs is not recommended.
- A sugar and yeast-free diet: many sufferers follow this, in common with sufferers from *Candida Albicans* (Thrush) a yeast infection of the gut. It is thought that stress can lead to a weakening of the immune system, thus allowing this infection to flourish.
- Relaxation techniques such as meditation, the Alexander technique and yoga are often practised.
- Homeopathy.
- Acupuncture.
- Herbal treatments, for example with evening primrose.
- Counselling: this can enable a person to lead a less stressful lifestyle, thereby reducing his or her propensity to further bouts of ME.

 Case study

Holly's story

Before becoming ill with ME, Holly, aged 32, had led an active life both at work as a social worker and outside her job, having many interests which occupied most of her spare hours. She made little time for relaxation and her diet was high in sugar and carbohydrates. Her emotional history had been stressful. When she became ill, she suffered from most of the common symptoms of ME and was bedridden for three months. After numerous setbacks and relapses, she is now in the fifth year of her illness and has used diet, homeopathy, herbal treatments and counselling as her path to recovery. The most difficult experiences for Holly were the financial implications of being ill. She lost her job and has been living on state benefits; she has found her practical circumstances difficult to reconcile with her need for relaxation and a reduction in stress. After five years out of work it will be difficult for her to find a job, particularly with this history of ill-health. She says that counselling has empowered her to face the stresses and difficulties which the future might hold, without becoming ill again.

Activity

Stress-related illness

Study Holly's story, then answer the following questions:

1 What advice and recommendations should be made to a person with ME pre-disposing factors, to avoid contracting ME?

2 What support should be made available to people with ME by:

   a the NHS;

   b the DHSS;

   c the workplace;

   d friends and family?

3 Many ME sufferers feel isolated as there is still a lot of ignorance about the illness. How could this be combated?

Reducing the likelihood of ill-health

This area covers education programmes aimed at increasing awareness about the ways in which ill- health can be prevented. These programmes focus on:

- immunisation;
- heart disease;
- substance abuse: smoking, alcohol, drugs;
- sexually transmitted infections;
- cancer.

Immunisation

Immunisation is the use of vaccines to protect people from disease. As babies and children are particularly vulnerable to infection, they are offered immunisation, but parents or guardians must give their written consent. In the UK parents can choose whether to have their children immunised. The advantages of immunisation include:

- Children who are not immunised run a risk of catching diseases and having complications.
- Immunisation is the safest way to protect children from particular diseases that may have long-lasting effects.
- Having children immunised at an early age means they are well protected by the time they start playgroup or school where they are in contact with lots of children.
- Immunisation also protects those children who are unable to receive immunisation, by providing what is called **herd immunity**: this is a term used to describe partial uptake of immunisation, where enough people are immunised to prevent the spread of the disease.

Table 3.3 The current recommended immunisation schedules in the UK

Age	Disease	Vaccination method
2 months	Polio Hib* Diphtheria Tetanus Whooping cough	By mouth One injection
3 months	Polio Hib Diphtheria Tetanus Whooping cough	By mouth One injection
4 months	Polio Hib Diphtheria Tetanus Whooping cough	By mouth One injection
12 –15 months	MMR:† Measles Mumps Rubella	One injection
3–5 years	Measles Mumps Rubella Diphtheria Tetanus Polio Whooping cough	One injection By mouth
10–14 years School Leavers 13–18 years	BCG (tuberculosis) Diphtheria Tetanus Polio	Skin test followed by one injection; if required One injection By mouth

Meningitis C vaccine: The new immunisation will be given to children aged 2, 3 and 4 months and around 13 months with their routine immunisations. Extra appointments will be organised where necessary. Depending on their age, all other children will be invited through their GP, school or college to have the vaccine in a special catch up programme.

*Hib : Vaccination against the bacteria haemophilus influenzae, type B, which may cause meningitis (cerebrospinal meningitis) and infection of the epiglottis (back of the throat).

†MMR: Vaccination against measles, mumps and rubella (German measles).
The vaccinations at the ages of 2 months and 3–5 years are usually combined with routine children's medical examinations.

The Department of Health issues the following guidelines:

- Children should *not* be vaccinated if they have a fever. When children have a fever, the vaccination should be postponed. If the child just has an ordinary cold, but their temperature is normal, it is safe for them to be vaccinated.
- Side effects to the vaccines do occur, but **allergy** to the vaccines is **very** rare:
- The vaccines for diphtheria-tetanus-whooping cough, Hib and diphtheria-tetanus may cause a red area and swelling to occur on the vaccination spot. However, it will disappear within a few days. A fever may also be noticed on the day of the jabs and for 7–10 days later.
- The MMR vaccine may cause a brief reaction that may begin at any time from a few days to three weeks after the vaccination. The child may have symptoms like the diseases, which are being vaccinated against, but only in a mild form. That is, a cold, a skin reaction, a fever and perhaps swollen salivary glands. The child will not be contagious.

The meningitis C vaccine may have the following effects:

- **Babies**: Some swelling and redness where the injection is given.
- **Toddlers over 12 months**: Some swelling and redness where the injection is given. About one in four toddlers may have disturbed sleep. About one in 20 toddlers may have a mild fever.
- **Pre-school children**: About one in 20 may have some swelling at the injection site. About one in 50 may have a mild fever within a few days of the vaccination.
- **Children and young people**: About one in four may have some swelling and redness at the injection site. About one in 50 may have a mild fever. About one in 100 may have a very sore arm from the injection, which may last a day or so.
- On very rare occasions, vaccinations may cause serious complications.

Alternatives to immunisation

There is no proven, effective alternative to conventional immunisation. **Homeopathic medicine** has been tried as an alternative to the whooping cough vaccine but it was not effective. The Council of the Faculty of Homeopathy (the registered organisation for doctors qualified in homeopathy) advises parents to have their children immunised with conventional vaccines.

Activity

1   Find out how parents receive information about having their children immunised.

2   Do you think immunisation should be made compulsory (as it is in some countries) to eradicate childhood illnesses?

Drugs

A drug is any chemical substance that changes the function of one or more body organs or alters the process of a disease. Drugs may be:

- prescribed medicines, for example, antibiotics;
- over-the-counter remedies, for example, paracetamol or cough medicines;
- alcohol, nicotine (in tobacco) and caffeine (in coffee and other drinks).

When their use is considered harmful or socially unacceptable, this is termed **drug abuse**. Many more deaths and illnesses are caused through the use of legal drugs than through the use of illegal drugs.

Drug dependence

Drug dependence is the compulsion to continue taking a drug, either to produce the desired results, or to prevent the ill-effects that occur when it is withdrawn. There are two types of drug dependence:

1 **Physical dependence** is when someone has taken drugs in quantity for a time and comes to rely on the use of a drug in order to feel well and for their body to function 'normally'. It usually happens when the body has built up a tolerance to the drug and in its absence, physical withdrawal symptoms appear. It mainly occurs with **depressant drugs** such as **alcohol, barbiturates, heroin** or **tranquillisers**. However, the deep depressions and even suicidal feelings that can follow **cocaine** and **ecstasy** use could be counted as physical dependence, because users will take *more* of the drug to escape these feelings.

2 **Psychological dependence** is when the user experiences an overwhelming desire to continue with the drug experience. This can be because of the pleasurable effects and the desire to keep experiencing them. It can, however, also represent some sort of psychological prop. The drug experience can become a way of blocking out reality, making life bearable and a way of facing the world. Without the prop life seems worthless. It can happen with any drug or any activity which takes over a person's life including eating, sex, work, or jogging.

Drug tolerance refers to the way the body gets used to the repeated presence of a drug, meaning that higher doses are needed to maintain the same effect. The body learns to tolerate the drug in the system. Alcohol, barbiturates, heroin and **amphetamine** are all drugs to which the body can build up tolerance.

There are four main groups of drugs which are commonly abused:

- . stimulants
- depressants;
- hallucinogens or psychedelics;
- analgesic drugs.

1 A **stimulant** is a drug that speeds up the central nervous system to *increase* neural activity in the brain. They are rarely prescribed for any medical problem. Such drugs tend to make people feel more euphoric, alert and wide-awake, and are sometimes called 'uppers'. Examples are amphetamines, nicotine (in cigarettes), cocaine and crack, caffeine and ecstasy.

2 Depressants are drugs that slow down the central nervous system to *suppress* neural activity in the brain. Large quantities make people feel sleepy. They are sometimes called 'downers'. Very large doses can lead to fatal overdose as the vital systems of the body such as breathing are slowed to the point where they stop. Examples are alcohol, sleeping tablets, tranquillisers, solvents (as in glue-sniffing).

3 An **hallucinogen** is a drug which alters **perception**: the way you see, hear, feel, smell or touch the world. This can mean that the senses can get all mixed up or changed. People may see colours much more brightly or hear sounds differently, or say that they can 'hear' colours and 'see' sounds. They might also see things that aren't there, which some people find very frightening. Examples are LSD and magic mushrooms and the strongest types of cannabis are hallucinogenic; to a certain extent, ecstasy can also be hallucinogenic.

4 Analgesic drugs are used medically to treat moderate and severe pain. Abuse of analgesic drugs for their euphoric (or intoxicating) effects often causes tolerance and both physical and psychological dependence. Examples are heroin, morphine, methadone, pethidine, codeine and opium

Illegal drug abuse

Illegal drugs are those that are banned for any *non-medicinal* use by the **Misuse of Drugs Act**. Table 3.4 gives information on the most commonly used of these. Banned drugs are placed in different classes – Class A offences carry the highest penalties and Class C offences the lowest penalties.

Types of drug use

1 Experimentation. Some people take a drug because they are curious about what the effects feel like.

2 Recreational use. Most young people who take drugs take them in particular social settings – at a club or a party, for example. They may not suffer any major harmful effects to their health, although occasionally young people die from a strong adverse reaction.

3 Problem drug use. Some people may need to take a drug just to feel able to cope with everyday life. Their drug use is likely to affect their health and they may experience:

- mental health problems, such as anxiety, depression or inability to concentrate;
- loss of friends;
- money problems;
- trouble with the law.

Illegal drug taking is *not* a part of normal life, and most people who do try drugs do not continue using them. More young people experience problems caused by drinking too much alcohol than from drug use.

Why do people take drugs?

Surveys of young people in Britain suggest many are experimenting with illegal drugs. The misuse of drugs and solvents appears to be widespread in secondary schools. In the UK, drug use often starts at around the age of 13, yet drugs education may not start until the age of 14–16. Many adults think that young people use illegal drugs only if they are having problems. This is

A Guide to Illegal Drugs

Drug name	Alkyl Nitrates
Other names	• Poppers • Amyl nitrate, butyl nitrate, isobutyl nitrate • Product names include: Ram, Thrust, Rock Hard, Kix, TNT, Liquid Gold
What it looks like	• Clear or straw-coloured liquid in a small bottle • Vapour which is breathed in through the mouth or nose from a small bottle or tube.
Effects	• Brief but intense 'head rush' • Flushed face and neck • Effects fade after 2 to 5 minutes
Health risks	• Headache, feeling faint and sick • Regular use can cause skin problems around the mouth and nose • Dangerous for people with anaemia, glaucoma, and breathing or heart problems • If spilled can burn the skin • May be fatal if swallowed • Mixing Viagra with alkyl nitrates may increase risk of heart problems
Legal status	• Amyl nitrate is a prescription-only medicine • Possession is not illegal, but supply can be an offence

Drug name	Amphetamines
Other names	• Speed, whizz, uppers, amph, billy, sulphate
What it looks like	• Grey or white powder that is snorted, swallowed, smoked, injected, or dissolved in drink • Tablets which are swallowed
Effects	• Excitement – the mind races and users feel confident and energetic
Health risks	• While on the drug, some users become tense and anxious • Leaves users feeling tired and depressed for one or two days and sometimes longer • High doses repeated over a few days may cause panic and hallucinations • Long-term use can lead to mental illness • Mixing Viagra with amphetamines may increase the risk of heart problems • Heavy, long term use can lead to mental illness • Mixing Viagra with amphetamines may increase the risk of heart problems
Legal status	• Class B (but Class A if prepared for injection)

Drug name	Cannabis
Other names	• Marijuana, draw, blow, weed, puff, shit, hash, ganja, spliff, wacky backy **Cannabis is the most commonly used drug among 11 to 25 year olds**
What it looks like	• A solid, dark lump known as 'resin' • Leaves, stalks ands seeds called 'grass' • A sticky, dark oil • Can be rolled (usually with tobacco) in a spliff or joint, smoked on its own in a special pie, or cooked and eaten in food
Effects	• Users feel relaxed and talkative • Cooking the drug then eating it makes the effects more intense and harder to control • May bring on a craving for food (this is often referred to as having the 'munchies')
Health risks	• Smoking it with tobacco may lead to users becoming hooked on cigarettes • Impairs the ability to learn and concentrate • Can leave people tired and lacking energy • Users may lack motivation and feel apathetic • Can make users paranoid and anxious, depending upon their mood and situation • Smoking joints over a long period of time can lead to respiratory disorders, including lung cancer
Legal status	• Class B (but Class A penalties can apply to cannabis oil). NB Proposed change to Class C is imminent

Drug name	Ecstasy
Other names	• E, doves, XTC, disco biscuits, hug drugs, burgers, fantasy • Chemical name:MDMA (currently many tablets contain MDEA,MDA, MBDB) **4% of 16 to 25s have used ecstasy in the last 3 months.**
What it looks like	• Tablets of different shapes, size and colour (but often white) which are swallowed
Effects	• Users feel alert and in tune with their surroundings • Sound, colour and emotions seem much more intense • Users may dance for hours • The effects last from 3 to 6 hours
Health risks	• Can leave users feeling tired and depressed for days • Risk of overheating and dehydration if users dance energetically without taking breaks or drinking enough fluids (users should sip about a pint of non-alcoholic fluid such as fruit juice, sports drinks or water every hour) • Use has been linked to liver and kidney problems • Some experts are concerned that use of ecstasy can lead to brain damage causing depression in later life • Mixing Viagra with ecstasy may increase the risk of heart problems
Legal status	• Class A • Other drugs similar to ecstasy are also illegal and Class A

Drug name	Gases, Glues, and Aerosols
Other names	• Products such as lighter gas refills, aerosols containing products such as hairspray, deodorants and air fresheners, tins or tubes of glue, some paints, thinners and correcting fluids
What it looks like	• Sniffed or breathed into the lungs from a cloth or sleeve • Gas products are sometimes squirted directly into the back of the throat
Effects	• Effects feel similar to being very drunk • Users feel thick-headed, dizzy, giggly and dreamy • Users may hallucinate • Effects don't last very long, but users can remain intoxicated all day by repeating the dose
Health risks	• Nausea, vomiting, black-outs and heart problems that can be fatal • Squirting gas products down the throat may cause body to produce fluid that floods the lungs and this can cause instant death • Risk of suffocation if the substance is inhaled from a plastic bag over the head • Accidents can happen when the user is high because their senses are affected • Long-term abuse of glue can damage the brain, liver and kidneys
Legal status	• It is illegal for shopkeepers to sell to under 18s, or to people acting for them, if they suspect the product is intended for abuse

Drug name	Heroin
Other names	• Smack, brown, horse, gear, junk, H,jack, scag
What it looks like	• Brownish-white powder which is smoked, snorted or dissolved and injected
Effects	• Small doses give the user a sense of warmth and well-being • Larger doses can make them drowsy and relaxed
Health risks	• Heroin is addictive (even when smoked) • Users who form a habit may end up taking the drug just to feel normal • Excessive amounts can result in overdose, coma, and in some cases death • Injecting can damage veins • Sharing injecting equipment puts users at risk of dangerous infections like hepatitis B or C and HIV/AIDS
Legal status	• Class A

Drug name	LSD
Other names	• Acid, trips, tabs, blotters, microdots, dots
What it looks like	• ¼ inch squares of paper, often with a picture on one side, which are swallowed. Microdots and dots are tiny tablets
Effects	• Effects are known as a 'trip' • Users will experience their surroundings in a very different way • Sense of movement and time may speed up or slow down • Objects, colours and sounds maybe distorted
Health risks	• Once a trip starts, it cannot be stopped • Users can have a 'bad trip' which can be terrifying • 'Flashbacks' may be experienced when parts of a trip are re-lived some time after the event • Can complicate mental health problems
Legal status	• Class A

Table 3.4 Facts about drugs

Figure 3.5 Why do people take drugs

not always true. They may be attracted to drugs for similar reasons as they are to alcohol (see Figure 3.5)

Risks of using illegal drugs

The following are risks involved in using *any* illegal drug:

- users can never be sure of exactly what they are taking;
- what is taken is unlikely to be pure, and users won't know what it has been mixed with;
- not knowing the strength of what has been bought could lead to an accidental overdose;

- users can't be sure of what effect a drug will have, even if they have taken it before;
- it is often very dangerous to mix different drugs, including drugs and alcohol;
- sharing needles or syringes carries a serious risk of dangerous infections being spread such as HIV and hepatitis B or C;
- a drugs conviction can cause problems obtaining a travel visa, and can affect job prospects.

Table 3.5 What to do in an emergency

Symptom	Response
tense and panicky	• calm them and be reassuring
	• explain that the feelings will pass
	• settle them in a quiet, dimly lit room
	• if they start breathing very quickly, calm them down and tell them to take long, slow breaths
very drowsy	• calm them and be reassuring
	• don't frighten or startle them, or let them exert themselves
	• never give coffee – or any other stimulant – to rouse them
	• if symptoms persist, place them in the recovery position
	• call an ambulance if necessary
unconsciousness	• call an ambulance
	• place them in the recovery position so they won't choke if they vomit
	• check breathing – be prepared to do mouth-to-mouth resuscitation
	• keep them warm, but not too hot
For all symptoms	• stay with them at all times
	• if you know what drug has been taken, tell the ambulance crew; if you have a sample of the drugs, give them to the ambulance crew

What to do in an emergency

Drugs affect everyone differently. It is not always possible to tell if someone has taken drugs. However, it is important to know what to do if you suspect that someone has reacted badly to a drug (see table 3.5).

Activity

1 Draw up a chart showing the 'pleasant' and 'unpleasant' effects of ecstasy, amphetamines and cocaine.

2 Choose one of the following drugs and research it:

   • Alcohol

   • Tobacco

   • Cocaine

   • Heroin

Include as much information as you can. Use your library's resources centre and internet sites such as the BBC sites and consumer support groups.

The project should be well illustrated and presented, and include the following information:

   • What is the drug, how is it taken and what are its effects?

   • Who uses the drug and why?

   • How can health educators change the patterns of drug abuse?

Alcohol

Alcohol is probably the most commonly abused drug in the developed world. It is absorbed into the body through the stomach and intestines and distributed throughout the body by the bloodstream. In pregnant women, alcohol crosses the placental barrier to reach the developing baby.

Calculating the amount of alcohol

All alcoholic drinks contain pure alcohol (ethanol) in different amounts. You can compare the amount of alcohol in different types of drink using 'units'. All alcoholic drinks containers show the amount of alcohol they contain. By law they have to be labelled with the **alcohol by volume (%ABV)**. This number shows the percentage of the drink that is pure alcohol – the higher the number, the stronger the drink.

You can work out how many units are in a drink by multiplying the %ABV by the quantity in millilitres and dividing by 1000.

So a 330 ml bottle of lager at 5% abv can be worked out as:

$$330 \times 5 = 1650/1000 = 1.7 \text{ units of alcohol}$$

Many drinks now are also being labelled with the number of units of alcohol they contain – this makes it much easier to keep track of how strong certain drinks are.

Each of these drinks contains one unit:

   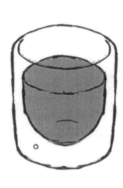   

A small glass of wine = 1 unit   A 25ml pub measure of   Half pint of ordinary strength
                                       spirit = 1 unit   lager/beer/cider = 1 unit

(NB A 330 ml bottle of alcopops (5% ABV) = 1.7 units)

Figure 3.6 Measuring alcohol as units

How does alcohol affect physical and mental behaviour?

The short-term effects of alcohol are almost immediate as it enters the bloodstream within minutes of taking a drink. It is carried to all parts of the body including the brain. The effects can take hours to wear off and the time it takes depends on:

- how much has been drunk and how quickly;
- what sort of drink (stronger drinks such as spirits and fizzy drinks such as sparkling cider are absorbed more quickly);
- how used people are to drinking alcohol;
- size and weight of the drinker.

Even in small amounts, alcohol affects:

- physical co-ordination;
- reaction times;
- judgement.

It takes about an hour for an adult body to get rid of one unit of alcohol. This may be slower in young people, and depends on drug tolerance and body weight.

The long-term effects are shown in Figure 3.7.

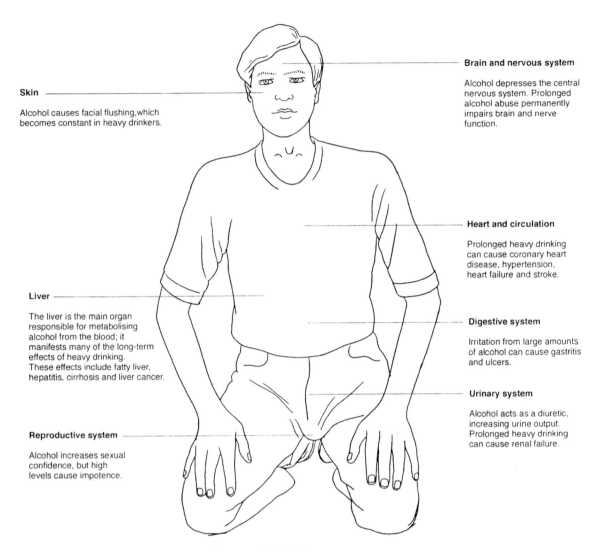

Skin

Alcohol causes facial flushing, which becomes constant in heavy drinkers.

Brain and nervous system

Alcohol depresses the central nervous system. Prolonged alcohol abuse permanently impairs brain and nerve function.

Heart and circulation

Prolonged heavy drinking can cause coronary heart disease, hypertension, heart failure and stroke.

Liver

The liver is the main organ responsible for metabolising alcohol from the blood; it manifests many of the long-term effects of heavy drinking. These effects include fatty liver, hepatitis, cirrhosis and liver cancer.

Digestive system

Irritation from large amounts of alcohol can cause gastritis and ulcers.

Urinary system

Alcohol acts as a diuretic, increasing urine output. Prolonged heavy drinking can cause renal failure.

Reproductive system

Alcohol increases sexual confidence, but high levels cause impotence.

Figure 3.7 Long-term physical effects of alcohol

Alcohol abuse

Alcohol-related problems occur at all educational and social levels and in every age group. There are several signs that a person is having difficulty controlling their alcohol intake:

- drinking for relief from pain and stress;
- pattern drinking (drinking every day or every week at a certain time, particularly in the morning);
- making alcohol the centre of life or of all pleasurable leisure activities.

Some quick alcohol facts

- The heaviest drinkers are 18–25 year olds, of both sexes on a Friday or Saturday night.
- 78% of all assaults are alcohol related.
- Drink plays a part in 50% of all murders.

- Alcohol is involved in 40% of all domestic violence incidents.
- One third of divorce petitions cite alcohol as a contributory factor.
- One in 3 drivers killed in road accidents were over the limit
- 1000 children under the age of 15 are admitted to hospital each year with acute alcohol poisoning
- Being drunk is no excuse if you end up in court on a charge of criminal damage or violence.

Warning

If you are going to drive you shouldn't drink. Even small amounts of alcohol increase the risk of an accident. Anyone caught driving above the legal limit will lose their driving licence for at least a year, face a stiff fine and may end up in prison.

Recommended guidelines on alcohol intake

The daily benchmarks (below) for adult men and women are a guide to how much you can drink without risking your health. These benchmarks are not appropriate for young people, pregnant women and specific circumstances, for example driving.

- Men: 3–4 units daily
- Women: 2–3 units daily

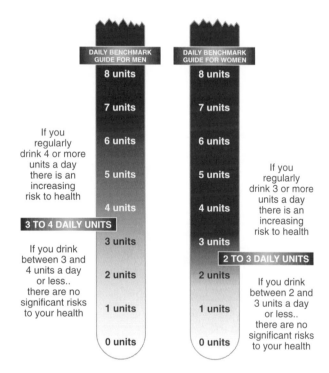

Figure 3.8 Daily benchmark guide for safe drinking

Activity

Researching alcohol abuse

1 Describe some of the ways in which people who drink excessive amounts of alcohol endanger

a themselves

b other people.

2 Find out why women are more sensitive to comparable doses of alcohol than are men.

3 Collect advertisements for drink from magazines, and also the posters and ads put out by bodies such as Alcohol Concern, Drinkwise and the Health Development Agency, which warn of the dangers of heavy drinking. In groups, discuss which posters are more effective – and why?

4 Research the condition known as Foetal Alcohol Syndrome. How many babies are affected each year in the UK and what problems does it present?

5 Find out what treatment or therapy is available for people with a drinking problem (alcoholism) in your area? What does the self-help group Alcoholics Anonymous offer?

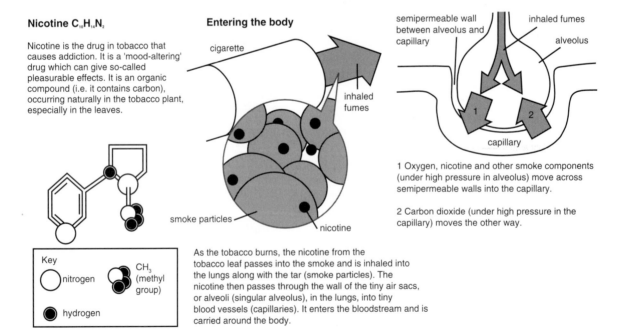

Nicotine $C_{10}H_{14}N_2$

Nicotine is the drug in tobacco that causes addiction. It is a 'mood-altering' drug which can give so-called pleasurable effects. It is an organic compound (i.e. it contains carbon), occurring naturally in the tobacco plant, especially in the leaves.

Entering the body

cigarette

inhaled fumes

smoke particles

nicotine

semipermeable wall between alveolus and capillary

inhaled fumes

alveolus

capillary

1 Oxygen, nicotine and other smoke components (under high pressure in alveolus) move across semipermeable walls into the capillary.

2 Carbon dioxide (under high pressure in the capillary) moves the other way.

Key

nitrogen

CH_3 (methyl group)

hydrogen

As the tobacco burns, the nicotine from the tobacco leaf passes into the smoke and is inhaled into the lungs along with the tar (smoke particles). The nicotine then passes through the wall of the tiny air sacs, or alveoli (singular alveolus), in the lungs, into tiny blood vessels (capillaries). It enters the bloodstream and is carried around the body.

Figure 3.9 How smoking affects your body

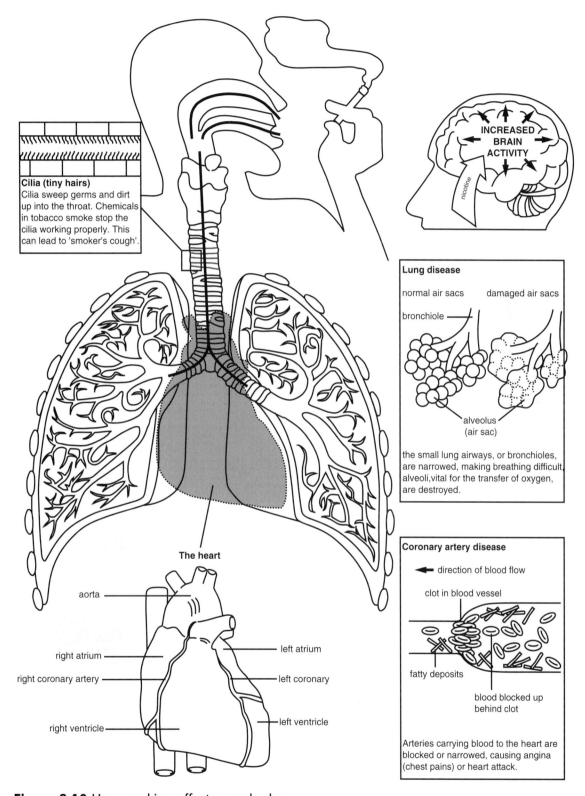

Cilia (tiny hairs)
Cilia sweep germs and dirt up into the throat. Chemicals in tobacco smoke stop the cilia working properly. This can lead to 'smoker's cough'.

INCREASED BRAIN ACTIVITY

nicotine

Lung disease

normal air sacs   damaged air sacs

bronchiole

alveolus (air sac)

the small lung airways, or bronchioles, are narrowed, making breathing difficult. alveoli, vital for the transfer of oxygen, are destroyed.

The heart

aorta

right atrium

right coronary artery

right ventricle

left atrium

left coronary

left ventricle

Coronary artery disease

← direction of blood flow

clot in blood vessel

fatty deposits

blood blocked up behind clot

Arteries carrying blood to the heart are blocked or narrowed, causing angina (chest pains) or heart attack.

Figure 3.10 How smoking affects your body

Smoking

Smoking is the largest single cause of preventable disease and premature death.

How smoking affects your body

Figures 3.9 and 3.10 show the physical effects of smoking. Many diseases and health problems are caused or complicated by smoking; these include:

- cancer: of the mouth, lip, larynx, oesophagus, lung, pancreas, cervix, stomach, bladder and kidney. NB The direct evidence that cigarette smoking causes cancer of the lung is clear – fewer than 10% of lung cancers occur in non-smokers
- chronic lung disease: bronchitis and COLD, Chronic Obstructive Lung Disease
- leukaemia
- emphysema
- fertility problems
- early menopause
- cataracts of the eye
- stroke
- sickle-cell anaemia
- stomach ulcers

Some quick smoking facts

- Smoking causes 31,820 deaths from lung cancer every year in the UK, and overall results in approximately 120,000 deaths each year.
- If you regularly smoke and drink, you are more likely to get cancer of the throat than someone who doesn't. If you do contract it you have a high chance of dying within five years.
- It is not only smoking cigarettes that is dangerous and puts your health at risk, cigars and pipes also increase your chances of getting cancer.
- Although lung cancer caused by smoking is the most common cancer in men and the second most common in women, smoking can also cause cancer of the throat, mouth, gullet, larynx, bladder, kidney, pancreas and stomach.
- Apart from the serious risk of cancer that you undertake when you smoke there are also other negative health implications: tar builds up on your lungs and your lung capacity is reduced, which can lead to a difficulty when breathing, and your chances of a heart attack are increased.
- On average, babies whose mothers smoke throughout pregnancy weigh 200g less at birth than babies of non-smokers.
- Giving up smoking reduces the risk of premature death; the risks return to those of a non-smoker within five to ten years.
- The best way to reduce the risk of getting cancer whilst simultaneously improving your general health and appearance is to stop smoking.

Why do people start smoking?

Smoking usually begins in adolescence. Various factors combine to make it more likely that a young person will smoke; these include:

- Availability: if cigarettes are readily available at home.
- Role models: if role models, e.g. parents, teachers and friends smoke.
- Peer pressure: there is a strong need to conform to the norms of one's peer group.
- Confidence: smoking is a social habit which gives confidence.
- Rebellion: as a gesture of defiance against authority.

Studies have shown that a teenager who smokes just two or three cigarettes has a 70% chance of becoming addicted.

Passive smoking

Breathing other people's smoke is called passive, involuntary or second-hand smoking. The non-smoker breathes **sidestream** smoke from the burning tip of the cigarette, and **mainstream** smoke that has been inhaled and then exhaled by the smoker. The smoke emitted from the end of a burning cigarette has *double* the concentration of nicotine and tar when compared to the smoke actually inhaled by the smoker (through a filter). It also contains three times the amount of benzopyrene (a known carcinogen) and five times the amount of carbon monoxide (a poisonous gas). The risks to non-smokers of passive smoking include:

- **Cot death.** World Health Organization figures indicate that babies are at five times greater risk of cot death if their mothers smoke.
- **Asthma.** Children also have a 20–40% increased risk of asthma if they are exposed to tobacco smoke, and a 70% increased risk of respiratory problems if their mother smokes. People whose partners smoke are nearly five times more likely to develop asthma in adulthood than those who are not exposed to passive smoking, according to new research.
- **Heart disease.** Short term exposure to tobacco smoke also has a measurable effect on the heart in non-smokers. Just 30 minutes' exposure is enough to reduce coronary blood flow. A study published in 1997 by the American Heart Association found that the risk of heart attack and subsequent death is 91% higher (i.e. almost double) for women who were regularly exposed to second-hand smoke and 58% higher for those who were only occasionally exposed.
- **Respiratory problems.** In the UK, long term exposure to second hand cigarette smoke has been shown to increase the risk of **lung cancer** by 20–30%. Those who are exposed to second hand smoke at work are more than twice as likely to develop respiratory problems.

Giving up smoking

The Health Education Council gives the following advice to those who wish to give up smoking:

- Cut out the first cigarette of the day to start with, then the second, and so on.
- Start by cutting out the most 'enjoyable' cigarette of the day, such as the one after a big meal.
- Give up with a friend.
- Tell everyone you are giving up smoking.

Activity

Campaign against smoking

Set up a 'No Smoking' campaign in your school or college.

- Obtain posters from any organisation committed to helping smokers to give up, for example, the NHS site or ASH (Action on smoking and health). Or make your own using the quick facts section on page 130.

- Choose a prominent site to display posters and fact sheets – don't forget to ask permission.

- Obtain several **peak flow meters**. (A peak flow meter is a small device that measures how well air moves out of the airways). Health clinic and GP practices might be willing to loan them out. Learn how to use them and to instruct others in their use. (**NB** Follow the rules of hygiene.)

- Ask each volunteer if he or she smokes and offer them the chance to test their own peak flow rate.

- Record results from smokers and non-smokers on separate charts.

- At the end of the session, analyse the results and present them on a poster.

Lung diseases

Lung diseases, which include conditions ranging from asthma to lung cancer, are now the biggest killers in the UK, accounting for one in four deaths. Respiratory conditions are now the most common long-term illness among children. They are also responsible for most emergency hospital admissions in the UK. It is also the most common reason patients give for visiting their GP and is estimated to cost the NHS £2.5bn each year – more than any other disease.

Cancer

What is cancer?

There are over 200 different cancers, yet each starts in the same way – with a change in the normal make-up of a cell. Normal cells grow in a controlled way. But cancer cells are different from normal cells:

- They go on and on growing. One cell becomes cancerous. This grows into two, then four, then eight and so on. By the time a cancer is big enough to see on a scan, or to feel as a lump, there are billions of cells in the tumour.

- Cancer cells may not stick together well, and are able to spread around the body.

- Cancers start because some of the information that is carried in the cell's DNA has become altered. For example, this altered information might tell the cell to carry on growing instead of stopping.

- There are many different types of cells in the body and any of these can become cancerous. This is why there are so many different types of cancer.

- Cancer cells use the blood stream and the circulation of tissue fluid (in the lymphatic system) to spread around the body. In order to grow, a cancer needs a good blood supply, just like any other growing body tissue. The fact that cancers grow is harmful to the body because they damage the tissues around them.

- Cancers are also harmful because they can spread. Doctors use a system called **staging** to describe the size of a tumour and gauge whether it has spread. Many people will have their cancer diagnosed and successfully treated before it has spread. Some cancers are more likely to spread than others. Certain cancers are more likely to spread to particular parts of the body.

- The **immune system** may have a role to play in fighting the cancer. Cancer treatments such as chemotherapy and radiotherapy can weaken the immune system for a time. Some people have genes that make it more likely that they will get cancer, some have genes that protect them. Things around us can also damage our genes and make a cell cancerous. This includes poisons in **cigarette smoke** and **radiation**. The older a person gets, the more likely it is that they will get cancer.

- Cancers can cause different symptoms in different people because of where they are. A cancer may press on a nerve, or another body organ that is nearby. The place where the cancer starts also affects what treatment can be used because doctors have to take into account the risk of damaging neighbouring organs.

Cancer is the cause of a quarter of all deaths in the UK. Experts have estimated that more than 80% of cancers may be avoidable by changing lifestyles or the environment. In 1996 there were 156,000 deaths from cancer – nearly a quarter of these were from lung cancer and a further quarter were caused by cancers of the large bowel, breast and prostate. Cigarette smoking has been identified as the single most important cause of preventable disease and premature death in the UK.

Some quick cancer facts

- 30% of all cancer deaths are caused by smoking.
- Every year smoking causes over 30,000 deaths from lung cancer.
- 3% of all cancers are related to excess alcohol consumption.
- Heavy drinkers are at risk of cirrhosis of the liver, which can lead to cancer in later life
- About 35 % of cancers may be related to diet.
- Diets containing a variety of fruits and vegetables seem to protect against certain cancers.
- Too much sun can lead to skin cancer.
- Skin cancer is the second most common cancer in the UK.
- Britain has the highest death rate from breast cancer in the world.
- 16,000 women die each year from breast cancer in the UK.
- About 2,000 women in the UK die each year from cervical cancer (cancer of the cervix or neck of the womb).

- Testicular cancer is the commonest cancer in the UK in men aged 20–34, with 1000 new cases reported each year.

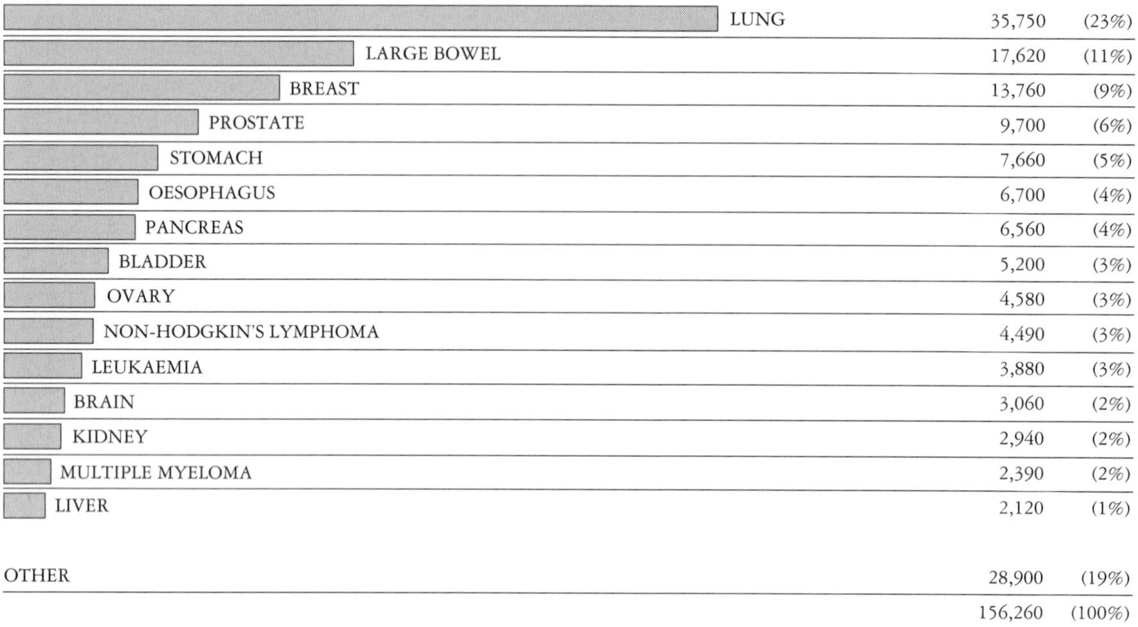

LUNG	35,750	(23%)
LARGE BOWEL	17,620	(11%)
BREAST	13,760	(9%)
PROSTATE	9,700	(6%)
STOMACH	7,660	(5%)
OESOPHAGUS	6,700	(4%)
PANCREAS	6,560	(4%)
BLADDER	5,200	(3%)
OVARY	4,580	(3%)
NON-HODGKIN'S LYMPHOMA	4,490	(3%)
LEUKAEMIA	3,880	(3%)
BRAIN	3,060	(2%)
KIDNEY	2,940	(2%)
MULTIPLE MYELOMA	2,390	(2%)
LIVER	2,120	(1%)
OTHER	28,900	(19%)
	156,260	(100%)

Figure 3.11 Deaths from different types of cancer

The risks of radiation

Radiation is used therapeutically to treat various forms of cancer, but it can also cause cancer. Everyone is exposed to that which comes naturally from the earth and the sky; other sources of radiation need to be fully monitored:

- X-ray examinations and treatment, including dental X-rays.
- Houses found on certain types of ground in some counties in England, Scotland and Wales are more likely to have high levels of radon, which is produced in granite and other rocks.

Reducing the risks of cancer

- Stop smoking, or better still don't start; after ten years your risk of lung cancer is about half that of a continuing smoker.
- Try to avoid places where you will be exposed to passive smoking.
- Know the limits of sensible drinking and keep within them.
- Eat more fruit and vegetables.
- Eat more starchy and fibre-rich foods.
- Eat less fatty foods.
- If you want to tan, do it gradually and protect against sunburn by using a sun lotion with the correct sun protection factor (SPF).
- Women aged between 50 and 64 should attend a breast screening centre every three years for mammography (X-rays) of both breasts; early detection gives a better chance of successful treatment.

- To reduce the risk of cervical cancer, use a barrier contraceptive (cap, condom, female condom or diaphragm) during intercourse; women aged 20–64 should attend a clinic for a free cervical smear test every 3 years.

- A good way of detecting testicular cancer in its early stages is for men to examine their own testicles.

- If you work with radiation, make sure that the safety regulations are fully observed.

- The radon level in your home can be measured by writing to NRPB.

Activity

Cancer risks

Prepare a fact file detailing the links between certain lifestyle practices and different types of cancer. Include information about cancer support groups.

Heart disease and stroke

There are two *main* types of coronary heart disease: angina and heart attack.

1 **Angina pectoris** is characterised by a crushing pain in the chest because of insufficient oxygen being carried to the heart muscles. It is often brought on by exercise or stress. The patient will usually have special tablets (glyceryl trinitrate or Trinitrin) that dissolve under the tongue and bring rapid relief

2 **Heart attack** is caused by either:

- myocardial infarction, when part of the heart muscle has died as a result of blood starvation;

- coronary thrombosis, when the blood supply to the heart muscles is stopped by a blood clot.

Both kinds of heart attack are usually caused by **atherosclerosis** – the build-up of fatty deposits, called atheroma, in the blood vessels.

Stroke

Stroke or cerebral vascular accident (CVA), occurs when an area of the brain is deprived of its blood supply for 24 hours or more – usually because of a blockage or burst blood vessel – causing vital brain tissue to die. It is caused by:

- atherosclerosis;

- weakening in an artery wall (aneurysm);

- atrial fibrillation – a kind of irregular heartbeat (arrhythmia); this can cause a blood clot to form in the heart which can shear off and travel to the brain.

Some quick heart disease facts

- One fatal **heart attack** occurs in Britain every three minutes. In about one-third of all heart attacks the patient dies before reaching hospital.

- An estimated 20% of deaths from heart disease in men and 17% in women are due to **smoking**.

- It is estimated that in the UK about 36% of deaths from heart disease in men and 38% of deaths from heart disease in women are related to **lack of physical activity**.

- Heart disease causes nearly one-third of all deaths in the UK in people under the age of 75.

- The UK has one of the highest levels of heart disease in the world.

- One reason why heart disease rates are high in the UK is because the average **diet** is so unhealthy. In particular, fat intake – especially of saturated fat – in the UK is too high, and fruit and vegetable consumption is too low.

- **Moderate alcohol consumption** (one or two drinks per day) is associated with a reduced risk of heart disease. At high levels of intake – particularly in 'binges' – the risk of heart disease is increased.

Reducing the risks of heart disease and stroke

- Don't smoke.
- Take regular exercise – a brisk walk for 20 minutes each day will improve circulation.
- Drink alcohol sensibly – think of a pint of beer or two glasses of wine as the maximum for one day.
- Eat healthily.
- Try to avoid stress.

 Activity

Lifestyles and health

Arrange a debate around a specific lifestyle issue, for example, diet, smoking or alcohol use. Suggested topics:

- Should overweight (obese) people or smokers be refused a heart transplant by the NHS?

- Should smokers pay compensation directly to those damaged by passive smoking?

- Should health professionals prescribe courses to change health-damaging behaviour (for example, a strictly monitored diet or an exercise programme at a leisure centre?

Sexually transmitted infections (STIs)

There are several different types of sexually transmitted infections (infection you can only catch through having sex with a partner). They cannot always be recognised because some do not have any signs or symptoms. Using a condom is not a 100% guarantee of not catching a STI but it does offer very good protection. STIs will not go away unless treated and some of them are easy to treat.

Table 3.6 describes the different infections, and how they may be recognised and treated.

Top tips if you've got an STI

- Make sure your partner is checked out and cleared of infection before you have sex again.
- Avoid sex until the STI has been treated and has gone away.
- Always use condoms if you have sex.
- If you are at all worried about having an STI, make sure you visit a GUM clinic.
- Once you become sexually active it is important to look after your sexual health by visiting a GUM clinic if you have had unprotected sex.
- If you're having sex, avoid catching a love bug... use a condom, it's the only way! You can't tell by looking – don't leave it to chance.

Remember – you can catch an STI the first time you have sex with someone!

Most sexually transmitted infections are treatable...just go to your local GUM clinic. A GUM clinic is one of the most confidential places you can visit. It's also free and totally non-judgmental. Even though these clinics are often found in hospitals, your medical records can never be passed on to your GP or other parts of the hospital. All you have to do for a test is turn up, and wait your turn.

(Material adapted from the family planning charity Marie Stopes International website: www.likeitis.org.uk)

Promoting personal safety

Many people believe that as individuals they have little control over risks to their health because of large-scale environmental problems – such as global warming or industrial pollution. While it is true that many environmental issues require global policies to be managed effectively, risks to one's immediate environment *can* be controlled.

Some quick accident facts

- Two-thirds of all fatal accidents involving school-aged children are the result of **road accidents.**
- In 1998, over 40,000 children were killed or injured on our roads.
- The severity of injury is closely linked to speed. Hit at 20mph, one in 20 pedestrians is killed, while at 40mph only one in ten survives. Drivers can make the biggest contribution to reducing road accidents by slowing down, especially when children are around.
- About 4000 people are killed in **home and garden** accidents in the UK each year and almost 3 million people seek medical attention in hospitals as a result of accidents at home.

Table 3.6 Sexually transmitted infections (STIs)

Infection	What is it?	How can I tell if I've got it?	What will clear it up?
AIDS and HIV	**HIV (Human Immunodeficiency Virus)** is a virus which damages the body's immune system. When someone has **AIDS (Acquired Immune Deficiency Syndrome)**, it means they are HIV+ and have gone on to get a series of serious illnesses. HIV can be passed on by having sex without a condom with someone who has HIV. HIV is only passed on through bodily fluids and blood, for example through sex, injecting drugs or from mothers to their unborn children.	You can't. The only way to tell if you have HIV is to have a blood test.	At present there is no cure for HIV or AIDS but new combination therapies mean improved management of the illness.
Chlamydia	This is the most common STI amongst young women and men. It's caused by a bacteria, which, if left untreated, can cause pelvic inflammatory disease (a disease that infects your pelvic region and can lead to infertility in women and men).	In 15–20% of cases there will be symptoms 5–10 days after infection (look for a discharge and pain). However, *most* people do not get any symptoms.	Antibiotics after a simple chlamydia test at a genito-urinary medicine (GUM) clinic.
Genital warts	Genital warts are small fleshy lumps (like the warts you can get on your hands). They appear around your genitals and are caused by a virus called human papilloma virus (HPV).	The big problem with warts is that there are often no symptoms, or the warts develop inside the vagina (usually on the cervix) so you can't see them. If they do appear they may itch but are usually painless.	If you have been infected the good news is that in many cases the body's immune system will cause most warts to disappear without treatment after six months. Large visible warts need to be treated. You will be given a special lotion that you will be asked to apply to the warts. If this doesn't clear the warts, or the warts are in a tricky place, stronger lotions may be used. Occasionally, warts may be frozen or burned off, but usually this is not painful.

Infection	What is it?	How can I tell if I've got it?	What will clear it up?
Herpes	There are two types of herpes that cause small, painful blisters. Herpes Simplex Virus (HSV) Type 1, which usually causes cold sores, and HSV Type II, which causes genital sores. Herpes Type 1 is passed by kissing and herpes Type II is passed through sex. Type 1 can become Type II, through oral sex.	Look for small, painful clusters of sores It can be diagnosed from a sample taken for testing, or a doctor may know just by looking. Remember, herpes is highly infectious and during an outbreak you should avoid sex and kissing (if you have cold sores). Outbreaks are treated with salt baths and/or medication.	There is no cure for herpes.
Gonorrhoea	Gonorrhoea is a disease caused by bacteria. The danger of this is, if left undiagnosed, it can cause pelvic inflammatory disease and infertility.	In five out of every six cases, there are no symptoms. Symptoms to look for are a discharge and a burning sensation when going for a wee.	Antibiotics.
Syphilis	An infection caused by a bacteria, which, if left untreated, can have very serious consequences.	A sore on your genitals, and a rash. If left untreated, the symptoms become severe.	Syphilis can be cured with one course of antibiotics.
Pubic lice	Also known as crabs, pubic lice are small insects that are spread through sex and intimate contact (bedding, towels etc.).	You'll have severe itching throughout your pubic region.	Usually a doctor will be able to tell if you have pubic lice and will prescribe a lotion to kill them off.
Trichomoniasis	This is an infection that affects the vagina, cervix, urethra and bladder.	Look for a greenish-yellow discharge with a strong and offensive smell, itching of the vagina and a burning when going for a pee. Boys/men have no symptoms.	A swab will be taken and antibacterial drugs prescribed.
Hepatitis B	This is a serious condition that causes inflammation of the liver caused by a virus passed on through vaginal or anal intercourse.	Usually there are no symptoms but look for unusual tiredness.	There is no effective cure, but in some cases your body fights off the virus and the infection goes away.

- There were 656 deaths associated with **work activities** in Great Britain during 1997–8.
- Nearly one-third of home fire victims are killed in fires that are related to cigarette smoking.
- Around half of pedestrians aged between 16 and 60 killed in road accidents have **blood alcohol levels** above the legal drink drive limit.

Many deaths can be avoided if simple precautions are taken.

Table 3.7

Fire safety	Home safety	Road safety
• Install a smoke alarm in your home, a least one per floor, and check regularly that it is working correctly. Replace the batteries as soon as they are low.	• Make sure pan handles are turned to the back of the hob while cooking.	• Infants and children should always ride in approved child car safety seats that are correctly adjusted and installed. Look for car seats with a British Standard kitemark. Other passengers should wear car seat belts.
• Extinguish all cigarettes carefully, especially before retiring for the night. Never smoke in bed.	• Store sharp objects such as scissors, razors and knives in a drawer.	• Never fit a rear-facing child safety seat in a passenger seat fitted with an airbag.
• Don't overload electrical sockets.	• Keep medicines and vitamins in a cupboard out of children's reach.	• If you are cycling, wear a helmet that meets a recognised safety standard. When riding in the dark, use front and rear lights (and have a rear reflector fitted) as required by law. Try to wear something fluorescent and reflective so that you can be seen more easily by other road users.
• Keep a fire extinguisher in the kitchen and learn how to use it properly.	• Store cleaning chemicals in a cupboard with a safety catch or in a high cupboard.	• Teach children how to cross roads safely and wherever possible cross at a zebra or pelican crossing.
	• Keep the stairs clear of toys and other items that could trip you up.	• Do not drink and drive and, even if you are not driving, don't put yourself at risk of road accidents by drinking too much. Alcohol affects physical coordination and reaction times so people who are drunk are more likely to be involved in accidents. Half of all pedestrians aged between 16 and 60 killed in road accidents are over the legal drink drive limit.
	• Fit locks on children's bedroom windows and keep furniture away from the window to prevent them climbing up to the window sill.	• Do not use mobile phones while driving. They distract you from driving safely.
	• Remove any potentially poisonous house plants.	• Observe speed limits, particularly in built-up areas and when children are about.
	• Never leave babies and small children unattended in the bath or near other sources of water, even for a short time.	
	• Avoid trailing wires and clutter in walking areas.	
	• Remove or repair frayed carpet edges.	

Figure 3.12 Step up to Safety: health promotion leaflet for elderly people

The Department of Education and Employment are developing the following pieces of software aimed at making the journey to school safer:

- Mapping software that will enable pupils to map safer, healthier and more sustainable routes to school
- Car-sharing database that will allow schools to develop a car-sharing scheme aimed at reducing the health and safety risks of the 'school run'.

 Activity

Road safety

Find out about recent campaigns to improve road safety awareness, for example, TV and poster adverts that focus on using seat belts, crossing the road safely and not drinking when driving. How effective and memorable are these ads? Can you think of a more effective way of getting the message across?

Origins of educational activities

Educational promotions for health and social well-being may be launched for many reasons, including the following:

- to meet international targets for health and social well-being;
- to meet national targets for health and social well-being;
- to address local/regional issues for informing social policy.

International targets

The World Health Organisation (WHO)

The WHO Regional Committee for Europe outlined 21 targets for health – called **HEALTH 21**. These targets are much less specific in their aims than the national targets set by Government Departments. Examples include:

- **Healthy start in life.** By the year 2020, all newborn babies, infants and pre-school children in the region should have better health, ensuring a healthy start in life.
- **Health of young people.** By the year 2020, young people in the region should be healthier and better able to fulfil their roles in society.
- **Healthy ageing.** By the year 2020, people over 65 years should have the opportunity of enjoying their full health potential and playing an active social role.
- **Improving mental health.** By the year 2020, people's psycho-social well-being should be improved, and better comprehensive services should be available to, and accessible by, people with mental health problems.

National targets

'Saving Lives: Our Healthier Nation'

This is a government national action plan to tackle the problem of poor health. It proposed a three-way partnership – between individuals, communities and government agencies to combat the 'four big killers' faced by people in the UK today:

- Every year **cancer** kills 127,000 people;
- Every year **heart disease and stroke** kill 214,000 people;
- Every year 10,000 people are killed by **accidents**;
- Every year **suicide** kills 4,500 people.

NB: Since the setting up of the **national action plan**, lung disease has been identified as a major health problem in the UK.

Tackling inequalities in health and social care

While overall life expectancy in England has been improving, the health gap between the rich and the poor has been widening. The stark fact is that a poor person is more likely to be ill and to die younger. Health inequalities are also evident for factors such as gender and ethnicity where differences in health can be similarly striking. The reasons for health inequalities are

Table 3.8 NHS Plan for tackling inequalities: (Access to NHS services; Children: ensuring a healthy start in life; Reducing smoking)

Access to NHS services	Children: ensuring a healthy start in life	Reducing smoking
• Allocating NHS resources to different parts of the country. • Fairer distribution of GPs. There will be a new way of distributing resources to address inequities in primary care services. • 200 new Personal Medical Services schemes principally in disadvantaged communities by 2004. • Health centres in the most deprived areas will be modernised. • The development of a new Health Poverty Index. • Health inequalities and equitable access to healthcare will for the first time be performance managed using the Performance Assessment Framework. • Free translation and interpretation service from every NHS premises by 2003.	By 2004 there will be: • An expansion of Sure Start to cover a third of all children under four living in poverty. • A new children's fund worth £450 million over three years. • A reform of welfare foods, with increased support for breastfeeding and parenting. • Full implementation of the Teenage Pregnancy Strategy. • Effective and appropriate screening programmes for women and children. • A new sexual health and HIV strategy. • Access to the Connexions Service, either through a Connexions Personal Advisor, drop-in centre, telephone or Internet-enabled support for every young person aged 13 to 19. • An additional 6,000 severely disabled children will receive a co-ordinated care package from health and social care services.	• Make Nicotine Replacement Therapy (NRT) available on prescription, to complement buproprion (Zyban) in 2001. • Ask the National Institute for Clinical Excellence to advise GPs on the most appropriate and cost-effective prescribing regimes for NRT and buproprion. • Ask the Committee on Safety of Medicines to consider whether more NRT can be made available for general sale. • Focus the efforts of specialist smoking cessation services on heavily dependant smokers needing intensive support and on pregnant smokers as part of ante-natal care. • If successful, this programme will mean that by 2010, approximately 55,000 fewer women will be smoking in pregnancy and at least 1.5 million smokers will have given up smoking. • In addition to the **Smoking Kills** target of reducing smoking in adults from 28% to 24% by 2010, the Cancer Plan (September 2000) announced new national and local targets to address the gap between socio-economic groups in smoking rates and the resulting risks of cancer and heart disease: • Smoking rates among manual groups will be reduced from 32% in 1998 to 26% by 2010. • Local targets will be set making explicit what this means for the 20 health authorities with the highest smoking rates. • Funding for smoking cessation work with black and minority ethnic groups has been increased to £1 million. • There will be new pilots in 10 deprived areas to reduce smoking prevalence in communities where there are particular opportunities for focused support, such as prisons and hospitals.

Table 3.9 NHS Plan for tackling inequalities: (Teenage pregnancy; nutrition; drugs and alcohol-related crime)

Teenage pregnancy	Improving diet and nutrition	Tackling drugs and alcohol-related crime
• The appointment of a local teenage pregnancy co-ordinator in every social services area supported by eight regional co-ordinators. • Local reduction targets which seek the largest reductions in areas with the highest rates. By 2010 we are seeking a 60% reduction in under 18 conceptions in the worst fifth of wards, thereby reducing the level of inequality between the worst fifth of wards and the average by at least a quarter. • A national media campaign with adverts in teenage magazines and in local radio. • The production of new guidance on sex and relationship education. • The production of new guidance for local co-ordinators on effective youth contraceptive services.	Action by 2004 includes: • A national five-a-day programme to increase fruit and vegetable consumption: • The National School Fruit Scheme which entitles school children aged four to six to a free piece of fruit each school day. • Five-a-day Community Projects have been set up to test the feasibility and practicalities of evidence-based community approaches to improving access to and increasing awareness of fruit and vegetables. National roll out begins in 2002. • Work with industry – producers, caterers, retailers – to increase provision of, and access to, fruit and vegetables. • A communications programme to increase awareness of fruit and vegetable consumption, particularly targeting those groups with the lowest intakes. • Evaluation and monitoring of the implementation and impact of the five-a-day programme. • A reform of the welfare foods programme to use the resources more effectively to ensure children in poverty have access to a healthy diet. • Increased support for breast feeding – inequalities in breast feeding exist, for example, over 90% of mothers in social class I breast feed their babies initially, compared to only 50% of mothers in social class V. • Reduce salt, sugar and fat in the diet: work with the Food Standards Agency and the food industry to improve overall balance of the diet. • Local action to tackle obesity and physical inactivity informed by advice from the Health Development Agency. The recent National Audit Office report on 'Tackling Obesity in England' highlighted that most adults are now overweight, and one in five is obese. • Hospital nutrition policy to improve the outcome of care for patients.	The new National Treatment Agency (NTA) came into being on 1 April 2001, and will have a budget that pools resources spent on services from health and other agencies. • The main purpose of the Agency will be to ensure that those requiring treatment are able to access quality services regardless of their route of referral. • Ministers have decided to set up the National Treatment Agency as a Special Health Authority. • The NTA will deliver the three key quality improvement elements of clear quality standards, effective local delivery and strong monitoring mechanisms. • The NTA will make a difference by setting standards of treatment provisions and commission, performance monitoring and development and tackling variations in treatment standards and availability. • The Agency will put in place new structures and mechanisms to ensure that every drug treatment programme is aimed at the outcomes of the best.

complex and tackling them is a tough challenge that requires concerted action at all levels. Tackling wider influences (or determinants) such as: poverty, education, social exclusion, employment, housing, and the environment will be key, and will involve contributions and partnership working from all Government departments as well as at a local level within individual communities. **The NHS Plan (2001)** gave a number of commitments on health inequalities – see tables 3.8 and 3.9.

The NHS cancer plan

This promises action on:

- preventive work to reduce risk;
- earlier detection;
- improved community support for sufferers;
- faster access to treatment;
- national standards of treatment;
- improved palliative care;
- a strengthened research base.

Performance targets

These include a maximum one-month wait:

- from urgent GP referral to treatment for children's and testicular cancers and acute leukaemia by 2001;
- from diagnosis to treatment for breast cancer by 2001;
- from diagnosis to treatment for all cancers by 2005.

There will be a maximum two-month wait:

- from urgent GP referral to treatment for breast cancer by 2002;
- from urgent GP referral to treatment for all cancers by 2005.

Other new measures include:

- a target to reduce smoking rates among manual workers from 32% in 1998 to 26% by 2010;
- £50m more investment and additional Lottery cash for palliative care and hospices.

Local and regional issues for informing social policy

Local **health promotion units** have a role in ensuring that national targets are achieved. The government has also set up **Health Improvement Programmes (HimPs)**, and **Health Action Zones (HAZs)**

Health Improvement Programmes (HimPs)

These are a partnership between:

- Health Authorities (including Primary Care Groups), Primary Care Trusts, NHS Trusts, to develop the aims and the objectives of the NHS;
- NHS bodies and local authorities to promote the health and well-being of the local populations.

Current Health Improvement Programmes aim to:

- improve health and tackle inequalities;
- modernise and improve local services;
- provide a more comprehensive and effective planning process within the local health care system;
- support the development of partnerships with local authorities, the voluntary sector and other organisations.

HImPs will involve:

1 Those who use local services – either as patients or carers – the voluntary sector, local communities etc. need to input into the current HImPs so they feel ownership of its objectives and are committed to its implementation. Here it is important to involve those groups (children, black and minority ethnic groups and older people) who are under-represented or hard to reach under the NHS's traditional consultation methods.

2 Others with an interest or contribution to offer: trade unions, TECS, local schools, employers, including their occupational health services, the Health and Safety Executive, relevant colleges and universities etc.

Health Action Zones (HAZs)

These are partnerships between:

- The NHS;
- local authorities;
- community groups;
- the voluntary and business sectors located in deprived areas with poor health status and significant service pressures.

The function of HAZs is to:

- trigger health action programmes;
- develop and implement a health strategy to deliver within their area measurable improvements in public health and in the outcomes and quality of treatment and care.

Educational programmes and activities for health and social well-being

The focus of health promotion activities

The main aims of health education programmes are to:

- raise individual and population awareness about health issues;
- provide information and advice;
- develop personal strengths and abilities;
- support people to make changes.

Whether health and ill health is seen as the consequence of individual lifestyles or as a response to the social environment will affect the focus of health promotion activities. Health promotion activities can have a variety of objectives:

- to prevent disease;
- to ensure that people are well informed and able to make choices;
- to change behaviour;
- to help people acquire skills and confidence to take greater control over the factors influencing their health;
- to change policies and environments to facilitate healthy choices.

Health promotion involves working with individuals, communities and society

The new health strategy, 'Our Healthier Nation', recognises the role of individuals in determining their own health but also sees a role for communities and government in tackling the root causes of ill health. Individual practitioners may be engaged in:

- advice and information giving;
- education and training;
- policy work and lobbying;
- community development;
- interagency collaboration;
- research, profiling and monitoring;
- media development and campaigns.

Significant educators of health and social well-being

Organisations

Table 3.10 Organisations involved in health education

World Health Organisation (WHO)
For detailed information (see Chapter 5, page 266)

HealthPromis: the national database for health promotion for England, containing references and links to a range of sources.

Health Development Agency (HDA) for England: The HDA aims to improve the health of the people of England through research, capacity-building, monitoring and setting standards. (This used to be known as the Health Education Authority.)

Health Education Board for Scotland

Health Promotion Wales

The Health Promotion Agency for Northern Ireland

Government departments
The Department of Health, (DOH), The Department of Health and Social Security, (DHSS); Department for Education and Employment (DfEE); Ministry of Agriculture, Fisheries and Food (MAFF); Department of the Environment (DofE); Department of Transport; Central Office of Information etc.

UK Public Health Association
The United Kingdom Public Health Association (UKPHA) is an independent UK wide voluntary association, bringing together individuals and organisations from all sectors, who share a commitment to promoting the public's health. It is a membership based organisation that aims to promote the development of healthy public policy at all levels of government and across all sectors, and to support those working in public health either professionally or in a voluntary capacity. The UKPHA is a registered charity.

National Health Service (NHS)
Health Improvement Programmes (HiPs).
NHS Direct.
For detailed information, see Chapter 1.

Health and Safety Executive (HSE)
For detailed information, see Chapter 5 (pages 273–4).

Local Education Authorities
Schools, colleges, school and college nurses.

Social Services
Parenting skills programmes and child protection.

Voluntary Agencies
Most voluntary organisations offer information and advice on health education specific to their interest, for example, RNIB, Age Concern, ROSPA, NCH etc. They are available online and usually have telephone helplines.

Local police forces
Citizenship programmes, road safety, home safety and personal safety.

Commercial organisations
Private preventive medical companies, for example BUPA, PPP. Manufacturers and retailers of 'healthy' products, such as Flora, Benecol etc.

Community groups
Local groups e.g. neighbourhood Watch, Friends of the Earth, Community centres.

The mass media
Newspapers, magazines, TV and radio.

People who work in health education

- **Health and social care professionals:** nurses, doctors, midwives, health visitors, health promotion officers, occupational health nurses.
- **Environmental health officers**
- **Health and safety officers**
- **Housing officers**
- **Youth workers and social workers**
- **Community liaison police officers:** specialist police officers visit schools to advise and teach children about healthy living practices, such as road safety, personal safety and substance abuse
- **Teachers and lecturers**
- **Family and friends**

Professionals work with individuals and with communities; each area requires different skills and strategies:

Supporting individual change

Health education with individuals involves:

- Helping individuals identify risks to their health and to assess the costs and benefits of change.
- Providing information.
- Developing a relationship of trust and mutual respect with a client.
- Being aware of other factors, such as the views of significant people in the client's life and the individual's own self esteem, that could influence the situation.
- Knowledge of health psychology: Naidoo and Wills (1994) suggest that before change can take place, six conditions must be met:

1 **The change must be self-initiated.** Some clients resist pressure from others to change their behaviour.

2 **The behaviour must become important.** Many behaviours, for example, smoking, have become a habitual part of the client's life. Something must happen to draw the individual's attention to the behaviour and prompt a reappraisal.

3 **The importance of the behaviour must emerge over a period of time.** The new behaviour (i.e. not smoking) must become a normal and accepted part of the individual's life. This process takes time.

4 **The behaviour is not part of the individual's coping strategies.** It is more difficult to change if the risky behaviour helps the individual to cope with other difficulties (for example smoking helps the person to feel less stressed). In some circumstances, it is possible to suggest alternative coping strategies.

5 **The individual's life should not be problematic or uncertain.** People who are already experiencing stress, perhaps because of poverty or significant life events, may find it more difficult to change their health behaviour.

6 Social support is available. The presence of other people who are interested in the behaviour change can be of immense help to the individual

Working with communities

There are many different kinds of communities. A community can be made up of individuals:

- living in the same geographic area;
- belonging to the same ethnic group;
- of the same age;
- working for the same organisation;
- sharing the same culture or sexual orientation.

Most people belong to several communities.

Health education with communities or groups of people involves:

- involving the group or community in planning their own health care – leading to empowerment;
- helping people to understand the influence of social factors on their health (see pages 93–94);
- initiating or facilitating support groups;
- working with other agencies;
- profiling health needs of local people;
- lobbying and campaigning.

Health educators must be good communicators. Whether communicating with an individual or with a group, the message conveyed must be clear, unambiguous and relevant.

Objectives of educational activities

Various sources of information or data are used to identify the aims and objectives of health education campaigns. These include:

Epidemiology

This is the study of the distribution and determinants (or decisive factors) of disease in communities; epidemiological data indicates how:

- How many people are affected by a health problem (**morbidity** statistics).
- How many people die from a particular health problem – if potentially fatal (**mortality** statistics).
- Who are most at risk, for example which age groups, men or women; which occupation; which geographical area; smokers or non-smokers; active or sedentary people etc.

Descriptive studies

These describe the situation, for example, describing the distribution of a certain disease in relation to the age of a given population.

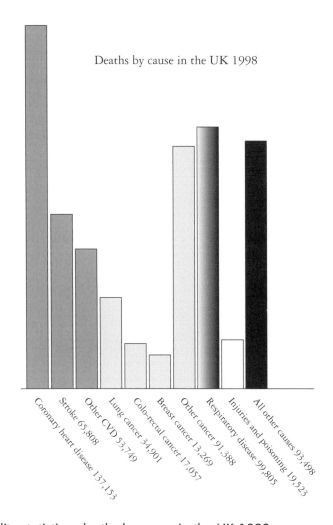

Deaths by cause in the UK 1998

Coronary heart disease 137,153
Stroke 65,808
Other CVD 53,749
Lung cancer 34,901
Colo-rectal cancer 17,057
Breast cancer 13,269
Other cancer 91,388
Respiratory disease 99,805
Injuries and poisoning 19,523
All other causes 93,498

Figure 3.13 Mortality statistics: deaths by cause in the UK 1998

Analytical studies

These try to explain the situation by formulating and testing **hypotheses**, for example, trying to explain why a certain disease affects predominately males over the age of 60 in a given population.

Different study designs can be used in different situations and can use a mixture of **descriptive** and **analytical** approaches. Study designs can also be categorised as:

- **non-experimental**, where there is no **intervention** by the researcher, for example, case studies and surveys. Most surveys are **cross-sectional** (based on a random cross section of the population of interest, carried out at one point in time). **Longitudinal** surveys are carried out at more than one point in time, and aim to analyse cause and effect relationships. Most longitudinal studies follow-up the same population over time (for example, to measure the incidence of disease, and cause-effect relationships).

- **experimental** (intervention study), where the researcher *does* intervene, designed to test a cause- and-effect **hypothesis**. However, they can be carried out only if it is feasible and ethically justified to manipulate the postulated cause, for example, fluoridate the water supply of some towns, but not others, then compare the level of dental caries in children.

Table 3.11 Models and approaches in educating for health and social well-being

	Medical, preventive interventionist	Behaviourist	Empowerment	Educational	Social change
Aims	• medical interventions • disease reduction • compliance • scientific (e.g. epidemiology), • expert-led (top-down)	• encourage individuals to adopt healthy behaviours – key to improved health • health belongs to the individual – is their choice	• help people identify own health concerns – gain skills, ability, confidence to deal with them. • health educator facilitates (bottom-up) • self-empowerment, community empowerment	• provision of knowledge and skills to enable informed choice about behaviour. • does not aim to persuade or motivate in particular direction – but intended to lead to voluntary choice	• policy and environmental changes • to make the healthier choice the easier choice
Methods	primary preventive services (e.g. immunisation)	• mass media (e.g. HDA) • expert-led (top-down) but adaptable – could be client-led (bottom-up)	• developing plan with patient or client (e.g. nurses – care-plan) • client identifies areas for change • community development – identify shared concerns – plan action	3 aspects of learning: • cognitive (information and understanding) • affective (attitudes and feelings) • behavioural (skills) • teacher/facilitator • counselling, group discussion, role play	• targeting groups – organisational level (top-down) • public health legislation • support of groups or populations • lobbying, policy planning
Evaluation	• **short-term:** uptake of preventive services • **long-term:** morbidity and mortality rates	• is the result a change in behaviour? – problems with measuring behaviour	• extent to which specified aims met (outcome evaluation) • how group has been empowered (process evaluation)	• increased knowledge	• effectiveness of policy change
Disadvantages	• does not promote positive health • ignores social/environmental aspects of health • dependent on expert medical knowledge • removes health decisions • reinforces the medical model and medical hierarchy	• ignores social/economic factors • can lead to victim blaming (i.e. passive smoking issue) • expert-led • social engineering • targeting certain groups – can be manipulative	• evaluation problematic – long-term – difficult to decide the causes of change. • community development time-consuming and expensive • relinquishing control difficult for many professionals	• ignores social/economic factors • information alone insufficient to change behaviour	• long term and expensive • politically sensitive, e.g. no smoking policy in all public places, advertising and sponsorship of smoking

A **randomised controlled trial (RCT)** is the experimental approach of choice when assessing the effect of any type of health care **intervention**. The intervention could be:

- a new drug treatment compared to an existing medication;
- a new service, for example, practice nurse-led clinics for diabetes compared to routine general practice care.

These clinical trials must be carefully designed and conducted. The strength of an RCT lies in the *randomisation* of individuals from a defined sample population into either an 'experimental' group or a 'control' group.

Models and approaches

Models and approaches in educating for health and social well-being

The main models or approaches to health education are described briefly in Table 3.11. Professionals in the field of health education need to adapt and combine different approaches, or models, to suit the desired outcome of the programme.

Planning health education campaigns

All health education programmes need to be carefully planned. This planning process can be broken down into the following stages:

The eight stages of a health education programme

Stage 1: Identify the health issue

Examples are heart disease and the role of stress; exercise; nutrition; substance abuse; sexually transmitted infections; personal safety; road safety; immunisation, etc.

Stage 2: Identify the target group

Examples are middle-aged men who are at particular risk from heart disease; young people who have just started or may be tempted to start smoking. The age of the target group – that is, whether they are children, adolescents or adults – will affect the way health education advice is presented to them. It is important to be aware of the different needs of the audience to ensure that appropriate information and resources are used.

Stage 3: Identify the aims and objectives of the campaign

Aims

The aims or goals of the campaign are broad statements of what you are trying to achieve from a single session or event, or from the whole campaign. Examples are

to examine the issue of sexually transmitted infections; to increase knowledge of healthy eating.

Objectives

The objectives are more specific aims. They help you to pinpoint the most realistic method of presenting health advice and information and to evaluate your success in achieving them. Examples are

to provide parents with up-to-date information on immunisation so that they can make an informed decision regarding their own children; to prepare a display on 'Safe Sex' – outlining the risks of contracting a sexually transmitted infection; to devise a questionnaire for adolescents to assess their knowledge about the effects of alcohol on behaviour.

Stage 4: Planning to achieve the aims and objectives

Having identified your objectives, you now need to decide on the method of presentation. This will depend on such factors as cost, size of target group, ease of delivery, availability of material and/or equipment, and appropriateness for the target group. Suitable methods may include:

- display, perhaps tying in with a national awareness day or week, for example, AIDS awareness week or National No Smoking Day;
- video programme;
- leaflets;
- group workshops;
- formal lecture with slides or OHP transparencies.

Stage 5: Identify resources and equipment

The choice of resources and equipment will depend on several factors:

- availability of resources, for example, size of room, video rental, access to display boards and materials;
- cost of equipment;
- time available for activity;
- knowing how to operate equipment, for example, the use of a slide machine or OHP;
- relevance to the target audience.

Stage 6: Planning the content and method of the programme

This is where you work out *exactly* how to present the information, using the resources available. The objectives and the target group will guide your choice of method, but it must be one with which you feel confident. The more effort you put in at this stage, the greater the chance of success.

Guidelines for a presentation

- Produce a detailed time plan.
- Allow time to introduce yourselves and the topic.
- Do a timed test run to ensure that you have enough material.
- Check the room for seating arrangements and equipment.
- Rehearse the delivery of the talk – try to use prompt cards which emphasise *key points* even if you have written out the whole talk. Remember to maintain eye contact with your audience – this is difficult to do if you are reading large amounts of text.

- Sum up the main points.
- Discussion time – let your audience know that there will be time for any questions or debate at the end. You may need to initiate this by asking a question yourself – have a few ideas ready or split the audience into smaller groups for the discussion of key points and arrange for these groups to give feedback to the whole group.
- Empowering the audience – individuals need to make choices themselves. Your task is to present them with clear, relevant and above all *accurate* information. If you don't know the answer to any question, admit it and apologise!

Stage 7: Implementation

Carry out the plan and remember to evaluate the programme as you go along.

Stage 8: Evaluation

Evaluation is an important part of any health education activity; it allows you to **assess** and **review** all aspects of the programme. Always refer to the original aims and objectives and ask if these have been achieved. Before ending your presentation, ask the audience to complete an (anonymous) evaluation form so that you can review the outcome of the session.

Questionnaire on presentation on
SMOKING AND HEALTH

We would be very grateful if you could spare a few minutes to complete this form. Any information received is confidential and will help us to improve our technique.

On a scale of 1–5 (1 = poor; 5 = good):

a) How would you rank the information on smoking and risks to health?

1 2 3 4 5

b) How useful was the information on ways to stop smoking!

1 2 3 4 5

c) How would you rank the OHP charts and diagrams as a learning tool?

1 2 3 4 5

d) How would you rank the display on 'Smoking: the facts'?

1 2 3 4 5

e) Did the session cover all you expected? Yes/No

Any other comments: ....

....

....

....

Thank you very much for your cooperation.

Figure 3.14 Sample evaluation form

Methods of educating for health and social well-being

Presenting the facts

The media have an important role to play in providing individuals with the information necessary to make decisions which may affect their health and that of their families. People are often confused by the sheer amount of sometimes conflicting advice they receive on health issues, for example, red wine is claimed to help protect against heart disease and cancer, but it is not always clear how much wine is beneficial and how much would be harmful in other ways. Most newspapers rely on interviews with 'experts' to present information about health issues, but there can be disagreement. For example:

- The link between BSE (Bovine Spongiform Encephalopathy) in animals and CJD (Jacob Kreutzfeld Disease) in humans.
- Repetitive strain injury – is this an occupational hazard? Experts disagree.
- Seasonal Affective Disorder (SAD) – often dismissed as a new neurosis.

Analogy

The most common analogy used in health education is that of the body as an *engine*. If it is looked after properly, given the right fuel and exercise, then it should give years of trouble-free service. Unfortunately this analogy does not take into account the inherited (genetic) dispositions we all have to certain disorders.

Shock/scare stories

Every decade has its share of shock stories. There is usually a 'knee-jerk' reaction by the public, but the adoption of avoidance strategies is sustained only if the initial scare is substantiated by informed debate and interest by health professionals. Examples include:

- The risk of listeria contamination of foods that have been cooked and then rapidly chilled.
- The role of toxins in cot mattresses as a contributory factor in cot deaths.
- The significance of aluminium-coated saucepans as a cancer risk.

Role models

Sports personalities and their lifestyles are very influential, particularly on young people, for example, the recent case of a footballer being treated for drug addiction received a lot of publicity and raised health awareness. Supermodels are often accused of promoting an unrealistic role model for adolescent girls – see page 101. Film stars and other people in the public eye advertise products and take part in health campaigns.

TV and radio

Programmes such as *Eastenders* and *The Archers* promote discussion on health issues, such as:

- child abuse;
- alcoholism and violence in the home;
- HIV/AIDS.

The role of the mass media in educating for health and social well-being

The mass media are the channels of communication to large numbers of people: they include: television, radio, magazines and newspapers, books and displays and exhibitions.

Health messages are conveyed through the mass media in various ways; these include:

- Planned deliberate health promotion, for example, displays and exhibitions on health themes, NHS or Health Development Agency adverts on television and in newspapers, Open University community education programmes on health.
- Books, documentaries and articles about health issues, for example, television programmes and magazine articles about diet, pollution or fitness.
- Health promotion by advertisers and manufacturers of 'healthy' products, for example, adverts for wholemeal bread or for low fat spreads, educational leaflets on 'feeding your baby' or 'slimming' which also promote the manufacturer's products.
- Discussion of health issues as a by-product of news items or entertainment programmes, particularly in 'soaps' where a character has a health problem.
- Health messages conveyed secretly, for example, well-known personalities or fictional characters refusing cigarettes or, conversely, chain-smoking.

Activity

TV and radio and health messages

1 In small groups, discuss a 'soap' on TV or radio. List all the health issues you can remember within the storylines:

- Do you think that TV or radio fiction is a good way of getting the message across? For example, have you learnt anything new?

- Does the inclusion of a telephone helpline detract from or enhance the impact of a health problem?

- Does the programme mirror real life or is it viewed as escapism?

2 Look at the TV listings for the next week. Make a list of all the programmes scheduled which have a health or social care focus. Arrange for each individual in your group to watch and analyse the message conveyed in the different formats, for example, documentary, soap, chat show, drama, film, etc. Discuss the impact of each format and its success in getting the message across.

The advantages and disadvantages of the different methods of health education are shown in Table 3.12

Ethical aspects of educating for health and social well-being

Any professional activity or campaign which 'interferes' in the lives of others will run into ethical problems. For example:

- Do health promotion agencies have a *right* to persuade or even coerce others into adopting a healthier lifestyle?

- Is there a risk that the individuals they target may suffer guilt and stress? Could they feel that they are being somehow blamed for their ill-health?

- Why should the general public take any notice of health 'experts' whose views often change over time or conflict with one another? (see page 155)

- How much should health professionals interfere in the legal pursuit of profits by a company which markets 'unhealthy' products such as cigarettes or fatty foods?

There have been many successful health campaigns over the last decades:

- **Grab 5:** The recent campaign led by Sustain (the alliance for better food and farming) to encourage primary school pupils to eat more fruit and vegetables (i.e. at least five portions per day.

- **Don't drink and drive campaigns:** These are run periodically on advertisement hoardings and on TV, but most frequently around Christmas and the New Year.

Table 3.12 The advantages and disadvantages of the different methods of health education

Resource method	Advantages	Disadvantages
Handouts and leaflets	• easy to produce • reduces need to take notes • information can be re-read as often as required	• not always read • can glance at information rather than read it carefully • difficult to obtain feedback
Display	• can be very attractive and eye-catching – especially when using a wide variety of interactive resources	• no captive audience
Posters	• can be very eye-catching when displayed in a prominent place	• often only glanced at – the overall message needs to be visually arresting
Videos	• can be useful as a trigger for discussion • useful for small to medium groups • can present information in a lively way	• danger of losing attention of audience if too long • must be previewed for relevance to target audience
Role play	• can be a lively way to encourage audience to think in depth about a health issue	• some people find role play threatening • may spend more time worrying about their 'acting' and not enough on the health issue
Presentations and workshops	• audience is captive – can't switch off or turn the page • information can be geared to the needs of the target audience • people have the opportunity to ask questions and to give feedback	• much depends on the skill of the presenter – to maintain audience attention • audience may be too shy to participate fully
TV and Radio	• can reach large numbers of people • can have a powerful instant impact through striking visual images • can raise awareness of a health issue which then stimulates group discussion	• difficult to obtain feedback • information or message may not be at the right level for a wide audience • audience can switch off if they don't like what is on
Newspapers & magazines	• can reach large numbers of people • information can be re-read whenever required • specialist magazines – such as *Top Sante* can target information at a particular audience	• difficult to obtain feedback • newspapers have a wide audience, so hard to target information • expensive to buy space in national newspapers and magazines • readers can ignore certain pages

- **Avoiding the risks of cot death:** This campaign took the form of TV documentaries and leaflets in clinics and hospitals.

- **Immunisation campaigns:** These are very successful and have done much to reduce the incidence of infectious diseases. However recent controversies over possible side-effects of the combined MMR vaccine have raised an ethical dilemma for both health professionals and parents.

- **Safety in the sun:** the increased public awareness of the depletion of the ozone layer and the risk of skin cancer

Many other campaigns have had more limited success, for example, those which have focused on secondary health education such as persuading women to attend for breast cancer screening.

Example of a national health campaign

National campaign: Smoking kills

The White Paper **Smoking Kills** is the first ever, comprehensive, government strategy to tackle smoking. Overall the government aims to persuade more smokers to give up, to aid them in doing so and to persuade non-smokers, particularly children, not to start.

The targets are:

- To reduce the number of 11–15 year-olds who smoke from 13 % in 1996 to 9% in 2010, with a fall to 11% by 2005.
- To help adults, especially the disadvantaged, to stop smoking. The target is to reduce the overall smoking rate in all social classes from 28% in 1996 to 24% in 2010, with a fall to 26% by 2005.
- To give special support to pregnant smokers and reduce the percentage of women who smoke in pregnancy from 23% in 1995 to 15% by 2010, with a fall to 18% by 2005.

(*All these targets apply to England only.*)

Target audiences

The key target audiences are:

- adult smokers aged 25–45;
- young people aged 11–16;
- pregnant women;
- ethnic minorities.

This campaign emphasises that:

- giving up is a *process*, and that relapsing is a natural part of that process;
- most smokers don't give up for good the first time they try – it often takes five or six attempts;
- lapses are ok – what is not ok is giving up on giving up.
- becoming a non-smoker can be hard, and 'giver-uppers' need to persevere.

This campaign aims to offer these people support and encouragement.

NHS Smoking Helpline – 0800 169 0 169

This helpline provides information and support for smokers who want to give up. People can also order written material via the phone line. Details of smoking cessation services in local districts are available from the NHS Smoking Helpline, and callers can be referred to face-to-face support via this route.

Figure 3.15 Don't give up giving up

NHS Pregnancy Smoking Helpline – 0800 169 9 169

This was launched in September 2000, and is particularly aimed at younger pregnant women in low-income groups who are more likely to continue to smoke during pregnancy. Some of the less well known problems associated with smoking during pregnancy are highlighted along with a supportive message encouraging women to call the NHS Pregnancy Smoking Helpline.

Promotional material

There are a number of leaflets, posters and stickers available through the website and the telephone lines. The campaign leaflet, 'Don't give up giving up', is available to order in a large range of languages, on audio cassette and in large print, Braille and learning disability versions.

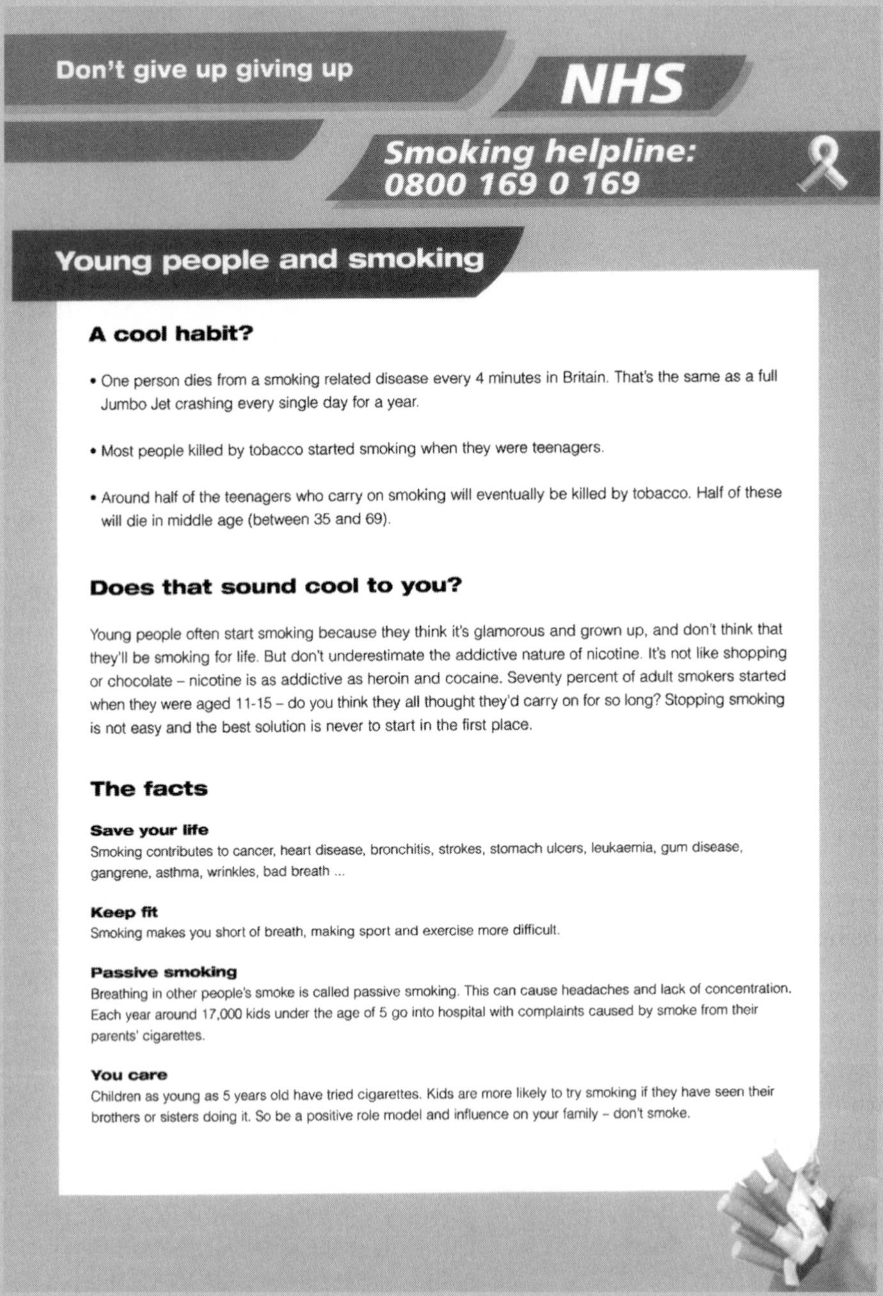

Don't give up giving up

NHS

**Smoking helpline:
0800 169 0 169**

Young people and smoking

A cool habit?

- One person dies from a smoking related disease every 4 minutes in Britain. That's the same as a full Jumbo Jet crashing every single day for a year.

- Most people killed by tobacco started smoking when they were teenagers.

- Around half of the teenagers who carry on smoking will eventually be killed by tobacco. Half of these will die in middle age (between 35 and 69).

Does that sound cool to you?

Young people often start smoking because they think it's glamorous and grown up, and don't think that they'll be smoking for life. But don't underestimate the addictive nature of nicotine. It's not like shopping or chocolate – nicotine is as addictive as heroin and cocaine. Seventy percent of adult smokers started when they were aged 11-15 – do you think they all thought they'd carry on for so long? Stopping smoking is not easy and the best solution is never to start in the first place.

The facts

Save your life
Smoking contributes to cancer, heart disease, bronchitis, strokes, stomach ulcers, leukaemia, gum disease, gangrene, asthma, wrinkles, bad breath ...

Keep fit
Smoking makes you short of breath, making sport and exercise more difficult.

Passive smoking
Breathing in other people's smoke is called passive smoking. This can cause headaches and lack of concentration. Each year around 17,000 kids under the age of 5 go into hospital with complaints caused by smoke from their parents' cigarettes.

You care
Children as young as 5 years old have tried cigarettes. Kids are more likely to try smoking if they have seen their brothers or sisters doing it. So be a positive role model and influence on your family – don't smoke.

Figure 3.16 Young people and smoking leaflet

Activity

1   Select a recent health education campaign that you found memorable (such as the NHS anti-smoking campaign). Evaluate the success of the campaign, with particular emphasis on the following:

- A description of the aim of the campaign, for example, a new Government report may have highlighted an increase in alcohol-related road traffic accidents, which the campaign aims to address.

- A description of the methods used, for example, newspaper coverage, use of famous personalities, use of shock/scare tactics, and how these methods relate to the target population of the campaign.

2   Interview at least six individuals from the target group of the campaign, using a structured interview format (see main textbook for guidance).

3   Use the results of these interviews to draw conclusions and to make recommendations about the effectiveness of the campaign.

Evaluating promotional activities

Evaluation involves identifying and grading the criteria, values and aims of a project and collecting information to assess if they have all been met. Overall, the main aim of evaluating a health education campaign is to see whether it has achieved its **objectives**. The objectives of any campaign should be SMART:

S   Specific

M   Measurable

A   Agreed

R   Realistic

T   Timebound

The success of medical treatments is relatively easy to measure or evaluate – for example, the rapid recovery of servicemen with infections during the Second World War was certainly helped by the use of antibiotics, particularly penicillin. More recently, the use of drugs to treat and to prevent asthma has been successful. Most health education campaigns aim to increase public awareness and to affect lifestyle and behaviour; they are usually very difficult to evaluate. There are many reasons for this:

1   It is difficult to ensure strict comparability between the target group and a control group.

2   Any trial that aims to compare a target group with a control group must span a long period of time and cover a large population.

3   Primary prevention methods are usually matters of public policy, concerning healthy

individuals who are not actively seeking help or care. How do we decide whether their continuing good health is directly influenced by a campaign?

4 The mass media plays a large part in raising public awareness of health issues, but messages received via TV, radio and the press are often not acknowledged as being part of health education.

There are some issues which have not been the focus of recent health campaigns:

* Chlamydia: the most common sexually transmitted infection in the UK today and yet most people have never heard of it (see page 138).

* Dental decay: one of the most costly avoidable health problems.

* Head lice: the subject of infrequent campaigns, but a common problem in nurseries and schools

* Back pain: a very common reason for absence from work.

* Heart disease: experts disagree on the exact causes of heart disease, but it is the major killer of those over 75 in the UK.

Activity

Health campaign: group presentations

These could be arranged as a video or as an oral presentation, depending on the resources available. Discuss with your tutor how and when you are going to make your presentation. Draw up an *individual action plan*, following the advice on pages 153–154 to include:

1 Choice of health promotion area. Choose from:

* smoking;

* alcohol;

* drug abuse;

* safe sexual practices;

* stress and mental illness.

2 Detailed planning – delegate different responsibility for different tasks to each group member. The presentation should:

* only contain accurate information;

* outline your target group;

* include recommendations on ways in which the audience can contribute to their own health;

* provide a question-and-answer session at the end;

- ensure that all feedback made to the target audience is both constructive and non-judgemental.

After the presentation, write an individual evaluation of the exercise, commenting on:

- your own contribution;

- the audience response to your presentation;

- recommendations for the future (i.e. ways of improving the session).

Chapter 4

Promoting independence and autonomy

This chapter relates to Unit 21. Promoting and maintaining independence and autonomy is a key feature in health and social care work today. This chapter explores how health and social care services help to promote independence and autonomy among service users. This unit builds on Unit 1, Equal Opportunities and Clients Rights.

This chapter covers the following:

- how human needs relate to independence and autonomy;
- how care services and care workers attempt to promote independence and autonomy;
- social responses to people with additional care needs;
- the factors that influence the design and delivery of care services.

This chapter also contributes to the underpinning knowledge for NVQ Level 3 in Care.

Assessment

Unit 21 is assessed through your portfolio work. You will be asked to produce a case study of care practice in a health or social care setting that explores strategies designed to promote independence and autonomy. You may be able to find a client you can use for your case study on work experience or in your part time work in a care centre. Useful materials include care plans, policy documents, plans and policies that affect that particular client (for example, if you are basing your case study on someone with a learning disability the White Paper 'Valuing People' (Department of Health, 2001) covers how people with learning disabilities should be cared for and supported.)

If you use patient records, bear in mind the importance of confidentiality; the client and the home should not be identified, so you should give them an alternative name. The *Community Care* magazine is published weekly and provides case studies and useful material.

Sources of information

At the back of this chapter, there is a glossary and also a list of useful websites and addresses. Most of the key terms will be defined in the chapter. While you are reading this chapter, you should have the main textbook, *Advanced Vocational A Level in Health and Social Care*, available as you will need to refer to this for additional information. The use of the icon [] will prompt you to refer to the key text.

Human needs: independence and autonomy

Care workers need to recognise their clients as unique individuals, with individual and shared needs that influence their ability to be independent and autonomous.

Word check

Independence and **autonomy**

Independence and autonomy is about people have greater control over their lives, through making informed decisions about every aspect of their lives. Some clients may need support either through an advocate (who speaks for them) or by self-advocacy, when they can speak for themselves.

Case Study

A group of people with learning disabilities were going to be moved from a large institution into a small group home. The management did not discuss the proposals with them and the first they knew of the situation was when a relative read an article in the local paper. The proposed site for the home was on the outskirts of the town with no access to public transport. The group asked the local advocacy service to represent their interests and, at subsequent meetings, some of the residents and their advocate attended. As a result, the site for the home was changed and the residents' views were taken into account when designing it. Two of the residents were so encouraged by this process, they had additional training from the advocacy service so that they could represent the views of the residents themselves and also be involved in the development of their own care plans.

We can see from this case study that in order to become independent and autonomous, patients and clients must be given access to relevant information and also supported to be included in decision-making. Many people who have been in institutions for a long time, find they have become used to decisions being made for them, and they need a great deal of support to become independent. There are some groups of people who may never be able to become fully independent because of a range of disabilities, but care workers need to try to give their clients as many choices as possible. This could range from deciding on what clothes to wear to what to eat for breakfast. In recent years, organisations such as the British Council of Organisations of Disabled People, and the Independent Living Movement have promoted the rights of disabled people to have greater control over their lives. These movements have four key principles:

- that all human life is of value;
- that anyone, whatever their disability, is capable of exerting choices;
- that people who are disabled by society's reaction to physical, intellectual and sensory impairment and mental distress have the right to assert control over their lives;
- that disabled people have the right to participate fully in society.

The Human Rights Act (1998) came into force in October 2000, and this Act brings the rights outlined in the European Convention of Human Rights into English law for the first time. ◇ The Human Rights Act is designed to protect individuals from abuse by institutions and people working in these institutions, and to promote the rights of all groups in society. These rights include the right to privacy and family life, to liberty and personal freedom and the right to marry and have a family. These sections of the Act have great significance for care workers as we will see later in the chapter.

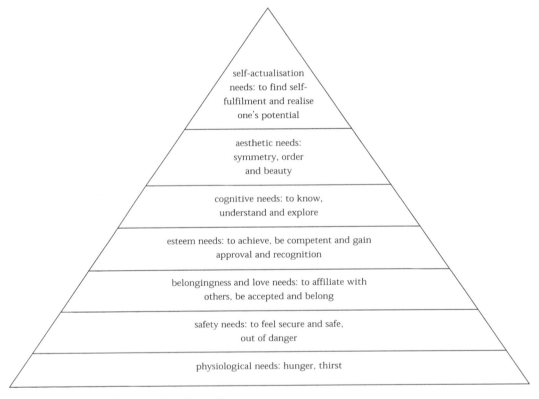

Figure 4.1 Maslow's hierarchy of needs

Universal human needs

There are certain universal needs which are common to all individuals. These have been defined by Abraham Maslow as:

- to have sufficient food and drink;

- to eliminate waste products;
- to breathe properly;
- to have the body at a comfortable temperature;
- to sleep and rest;
- to keep clean and maintain health;
- to wear suitable clothing;
- to be free from discomfort and pain;
- to feel safe.

Maslow (1908–70), an American psychologist, devised a hierarchy of needs. These needs are usually represented in the form of a pyramid with the most basic physiological needs at the base and the highest need – self actualisation – at the top (see Figure 4.1).

Activity

This model can be applied to each one of us at different stages of our lives. Look at the following case study.

Case study

Balkar is a 25 year old Asian man. At the moment he is a student at a local college. He has mild cerebral palsy which affects his speech and mobility, and he has difficulty communicating with fellow students. He has to allow extra time to get to college and to move between classes. He also suffers from arthritis.

Activity

Look at the Maslow model and identify those areas that may be a problem for Balkar. Can you think of any way in which you could assist Balkar so that he is able to fulfil these needs?

Comment

Many people have times in their lives when their needs are not met. Someone working in a dangerous environment where health and safety issues are not monitored, may not have their safety needs met, but after work they may go home to a loving family. A struggling artist or musician may go hungry or cold, but through their artistic work they may feel self-fulfilled. This is one of the problems with Maslow's model. There may not be a smooth progression from the bottom of the model to the top, and different people may see certain needs as very important at certain times of their lives. The main needs for everyone can be divided into:

- **physical:** the need for food, drink, warmth, exercise and freedom or relief from pain and discomfort;
- **intellectual:** having enough mental stimulation in order to keep the mind active;
- **emotional:** having a sense of belonging, helping people feel secure, valued and accepted;
- **social:** forming relationships with other people, living and working together.

In our society, certain groups such as those with a physical or learning disability will have difficulty in fulfilling some of these needs. In this chapter we will see how some client groups may be supported in order to achieve autonomy and fulfil their potential.

Definitions of disability

 Word check

Impairment

Any loss or abnormality of psychological, physiological or anatomical structure or function. Impairment does not necessarily mean disability. For example, people have short sight but this is remedied with the use of prescribed lenses or glasses.

Disability

The limitation of personal activity as a result of the impairment. The loss of the ability to perform an activity in the manner or within the range considered normal for a human being.

Handicap

The resulting personal and social disadvantage that limits or prevents the fulfilment of a role that is normal (depending on age, sex, social and cultural factors) for that individual.

Comment

You may notice that in these definitions the word 'normal' is used. What does this term imply? Normality is a relative term and may vary according to time and place. For example, it is normal for a young person to be able to perform physical tasks such as heavy lifting or a work-out in the gym, but once this young person reaches the age of 60, they may feel it is normal for the tasks they performed in their youth to be beyond them. When talking to patients over 75, people may assume that it normal for them to experience aches and pains, and not be able to perform the things they used to do. Deciding what is normal or not can be based on scientific and medical tests, such as a blood pressure reading, or on the subjective experience of the patient or client.

Always be careful when using this term, as what is seen as 'normal' or not can lead to labelling certain groups as 'abnormal', and the effects of this label can be very negative.

The medical model of disability

Labelling certain groups as disabled tends to focus on the impairments or disability of the individual. The key features of the medical model are as follows:

- people are identified according to their impairment;
- the focus is on the individual;
- the approach is measurable or quantitative;
- professionals are involved who decide the level of impairment using a scientific approach.

Criticisms of this approach include:

- people are seen as in need of care or treatment of the impairment, and this encourages the dependency of the individual;
- the individual is disempowered because the scientific approach is used;
- the subjective experience of the individual is ignored;
- the individual is seen as needing to fit in with society.

 Case study

Judy is a science teacher at a local college. She lost her left leg at the age of 12 as the result of cancer. She tried using an artificial limb but she fell down the stairs and this put her off, so she uses crutches. Judy went to college to study for a degree and she decided she wanted to teach. At her interview, Judy was asked about her disability. She explained that she used crutches and had no problems getting around.

When Judy started her job, she found there were a number of problems. There was a staff car park but often there were no spaces available so Judy had to park her car in the student car park, which was some distance away from the college entrance. Judy often had to carry a large bag with her. There was a lift in the college, which was a help, but Judy found that her timetable meant she had a lesson in one end of the college and immediately afterwards she had to go to the other end of the college for the next lesson. Although staff and students were friendly towards her, no one asked her if she needed any help. At the end of each day she was exhausted.

According to the medical model, Judy had been treated for her disability and was able to fit into society through her success in education and employment. But we can see that the medical model ignores aspects of society that need to be addressed.

The social model of disability

This model sees people with disabilities as being disabled by society. Three factors, in particular, disable people:

1 **Environmental:** this would include physical access to schools, shopping, leisure activities, transport.

2 **Social/Institutional arrangements:** this would include the organisation of work hours, training courses, care and health services.

3 **Attitudes:** this would include attitudes of employers, colleagues and the general public, and could be reflected in media articles, advertisements and interviews and consultations.

Look again at the case study. How could the college have helped Judy?

The provision of a disabled parking space in the car park would not just have helped Judy but other disabled visitors to the college. Timetabling could have taken account of the need for Judy to have adequate time between classes. This could help all staff! Sometimes people with disabilities find it difficult to ask for help as they feel they are lucky to find employment, especially if they have experienced discrimination. When employing a disabled person, their manager should ask them what support they need. This approach would help everyone. Students and staff could have training sessions on raising awareness of disability issues, so they are more aware of the needs of some people.

Activity

Look at the following examples. Decide whether they reflect environmental, institutional or attitudinal barriers, and suggest a solution for each example.

1 Mary is blind. She has a cervical smear test. The letter arrives at her home with the result.

2 Vikram uses a wheelchair since he had a car accident. His friends ask him out for a meal at a restaurant. When they arrive they find there are steps to the restaurant and the toilet is in the basement.

3 John has a hearing problem. He doesn't want people to know of his condition so he lipreads. Colleagues at work think he is ignoring them when he does not respond to them.

4 Caroline has multiple sclerosis and she cannot write. She wants to take a college course.

As we can see from these examples, according to the Social Model it is not the condition that is disabling but the social arrangements (environmental, organisational and attitudinal), that determine the degree to which the impairment is disabling (see Figure 4.2).

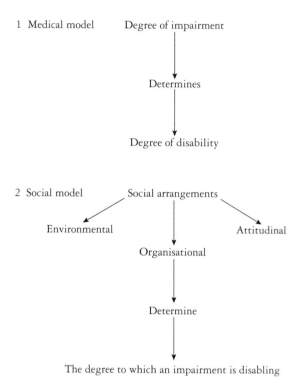

Figure 4.2 Medical and social models of disability

The Disability Discrimination Act (1995) ◇

There are four main areas covered by the DDA:

- access to goods and services – this could include a bank loan and insurance;
- getting and keeping a job;
- using public transport;
- buying or renting a home.

Access to goods and services

It is against the law for service providers to discriminate against disabled people. It is also against the law for them not to provide reasonable adjustments to enable disabled people to have access to their goods, facilities or services. Under the DDA, service providers have to:

- change policies, procedures and practices that discriminate. For example, if a video rental store only allows people to rent videos if they can show a driving licence as proof of identity, this would need to be reviewed as it discriminates against a disabled person who cannot drive;
- provide extra practical aids and services, such as information in braille or on tape;
- provide an alternative means of service where physical features such as buildings or access present difficulties. For example, if there is no lift to the second floor, service providers could shop for the disabled customer.

The DDA covers:

- corner shops, department stores;
- facilities such as libraries and leisure centres;
- services such as libraries, banks, restaurants and cinemas;
- In 2004, service providers will have to make physical alterations to buildings to provide access (for example, through ramps).

Activity

Undertake a survey of your local area to assess the provision for disabled people. Pay attention to areas such as banks, public telephones, shops, restaurants and cinemas. What provision is made for disabled people? What measures could be taken to improve services?

Disabled people are not just wheelchair users. What provision is made for people with other physical disabilities, such as visual impairment, or hearing impairment?

Employment

The DDA only applies to companies with more than 15 staff. Disabled people must not be treated less favourably than non-disabled workers. Recruitment and employment arrangements must reflect the needs of disabled people.

Activity

Look in the local or national papers at job vacancies. Does the employer offer to give details of the job in alternative formats such as large print or tape?

Using public transport

New public transport such as buses, coaches and trains will have to be built to enable disabled people to get on and off. Aeroplanes and ferries are not covered by the DDA.

Buying or renting a home

Disabled people cannot be asked to pay a higher rent. Health and social care workers need to be aware of the potential for additional support needs for people with disabilities and other service care users.

In the next section we will identify certain client groups who have additional support needs.

People with visual impairment

Sight loss is one of the commonest causes of disability in the UK. Almost one million people are blind or partially sighted. That is 1 in 60 of the population. One in seven of people over 75 are blind or partially sighted.

Causes of visual impairment in children

The main causes of visual impairment in children are:

- defects in the eyes from birth such as cataracts (cloudiness of the lens);
- nystagmus – involuntary movements (usually sideways) of the eyes;
- optic atrophy – damage to the optic nerve;
- retinopathy of prematurity – abnormal development of the retina in premature babies;
- hereditary factors such as retinoblastoma – a tumour of the retina that is often inherited.

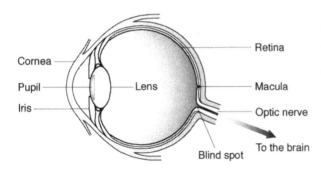

Figure 4.3 Diagram of the eye, showing the main parts

Causes of visual impairment in adults

The main causes of visual impairment in adults are diabetes and diabetic retinopathy. Retinopathy is common in people who have had diabetes for a long time. There are two types of retinopathy that can damage the sight. Both involve the fine network of blood vessels in the retina (Figure 4.3).

1 **Maculopathy.** The blood vessels in the retina start to leak and the central vision gets worse so it is difficult to recognise people's faces in the distance or to see small print. It is rare to lose all the sight with this condition.

2 **Proliferative diabetic retinopathy.** The diabetes causes the blood vessels in the eye to become blocked. New blood vessels form but this causes scar tissue to form in the eye and the retina may become detached. Without treatment, total loss of vision can occur.

Nystagmus

Although nystagmus usually occurs in the first six months of life, it can also develop later on. Many people with this condition register as partially sighted. It is caused by a defect in the eye, or in the visual pathway from the eye to the brain. It occurs in a wide range of eye disorders of childhood such as cataracts, glaucoma and some disorders of the retina. It can also be found in children with Downs Syndrome. Nystagmus is believed to affect one in 1000 individuals.

Glaucoma

Glaucoma is the name for a group of eye conditions in which the pressure of fluid in the eye is so high that it damages the optic nerve and causes gradual loss of vision. Glaucoma becomes more common after the age of 40.

Retinal detachment

Detachment of the retina is more common in middle-aged, short-sighted people. It is quite rare and affects one person in 10,000. When detached, the retina cannot make a clear picture from the rays coming into the eye, and vision becomes blurred and dim.

Treatment of visual impairment

Some conditions that cause visual impairment are treatable, particularly if detected at an early stage. Glaucoma can be treated by medical or surgical means, cataracts may be treated by the removal of the lens and the insertion of a plastic lens. Retinal detachment is treated by laser surgery. Table 4.1 shows the main people who work in eye services.

Table 4.1 People who work in the NHS eye services

Job title	Where they work	What they do
Optometrists	In hospital and high street practices	• Test sight • Prescribe glasses • Detect eye conditions • Provide advice
Dispensing opticians	In high street practices	• Fit and supply glasses and contact lenses. (*not* qualified to test sight)
Ophthalmologists (qualified doctors)	In hospital eye departments	• Treat eye disorders • Diagnose and treat eye defects and disease through surgery, drug treatment and other types of medical care
Ophthalmic nurses	In hospital eye departments	• Treat eye conditions and diseases

Issues for care workers who work with people with visual impairment

People with visual impairments have the same needs as everyone else. Until recently, many children and young adults who had visual impairment were sent to 'blind schools' and encouraged to follow traditional occupations that were seen as appropriate for blind people. Physiotherapy and piano tuning was seen as appropriate, and girls were encouraged to be typists. Because people with visual problems were excluded from main stream schooling, they often did not have the opportunities to go to college and university. Getting married and having children was seen as unlikely. Nowadays, opportunities have changed. Many people with visual impairment go to college and university, and there are also colleges, run by the RNIB, that prepare people for work.

Activity

Can you think of advantages and disadvantages to going to a mainstream school or a special school if you had visual problems?

Case study

Susan was born in London in 1946. She was 13 weeks premature and her sight was damaged by retinopathy of prematurity. Her parents were sighted. Throughout her life, Susan's mother blamed herself for Susan's condition. When Susan was 18 months old, she went to a Sunshine Home for the Blind until she was seven years old. She came home for the holidays. When she was seven, she went to another residential school where she stayed until she was 16. Susan cries when she remembers her life at the home. Although some of the staff were kind, others were very strict, slapping the children and giving them punishments. Susan remembers that if the children spoke after lights out, they were 'put on silence for a week', which meant that they had no communication with other children. The children were taught Braille and given a basic education, but Susan did not pass the 11-plus exam so she was seen as only being good enough to be an audio-typist.

When she was 16, Susan went to a college run by the RNIB. Most of the girls with Susan were taught to be audio-typists or switchboard operators. When Susan was 18, she came back to live with her mother and she worked as an audio-typist in a local office. Because Susan has lived in the same area all her life, people know her and she is able to get around quite independently. She uses a white stick.

Susan finds certain things difficult. When she sees a doctor either in the local clinic or in the hospital, she finds that all the information is given in leaflets. When she was recently referred to the local hospital, the staff were not aware she had a sight problem. She was given exercises to do, which were demonstrated by the physiotherapist, but as she couldn't see, it was difficult for her to follow what she should do. Susan goes to a local restaurant once a month with some blind friends. The staff read out the menu to her and cut up her food. When Susan goes to the bank, the assistants help her but she says she was never taught to write, so writing a signature is a problem.

Since Susan's mother died, Susan has moved to a flat on her own. She manages her cooking and washing as the microwave and washing machine have Braille buttons. Susan has to be careful when using the oven. Cleaning the flat is a problem as she cannot see where the dust is, so a cleaner comes in once a week to clean and iron. Susan manages to lead a full and independent life. She advises local groups on disability issues. She has a Braille watch, she listens to the radio and television and she is completing a degree with the Open University. Susan has travelled widely on her own. She finds that some countries have training programmes for their staff on how to support blind people but she has had some frightening experiences of being left alone on platforms of busy stations.

Susan relies on sighted friends to help her choose clothes and shoes and furnishings for the flat, but there are certain things that still remain a problem. On her last birthday, she could not read her birthday cards. In the past her mother always used to do this, so Susan had to ask a friend. Susan has a scanner that can be used for typed letters, but hand-written letters have to be read to her by a friend. Other problems include:

- *filling in forms;*
- *travelling by bus, getting on at a request stop and getting off at the correct stop;*
- *travelling by train if announcements are not given, especially if changes to platforms are made;*
- *access to GP services when she needs dressings or injections.*

 ## Activity

Can you think of ways in which Susan could be supported, enable her to overcome these problems. As we have seen in the Medical Model of Disability, the focus is on the individual with the disability, but if we apply the Social Model and identify the environmental and institutional barriers which Susan has experienced, we may be able to develop ways in which people like Susan can be fully independent.

The RNIB has a range of publications and catalogues for materials that support people with visual problems. Susan enjoys reading their publication, *New Beacon*, which is a magazine published in Braille, and you may know of local talking newspapers that tape record local news for people.

Nowadays professionals in health and social care are more aware of the importance of communicating appropriately with parents of children with visual problems and giving them support. The RNIB states there are guiding principles that all professionals should follow when they are involved with newly diagnosed blind and partially-sighted children:

- all children have the potential to lead fulfilling, happy lives, whatever their abilities or disabilities;
- negative attitudes towards disability undermine the development of children with visual or other impairments;
- professionals must promote the potential of each child and be willing to challenge negative attitudes in themselves or others.

For most parents, diagnosis of serious sight problems in their child is traumatic. Without sensitive and appropriate care, support and information, the negative effects can be far reaching. Even if medical treatment is not possible, considerable support and information are available. The RNIB conducted interviews with parents of children with sight problems and asked them what support they had received when they were first told their child had a problem. They found the following.

1 Parental trauma is increased by:
- negative attitudes from professionals;
- brusqueness and uncaring attitudes;
- no chance for discussion;
- being in public – no privacy to discuss the issues;
- poor communication between professionals.

2 Parents felt supported by:
- rapid referral to specialist;
- being respected and listened to;
- the presence of a relative or friend at consultations;
- sensitive clinicians;
- clear explanations about the eye and eye condition;
- being told exactly what is happening;
- honesty about uncertainty;
- being given privacy and time;
- attentive non-intrusive staff;
- early follow-up appointments with consultants;
- telephone numbers and a named person to contact;
- written information.

Although these results related to parents with children with sight problems, we can see that the supporting factors are relevant to all client groups in health and social care. The RNIB has produced an excellent booklet, 'One step at a time', for parents with visually-impaired children. This gives practical advice on how to develop the senses, establishing routines and learning to walk.

Visual impairment in adult service users

The RNIB produces leaflets that give advice on meeting people with visual impairment and how to guide them. If you are working with blind people, you may feel awkward about how to support them. Here are some basic guidelines.

1   Introduce yourself, say who you are and ask if you can do anything to help.

2   When you leave the person, say you are going.

3   When a blind person is in hospital as a patient, make sure they know the position of the light switches, the call system, radio and bedside locker. Let them know where the toilet and bathroom are located, and how they can summon help.

4   Make sure all staff know that the patient has visual impairment – some hospitals put a notice on the bed to warn staff.

5   When a meal is served, say what the meal is and offer to help them.

6   For visually-impaired people who are visiting the hospital and surgery, make sure any information is in accessible form, i.e. on tape or in Braille.

7   Interpersonal communication – your tone of voice is very important.

8   If you are guiding someone, explain things they cannot see, for example, if there are steps or stairs, are they going up or going down.

Many of the problems encountered by visually-impaired people are caused by the organisation of the environment. These include aspects of lighting, sound, walls and floor surfaces. The arrangement of furniture is also important. The RNIB produces a fact sheet outlining how staff working with visually-impaired people can improve the environment to promote independence. RNIB has a website that you could use as part of your studies: http://www.rnib.org.uk

Mental Health Problems

Mental health problems are common and affect most of us at some time. Most people who suffer from mental distress and who receive care from the health service do so in Primary Care. The number of consultations for mental distress account for a high proportion of GP appointments; only respiratory conditions are more common. Table 4.2 shows the population and estimated general practice prevalence of mental disorders, and Table 4.3 shows the difference between urban and rural environments. Look at Table 4.3 carefully. Can you think of reasons why there is a higher rate in urban areas?

Definitions of Mental Health

There are three broad approaches to the definition of mental health.

1   Mental health can be defined as the absence of signs and symptoms of mental illness.

2   Adopting a 'foundations of health' model, mental health is seen as a component of the physical, psychological and social foundations that constitute good health or overall well-being.

3   A focus on positive mental health, based upon self-esteem, self-regard, competence and social integration.

Table 4.2 Prevalence of mental health disorders

Diagnosis	Weekly prevalence per 1000 adults aged 16–64	Number of patients aged 16–64 on GP list of 1800 (assumes 63% of GP list is aged 16–64)
Mixed anxiety and depression	77	87
Generalized anxiety	31	36
Depressive episode	21	24
All phobias	11	13
Obsessive compulsive disorder	12	14
Panic disorder	8	9
All neuroses	160	182
Functional psychoses	4.4	5

Source OPCS Survey of Psychiatric Morbidity Report 1995, London. HMSO

Table 4.3 Variations in prevalence of mental disorders in adults aged 16–64 living in private households in Great Britain between rural and urban areas in the UK

Disorder prevalence per 1000 adults		Urban	Semi-rural	Rural
Neuroses	Women	216	156	150
	Men	133	117	78
Psychoses	Women	5	5	1
	Men	6	5	3

Source OPCS Survey of Ssychiatric Morbidity Report 1 1995, London. HMSO

The medical model of health tends to focus on the first definition, but increasingly professionals are focusing on the importance of social factors, such as poverty, affecting a person's mental health.

The Mental Health Needs Index (MINI index) calculates the relative mental health service needs between populations. It is based on 1991 census data. Figure 2.2 in Chapter 2 shows the MINI index scores for London. The scores are based on variables chosen on the basis of an established association with mental illness rates, covering areas such as social isolation, poverty, unemployment, sickness and quality of housing. The variables are:

- single, widowed, divorced;
- no car;
- permanently sick;
- unemployed;
- shared housing accommodation;
- hostel, lodging houses, etc.

Activity

Looking at the chart, identify the areas that are:

- better than the England average;
- worse than the England average.

From this exercise we can see the importance of social factors on mental health. Can you think why people who are unemployed, permanently sick, divorced or widowed are more likely to become mentally ill?

Conversely, why are people with mental health problems more likely to become unemployed or divorced?

Child and Adolescent Mental Health

In 1999 the Mental Health Foundation reported that 20% of children and adolescents were found to have mental health problems in Britain.

- Suicide and self-harm in adolescents has increased, and suicide is now the leading cause of death for young people.
- Eating disorders have increased in the last 25 years. One study in 1991 showed that 5% of female secondary school children had been diagnosed with bulimia nervosa.
- Drug and alcohol use is increasing, with young people using illicit drugs, such as cannabis, and drinking alcohol regularly.

Activity

Why is it so difficult to establish the use of drugs and alcohol among young people? What research methods could you use?

Explanations for the increase in child and adolescent mental health problems include the following:

- changing family structure – divorce, remarriage, increased single parent families;

- media influences – media images of life-style, slimness seen as desirable;

- increased availability of drugs and alcohol;

- changes in working life and education – many unskilled jobs done by school leavers have disappeared; adolescents spend longer in education and are dependent for longer on their parents.

A recent study into primary, middle and secondary schools in a South London area showed that the mental health issues that were most frequently mentioned by teachers as of most concern were:

- stress and stress management;
- low self-esteem and eating disorders;
- family breakdown;
- pressure to succeed;
- depression;
- bereavement;
- drugs;
- racism;
- abuse;
- peer pressure;
- formations of sexual identity;
- friendship problems;
- anger management;
- self harm.

The study made several recommendations for future practice in schools. These included:

- increase availability of counselling services for pupils and staff;
- specific mental health awareness training for teachers;
- accessible psychiatric services.

(Adapted from Chris Gilleard and Rose Lobo. *Education and Wellbeing in School.* May 2000. MSW Health Promotion Alliance)

Table 4.4 People who work in the NHS Mental Health Services

Name	Qualification	Role and responsibilities
Psychiatrist	Doctor specialising in mental health	• Diagnosis and general management of care of patients mental and physical health, including medication • Implement the Mental Health Act (sectioning patients)
Community Psychiatric Nurses (CPNs)	Registered mental health nurses with ENB training for community work	• Based in community care for people with mental health problems in their own homes • Can offer long-term support, counselling and medication, psychological therapies • Will be part of the hospital outreach team
Clinical psychologist	Degree in psychology and post-graduate qualification in clinical work	• Assessment of patients • Provide a range of treatments such as behavioural therapy and cognitive therapy
Psychotherapists and counsellors	Variety of qualifications	• 'Talking therapies', individual or group therapies
Occupational therapists (OTs)	Occupational therapy qualification (degree)	• Work in hospital and community • Help people develop confidence and skills in daily life • Creative therapies and practical skills training
Mental health – social worker	Social work qualification and mental health training	• Assessment of people with severe and complex needs • Work with health colleagues • Coordinate and monitor care plans • Ensure service users get the services they need
Approved social workers (in Scotland mental health officers)	Specialist training in mental health approved under the Mental Health Act (1986); Mental Health Act Scotland (1984); Mental Health Act N. Ireland (1986)	• Assessment for urgent admission to hospital • Supervision of clients under the supervised discharge scheme • Act as social service supervisors for mentally disordered offenders who are subject to Home Office supervision
Community care workers/support workers	Non-professional members of the mental health team; may have NVQ and other qualifications	• Support and encourage clients in different ways • Listening to them and helping with practical tasks • Finding them work and developing social skills

Mental Health Problems in Adults

In a GP surgery, every third or fourth patient seen has some form of mental disorder. In the last 30 years the number of hospital beds for people with mental health problems has fallen, while the number of GPs and psychiatrists has risen. Table 4.4 shows the specialist health professionals who work in mental health services. The Primary Health Care Team (PHCT) includes practice nurses, district nurses, health visitors, counsellors, clinical psychologists and school nurses, as well as GPs, all of whom may have a role in mental health care. The Community Mental Health Team (CMHT) may include nurses, occupational therapists, clinical psychologists, social workers and support workers, as well as psychiatrists. Families and friends, self-help and community groups also provide support to people with a whole range of mental disorders.

Word check

Psychosis

A collective term for the more severe forms of psychiatric disorder in which hallucinations and delusions may occur.

Acute psychotic disorders

These include schizophrenia and delusional psychosis. Patients may experience:

• hallucinations, for example, hearing voices when no one is around;

• strange fears or beliefs;

• disordered thinking and lack of insight into their condition;

• confusion;

• perceptual disturbances – visions.

The patient's family may report strange behaviour and speech. It is very important that the safety of the patient and of the family is considered. This may mean that the patient may be admitted temporarily to a hospital for proper assessment. However, many patients are supported in the community by the CMHT, but it is important that the correct diagnosis is made. Treatment will usually include drug therapy until the situation is stabilised.

Neurosis

A collective term for psychiatric disorders in which there are no hallucinations or delusions. The patient has the ability to understand the condition.

Case study

Sara is 45 years old. She was diagnosed at the age of 18 with schizophrenia. She exhibited strange behaviour at home: staying up all night to do washing and cleaning, and constantly walking about the local town, talking and singing. She never showed any violent tendencies to other people or to herself. Her parents were elderly and they could not cope with her. Sara is intelligent and lively but because of her constant activity she was unable to hold down a job.

Sara became a resident in a voluntary home for people with mental health problems. She enjoys her life in the home. The staff encourage her to be as independent as possible, she visits the local shops and buys her own clothes with an allowance from her benefits. Sara is very sociable. She enjoys helping round the home. She cleans her room (often at night), she does her own laundry and she spends a lot of time making her own clothes. She enjoys smoking and there is a smoking area in the home. Because of her unpredictable behaviour Sara can never be totally independent, but the care staff support her and she is visited by the local CPN who reviews her progress and her medication.

Forty years ago, Sara would have spent all her life in an institution, but with changes of medication, attitudes to mental illness and health policy, Sara can live in the community with support.

Depression

- Depression is a common illness and effective treatments are available.
- Depression is not weakness or laziness.
- Depression can affect a person's ability to cope.

A wide range of complaints may accompany depression. These include anxiety or difficulty sleeping (insomnia). At least four of the following symptoms are usually present:

- disturbed sleep;
- disturbed appetite (eating more or less than usual);
- guilt or low self-worth;
- pessimism or hopelessness about the future;
- decreased interest in sexual activity (decreased libido);
- poor concentration;
- suicidal thoughts or acts;
- low mood;
- loss of self-confidence;
- fatigue or loss of energy;
- agitation or slowing of movement or speech.

Symptoms of anxiety or nervousness are also often present.

Anti-depressant drugs may be used if the low mood has been present for at least two weeks and if four of the symptoms are present. However, there is no evidence that mild depression responds to anti-depressants. Some people may prefer not to take drugs but to use other therapies.

Depression in older people

People are living longer nowadays, and depression in older people is common. It is estimated that at least 15% of the over 65s living in the community suffer from depressive illness. Possible factors linked to depression in older people include:

- poor health;
- poverty;
- loneliness;
- bereavement;
- lack of a confiding relationship;
- family history of depression;
- previous history of depression.

Many older people feel that it is in some way shameful to feel depressed and they often believe there are no effective treatments. Here are two ways a care worker could support an older person with depression:

- Support groups offer an opportunity to meet other people who are in the same situation.
- Talking and being listened to by someone who shows empathy and acceptance is very helpful.

Post-natal depression

Post-natal 'blues' affect over 70% of women who have had a child. In 10–15% of cases these transient feelings of depression progress to post-natal depression. Post-natal depression is often not recognised because mothers are reluctant to admit that they are depressed. Mothers often say they cannot cope, or that their infant cries excessively or will not feed properly. Liaison between the health care team and the midwife during pregnancy, and the health visitor after the birth, will often identify those most at risk.

Support for post-natal depression

Support, help and counselling through a GP or health visitor may be sufficient, but a small number of women may need treatment in a specialist parent and baby unit. Women with postnatal depression should be referred to specialist services if they have severe symptoms and if the baby is seen to be at risk.

Depression in people from ethnic minority groups

Feelings of 'low mood' are often not recognised in non-western cultures. Feelings of depression are often expressed as problems with the 'heart' or 'soul'. Depression is a common symptom in people from ethnic minority groups. Factors that may increase the likelihood of depression include:

- 'culture shock' and readjustment;

- social deprivation, poor housing, unemployment;
- discrimination and prejudice;
- loss of social support.

It is important that health and social care workers recognise that mental illness may manifest itself differently in different ethnic groups. Therefore, it is important that all workers are culturally sensitive to the different client groups they are working with.

Some common therapies used in mental illness

Behavioural therapy

Behavioural therapy is based on the belief that many of our actions are the result of things we have learned. The behavioural therapist will look at certain behaviours and set objectives for the patient (with the patient's agreement). Behavioural therapy is good for treating phobias, obsessional and compulsive behaviour, some sexual problems and also for anxiety management.

 Case study

Salma was 45. Her two children had grown up, and Salma had started to think about getting a part-time job. However, one day Salma got on the bus to go for an interview and she suddenly panicked and had to go home. During the next few weeks she found it increasingly difficult to go outside her house, even to the local shop. In the end, she could not leave her home. Her husband went to see the doctor about her. The GP called and referred Salma to the CMHT. Salma was diagnosed as having agoraphobia. The CPN called on Salma and together they drew up an action plan.

Each day, Salma would go out of the front door of her house and walk along the path to the gate. Each day she went a little further. Once she was able to reach the gate without panicking, she decided to try to go to the local shop with her sister. Salma's progress was slow but in the end she was able to go out by herself and start thinking about planning for the future.

Anxiety management

This approach involves a mixture of behavioural strategies, often taught in a group setting to people with anxiety problems. The group programme will usually include education about the nature of anxiety, recognising hyperventilation (over-breathing, which can cause fainting), slow breathing techniques, relaxation training and, perhaps, assertiveness training.

Graded exposure

This is similar to behavioural therapy. People who avoid particular things (for example, spiders), or places (the dentist's surgery) are encouraged to gradually face the things they fear, starting with easy situations and building up slowly to harder things. Breathing and relaxation techniques are also used.

Cognitive therapy

Cognitive therapy is based on the idea that how you think determines how you feel. Cognitive therapy teaches the individual to recognise and challenge upsetting thoughts. Learning to challenge negative or fear-inducing thoughts helps people to think more realistically and feel better. Patients are given homework assignments.

Counselling

Counselling covers a range of skills and techniques. Counsellors may use cognitive and/or behavioural techniques. However, the main purpose of counselling is to provide a supportive and non-judgemental atmosphere for people to talk over their problems and explore more satisfactory ways of living. Counselling generally deals with specific life situations, such as bereavement, and is more short-term – usually 6 to 12 sessions in primary care – than psychotherapy.

Psychodynamic therapy (analytical psychotherapies)

These are usually offered by psychotherapy departments after assessment by a psychotherapist. They are based on psychoanalytical ways of understanding human development, developed by Freud and his followers. The therapy concentrates on the unconscious conflicts of the person. These therapies can be offered on an individual, couple, family or group basis. These sessions usually last up to an hour a week for a year or more.

Social responses to people with mental health problems

In 2000, the mental health charity, MIND, published results of a survey that found that negative stories in the media, which refer to 'psychos', nutters and maniacs, have a bad effect on people with mental health problems and cause them additional distress. According to the MIND report (2000), 'Stigma hurts, not only does it undermine mental health, but it also damages other aspects of life, like employment opportunities and relationships with family and friends. It plays a significant role in isolating and keeping people diagnosed with mental health problems at the very margins of society.'

Ignorance

About one third of the public do not know the difference between learning disability and mental illness.

Stigma

Why does it exist? Forty per cent of the public associate mental health problems with violence. According to MIND, the public is more at risk from young men under the influence of alcohol. Most violent crime is committed by people who do not have a mental health problem. Violence is not a symptom of schizophrenia.

The effects of stigma

1 **Prejudice:** 60% of people with mental health problems in the survey believe the discrimination they experience is directly related to media coverage; 37% felt that their family and friends reacted differently to them because of media coverage.

2 **Discrimination:** 47% of people with mental health problems in the survey have experienced discrimination in the workplace. Many people lose their jobs or may become unemployed due to the effects of medication or stigma. Most of the common mental health problems (for example, depression, anxiety, and prolonged stress) go away completely in a few months. Most people make a full recovery without much interruption to their working lives.

Mental health and employment

Employers should give greater support to staff with mental health problems. With the changes in legislation under the Human Rights Act, people who have mental health problems will have the same rights as other people related to employment.

Dementia

The number of people with mental health problems is growing rapidly (Audit Commission Briefing, January 2000). The two main categories of mental health problems in older people are functional illnesses (anxiety, depression and schizophrenia) and organic disorders (Alzheimer's disease, vascular dementias).

The incidence of dementia increases with age – with about 10% of 60–64-year-olds affected, rising to 34% of the over 90s.

In dementia the following symptoms may occur:

- decline in memory for recent events;
- decline in the ability to make a judgement and to think coherently;
- increased disorientation;
- decline in language use;
- patients may become apathetic or disinterested;
- there may be a decline in everyday functioning – dressing, washing, cooking;
- changes in personality or emotional control – may become easily upset and tearful.

Diagnosis of dementia

This may include tests of memory such as:

- the ability to repeat the names of three common objects such as apple, table, penny, and then recall them after three minutes (see if you can do this!).
- the ability to give own name and full postal address;
- the ability to identify the day of the week, month and year.

Many people with Alzheimer's disease, or dementia, live at home on their own, and care workers may have to decide what kind of support they need in order to maintain their independence or if they would receive more appropriate support in residential care.

Case study

Violet is a widow. She is 84 and lives on her own. She has lived in the same house for 60 years. There is no inside toilet, and the only heating is a coal fire in the living room. The water is heated by an immersion heater in the kitchen. Violet has been diagnosed with Alzheimer's disease and she was registered as partially-sighted 10 years ago. Her daughter visits her regularly – she lives an hour's drive away. Vi is very confused and neighbours have contacted the social services and police on numerous occasions, as she frequently runs about in the busy road in her nightdress. Recently, she was burgled when she let someone in the house as she thought she recognised him.

Social services provided Vi with a care assistant who comes to the house three times a week to help her with cooking, cleaning, laundry and shopping, but sometimes Vi won't let her in the house. Vi's social worker has met Vi and her daughter to discuss her future care. The social worker has a duty of care to Vi's general health and safety, and also to that of Vi's neighbours. Vi could be injured or put others at risk if she continues to live at home.

Activity

Bearing in mind the principles of promoting independence and autonomy, decide what may be the best solution for Vi's care:

1 If she stays at home (which is what she wants to do) how could she be supported?

2 What may be the problems if Vi goes into care? Remember older people can become very confused if they are moved from familiar surroundings.

Risk assessment

We can see from this case study that there are risks involved in the management of the care of many client groups. It is the duty of the professional worker to assess the risks of following a particular course of action. If Vi stays at home, she may have a serious accident or be at risk from abuse or attack. The social worker has to weigh up the advantages and disadvantages of leaving Vi where she is, or of moving her.

In our everyday lives we all take risks. We may decide to do a parachute jump, go skiing or travel home late on our own. Usually when we undertake an activity like this, we weigh up the problems that may occur and this will influence our decision. In community care, risks of allowing certain activities are also assessed. We may hurt ourselves or others by our actions. When care professionals carry out risk assessments, they may be dealing with clients with a range of problems, such as mental distress or learning disabilities, and their behaviour could have consequences for the safety of themselves and for others. This is what professionals need to consider on a frequent basis.

People with learning disabilities (PLD)

What is a 'learning disability'? There are different definitions of this term.

1 Generally, it means people with significantly lower than average intellectual ability. This affects their ability to cope in society.

2 It is a condition present from birth or early childhood, and can be caused by a number of factors. It may be due to a failure of development within the womb, problems occurring during or immediately after the birth, or infection or trauma in early childhood.

3 There are also certain genetic conditions, such as Downs Syndrome which may cause learning disability.

Some health problems or disabilities are more common in people with learning disabilities. These include:

• hearing and eyesight problems;

• communication difficulties;

• epilepsy;

• heart conditions;

• obesity;

• thyroid problems;

• a tendency to have mental health problems.

The term 'learning disability' was adopted by the Department of Health in 1992. However, some people prefer the term 'learning difficulty'. If an intelligence test (IQ test) was carried out on someone with a learning disability, they are likely to score an IQ of less than 70. Learning disability can be mild, moderate, severe or profound.

Traditionally, people with learning disabilities were cared for in institutions, but nowadays care in the community in small residential homes or supported units is preferred. Care of PLD is usually jointly delivered by the health services and the local authority. Many of the homes are run by voluntary or private agencies. These have to be registered and inspected by the local authority but, under the Care Standards Act, the responsibility for inspecting all care agencies will be taken over by the National Care Standards Commission (NCSC) from April 2002.

There have been several Government documents related to the care of PLD in recent years. In 1998 the Department of Health issued guidance about how health services for PLD should be provided ('Signposts for Success in Commissioning and Providing Services for PLD' 1998). This states that people with learning disabilities should:

• have their basic rights, and rights to access services, recognised;

• receive better information in appropriate formats;

• encounter staff with good communication skills;

• have personally-held health records;

- be able to give informed consent to treatment;
- have improved access to primary care (services based at GP practice level);
- receive assistance and support to use services (this could be through advocacy);
- be able to improve their health;
- be able to access health screening;
- have access to dental services that can meet their needs;
- have improved access for audiology (hearing) and visual services;
- have better experiences of out patient services at hospitals.

Local voluntary groups such as Mencap offer support to people with learning difficulties.

Advocacy

 # Case study

Advocacy Partners

Advocacy Partners was the first citizen advocacy organisation in the UK. It was founded in 1980. It is a voluntary organisation and receives its funding from local authority grants and charitable donations. The mission of the organisation is to:

- *represent the interests of vulnerable people;*
- *to bring vulnerable people into greater contact with social and community life;*
- *to enable vulnerable people to make their own decisions.*

A wide range of clients has been supported by advocacy partners – people with physical disabilities, mental health problems and learning disabilities. Because Advocacy Partners is based in an area where there are many long-stay institutions for people with learning disabilities, the group supports many clients who have been transferred into the community.

Citizen advocacy

Citizen advocates represent the interests of the client. They provide a link into community life for people who may be isolated and represent older people and people with learning disabilities. Citizen advocates are volunteers who are trained to fulfil their role.

Professional advocacy

The organisation employs staff who give a focused individual advocacy service. This service provides support and representation to people with complex needs and those who are experiencing major changes in their lives (for example, moving into the community from hospital).

Self-advocacy

The organisation provides independent support to people with learning disabilities. They facilitate self-advocacy groups, which enable people to support each other, raise common issues and ensure these are addressed.

Advocacy is about:

- speaking out for yourself;
- making sure people listen to what you have to say;
- having someone on your side to speak for you;
- making sure your rights are respected.

 # Case study 1

One of the people Advocacy Partners helped was Isabella, who had been labelled as having profound learning disabilities. Her advocate helped her find mainstream education classes, enabled her to get a place working on an urban farm and negotiated the additional support she needed to do these activities.

There are many problems for people with learning difficulties accessing medical care.

 # Case study 2

Jordan's carer was told by his GP that he could not have his cataracts treated as Jordan could not give consent and his behaviour would undermine the success of the operation. Jordan's advocate helped to ensure that issues of consent were clarified and that support was put in place so that the operation was successful.

From these case studies we can see the important role played by advocacy in supporting vulnerable people.

Services for people with learning disabilities

The White Paper 'Valuing People' was published in March 2001. This was the first White Paper on learning disability services for 30 years. It looked at the services for PLD from childhood to old age, health and social care services and also housing, education and employment.

The problems facing people with learning disabilities include:

- social exclusion – few PLDs are in work, day services are inflexible, training and education are poorly provided, and many are dependent on social security benefits;

- inconsistent services throughout the UK;
- little partnership work between health and social care, with little training for staff working with this client group.

The White Paper proposes to:

- tackle social exclusion;
- provide better life chances for people with learning difficulties;
- reduce variation in service provision;
- promote partnership working between health and social care agencies;
- raise standards;
- achieve value for money.

The proposals in 'Valuing People' are based on four key rights:

- **Civil rights;**
- **Independence;**
- **Choice;**
- **Inclusion.**

By 2004, 1500 people in long stay hospitals will be moved to more appropriate accommodation in the community. Accommodation can include a range of options, including village communities. The voluntary sector takes an important role in providing community support.

 Case study

Daisy has lived in a large hospital for people with learning difficulties since she was 14, when her family decided they could not cope with her any more. Daisy is now 35. The hospital is being shut down and the client group moved into the community. Daisy is excited about the prospect of having her own home. Daisy is sociable and her communication skills are quite good. She has made several friends in the hospital and she enjoys the weekly disco in the hall. She also enjoys going shopping in the nearby town, although she gets lost easily, so she is usually accompanied by a care worker when she goes out. Daisy has reasonable self-care skills. She can wash and dress herself, and she has learned how to use the washing machine and the microwave. Daisy's sister visits her every week.

Daisy is going to move to a house in the town. She will be with two other women whom she does not know, and whose communication skills are worse than hers. She will have her own room. Arrangements have been made for her to attend a day centre nearby. Daisy has always wanted to work with children and she had hoped to attend the local college. Daisy is so friendly she tends to speak to everyone she meets. Her sister is worrying about her meeting men.

Activity

Read the case study carefully and decide the following:

1 What are the positive aspects of the move for Daisy, and what are the problems?

2 How might an advocate support Daisy to achieve what she wants?

3 What additional support and training may Daisy need so that the risks attached to her living in the community may be reduced?

4 How might Daisy's care worker facilitate the transition from hospital to the community?

5 How can Daisy become fully integrated into the community?

Comment

People with learning disabilities often lack opportunities to meet other people and develop close relationships with them, and they can be effectively denied this basic human right. They are frequently denied sexual freedom and the consequent frustration can result in difficult behaviours. Daisy has a legal right to a sexual relationship, providing she gives consent and knows what consent means. However, consent is a problematic issue for people with learning disabilities. There have been cases reported in the media when parents of teenage girls with learning disabilities have applied to the Court for consent for their daughter to be sterilised to guard against unwanted pregnancy. Since the Human Rights Act, the Court is unlikely to give consent to such an operation without the informed consent of the person with learning disabilities.

Social exclusion

The Labour Government has expressed concern for people who do not seem to be part of society. Marginalisation is another term that is also used to describe how certain groups come to be excluded from various aspects of social and community life. There are four aspects of social exclusion:

1 Exclusion from participation in civil society through legal exclusion as people are not considered citizens. For example, certain groups may not be included on the electoral register if they move about the country trying to find work or employment.

2 Exclusion from access to housing and other services. Certain groups may have problems accessing these services because English is not their first language and there is no interpreting service available.

3 Exclusion from employment and actively contributing to society. An example of this would be lack of employment opportunities for people with disabilities.

4 Exclusion from access to the normal experiences of daily life. An example would be access to education for the children of travellers.

Achieving Social Inclusion

Objectives

1 We will seek effective solutions to housing need aimed at improving people's quality of life.

2 We will reduce health inequalities by working with the NHS, schools, employers and communities to promote opportunities for health and well-being and a healthy environment.

3 We will ensure that children and young people in need gain maximum life chance benefits from educational and training opportunities, housing, leisure and social care services.

4 We will increase opportunities for social inclusion through assisting those on low incomes to maximise their finances.

5 We will enable people with caring responsibilities to participate fully in the life of their community.

6 We will promote equality of opportunity and fair access for those at most risk of social exclusion because of gender, disability, sexual orientation, race, culture, religion or language factors.

7 We will increase the chances for vulnerable older people to achieve social inclusion.

8 We will ensure that we actively increase the potential for social inclusion of people with disabilities, learning difficulties or those experiencing mental health problems.

(London Borough of Sutton)

Figure 4.4 The social inclusion policy of the London Borough of Sutton

Certain groups who are most likely to be affected by social exclusion include:

- unemployed people;
- ethnic minorities – these may be refugees, asylum seekers, immigrants;
- homeless people;
- pensioners living on a limited income;
- single parents;
- disabled people;
- people who are long-term sick.

Socially excluded groups tend to have poorer health. Many local councils have developed social inclusion policies. Figure 4.4 shows an example of a social inclusion policy.

Activity

Look at Figure 4.4. In your groups, think how a local council would achieve some of these objectives and who would be involved.

For objective 3, the people who could be involved would include professionals from education, and childrens' and community care services. Children with mental health problems would be supported by the Children's and Adolescent Mental Health Services (CAMHS). Young children from poor families would be supported by Sure Start programmes. As we can see from this example, trying to reduce social exclusion for disadvantaged groups includes health, social care and education agencies; the voluntary sector would also be involved.

Your local authority should have a social inclusion policy document. Many local authorities have their own website and this is a useful source of information for your course.

Care practice

Good care practice includes strategies for promoting and maintaining independence and autonomy, and places emphasis on the individual rather than the disability, condition or treatment. Activities for Living (ALs) cover everyday activities that are essential to the process of living. The activities are complex and interrelated and form the basis of identifying care needs.

Table 4.5 shows the Roper Model of Activities of Living.

Look at the following case studies and identify the key needs of each client. Discuss in your groups how these needs could be met.

Case study 1

Sara (aged 18) is recovering from a car accident. She broke both her legs. The plaster casts have been removed, but Sara is nervous about regaining her strength.

Case study 2

Sam (aged 54) is in the coronary care unit. He still has a transfusion into his hand. He has difficulty washing and feeding himself.

Table 4.5 Roper's model of Activities for Living (AL). AL covers everyday activities that are essential to the process of living. The activities are complex and inter-related

Activity	Discussion	Comments
Communicating	The process of communicating includes speech, writing, non-verbal communication and interpersonal interaction	Assessment should identify communication problems resulting from illness, treatment or hospitalisation
Breathing	The process of taking in oxygen and exhaling carbon dioxide. Fluid loss also occurs	Does the patient breathe freely? Are there any problems because of illness/treatment?
Eating and drinking	The ability to suck, chew, swallow food, and to swallow fluids for growth and nourishment	Assessment should identify any problems with eating or drinking
Eliminating	The discharge of bowel and bladder movements is controlled by the patient	Does illness or hospitalisation cause problems with this activity?
Personal cleaning and dressing	Personal care of the body, including washing, bathing, hairwashing, care of nails and mouth, dressing	Does the person need assistance with any of these?
Controlling body temperature	Maintaining normal body temperature	Problems may include fever (pyrexia) or hypothermia or discomfort
Mobility	Co-ordinated movement to sit, stand, walk, bend, grasp, run etc.	Mobility may be affected by a range of factors
Work and leisure	Can the person go to work and undertake leisure activities to meet economic needs and prevent boredom?	Illness may affect economic needs and boredom
Expressing sexuality	Sexual needs and sexual differences	Opportunity and choice for relationships for certain client groups may be limited
Sleeping	Achieving a period of sleep to refresh person	Insomnia can be caused by a variety of problems e.g., depression
Maintaining a safe environment	Safety in the environment is an essential factor	Health and safety aspects in the care environment whether in hospital, residential home or client's own home

Source Roper, N., Logan, W. and Tierney, A., 1980

Case study 3

Michael (aged 75) has had a stroke which has affected his ability to speak and swallow.

Case study 4

Erina (aged 8) is in the children's ward of a cancer hospital. She is in an isolation unit while she is having her treatment which means she cannot play with the other children in the ward.

As you can see from these case studies, health and care workers need to look at ways to support their clients so that they can achieve their ALs. Sometimes professionals such as speech therapists and physiotherapists may be needed to assist the patient, but sometimes a carer can provide the support needed, especially if the patient is in their own home. As we have already discussed, everyone has certain physical, intellectual and emotional needs at every stage of their lives.

Training in daily living skills

Just as a child learns how to eat, drink, walk and talk and become independent, so do other client groups need support to become independent. With the closure of large institutions, more people are now being supported in the community. Because people who have been in an institution for a long time have become used to a routine, they may find it difficult to adapt to a life in which they have to make decisions and perform tasks that they never had to do in the past.

Activity

Christine was in a long-stay hospital since she was 15 years old. She has a learning disability. Now she is 50, the hospital is closing and Christine is being placed in a small group home in the same area.

Make a list of all the daily living skills you think Christine will need to learn in order to become more independent.

Your list could include:

- shopping;
- managing money;
- cleaning;
- using public transport;
- cooking;

- personal hygiene;
- using a washing machine.

Many of these things we do without thinking, but they are skills which certain groups of people have never had the opportunity to develop.

The Normalisation Model

This model was proposed in Scandinavia in the 1970s. The Jay Committee was set up in 1979 in the UK to discuss the care of people with learning disabilities. The Committee set out a model of care that should be based on the following principles (note the terminology that would not be used nowadays).

1 Mentally handicapped people have the right to enjoy normal patterns of life within the community.
2 Mentally handicapped people have a right to be treated as individuals.
3 Mentally handicapped people will require additional help from the communities in which they live and from professional services if they are to develop their maximum potential as individuals.

The influence of normalisation is clear in this document and is further highlighted in the service principles (Jay Committee 1979).

"1 Mentally handicapped people should use normal services wherever possible.
2 Existing networks of community support should be strengthened by professional services.
3 Specialised services for mentally handicapped people should only be provided if they are likely to meet additional needs that cannot be met by general services.
4 Maximum co-ordination of services is needed to meet the diverse needs of mentally handicapped people.
5 We need someone to intercede on behalf of mentally handicapped people in obtaining services."

These principles were developed and advocacy schemes were set up in many areas to support people with learning disabilities. However, in spite of the normalisation model being used as a basis for developing care, people with learning disabilities were still marginalised. The model was also criticised for the emphasis on people fitting in with society, 'becoming normal' rather than addressing the individual needs of clients and developing services that addressed those needs.

Social role valorisation

This concept is about improving the relations of people with learning disabilities with other groups in society, and is a development of the Normalisation Model. Key features of this model include:

- people with learning disabilities should be encouraged to develop their skills and increase their confidence in functioning in 'normal' situations;
- people with learning disabilities should not be hidden away in institutions but should take part in wider society;

- society should value and respect people with learning disabilities, rather than see them as second class citizens.

If you have the opportunity to work in a care setting for people with learning disabilities, whether it is a day centre or a small group home, make a note of the activities that seem to follow the model of social role valorisation.

Case study

Cherrytree House is a group home for people with learning disabilities. There are seven residents in the home, which is run by a charity. There are four men and three women in the home. The daily routine in the home is as follows:

7–8am

Residents get themselves ready for going to work, to college or to the day centre. They get their own breakfast. In the kitchen there is a rota for household duties, such as tidying up the lounge, preparing meals and clearing away after meals, which has been agreed with the residents.

8.30am

Residents are collected by minibus to go to the day centre, two go to college by public transport, two walk to work.

9am–3.30pm

Residents are occupied outside the home.

4pm

Residents return from their activities. They may look at the television in the lounge or in their own room, help to prepare the evening meal or visit local shops or the library.

6pm

Residents have their evening meal with the two care workers on duty. They discuss their day and clear up the kitchen.

7.30pm

Residents are occupied in a range of activities. This could include going to the pub, visiting friends, going to the cinema or staying in the home looking at television or listening to music.

Look at the case study and compare the residents' life with yours. Can you identify aspects of their lives which are the same or are different from yours? As we have already discussed, residents should be encouraged to be as independent as possible, but sometimes it may be more appropriate to collect residents and take them to a day centre than for them to travel independently. If we want people with learning disabilities to lead a 'normal' life we need to look carefully at care practice. In whose interest are decisions made about transport? Small group homes can become mini-institutions and this is an area that the home inspector will be looking at carefully.

Supported self help groups

Self help groups may be set up by clients themselves or by professionals. 'Don't Panic' is an example of a self-help group that supports people with panic attacks. Some self-help groups have professionals that support clients. An example of this would be a post-natal support group, which would be supported by health visitors and a Community Psychiatric Nurse (CPN).

Case study 3

A post-natal group in south London is a joint initiative between the local Community Trust's Post Natal Depression group and a local leisure centre. The group provides reassurance and advice, and a creche. The group wants to help the new mothers understand they are not alone. Some mothers refer themselves to the group, but most are referred by the GP or health visitor. The group meets in a leisure centre rather than a surgery or clinic, and this removes the stigma from the condition.

There are more than 1000 self-help groups in the UK and the following website gives you details of them: www.self-help.org.uk

Pressure group lobbying

Nowadays many people who are carers or users of services have an influence on service provision through lobbying. One person on their own will not have much influence, so many people come together to form pressure groups. Some charities such as Mencap have an important lobbying role nationally to influence decision making. Many voluntary organisations were originally set up to represent the interests of their client groups and to influence decisions. For example, Age Concern conducted research into the medical treatment of older people and found that many of them were denied treatment on the basis of age. They raised this issue with MPs and other health and care agencies.

The National Service Framework for Older People (NSF), 2000, has stated that NHS services will be provided on the basis of clinical need and that all health and social care services will not use age in their eligibility criteria to restrict access to available services. This could be seen as an example of the influence of lobbying. Local pressure groups are often formed. In a recent case concerning the closure of a long-stay hospital for people with severe learning and physical disabilities, the relatives opposed the closure decided by the health authority and took their case to judicial review. This meant that the High Court looked at the case and ruled in favour of the parents, and overturned the Health Authority's decision. These are examples of pressure group lobbying, both at a national and at a local level.

Individualised care planning

The care plan is based on the outcome of the assessment process. It should contain goals and prescribed medication. In the community setting in the past, the health worker and the social worker would perform separate assessments of need. This caused confusion for the client and was seen as a waste of resources. Nowadays, many areas are developing a single assessment approach, were either the nurse or the social worker performs one assessment to cover all areas of need. In nursing, the Activities of Living are often used as a basis for devising a care plan. Table 4.6 is an example of a care plan developed with a client with learning disabilities.

Table 4.6 Extract from an individual care plan for a client with learning disabilities

Name – Jatinder Khan

Date 11-6-01

Targets	How can the targets be met	Action to be taken	Whose commitment	Review date
To improve communication skills	Individual support and attendance at local college workshop	Plan individual sessions with speech therapist. Enrol on college makaton course	Alison Smith (key worker)	1-9-02
To develop personal relationships	Regular contact with family and friends and boyfriend	Discuss arrangements with staff; discuss possibility of attending family planning clinic	Alison Smith	1-9-02
To develop daily living skills	To learn to tell the time; to learn money management	Individual and group work	Alison Smith	1-9-02
To develop personal care skills	To wash hair independently	Individual support from care worker	Daphne Brown	1-9-02

Task-centred social work practice

Task-centred practice is used in assisting some physical and mental illnesses, but also in supporting behaviour modification programmes, so it is similar to the behavioural interventions we have already discussed. In task-centred work, social workers resolve problems presented by the clients. Task-centred work is concerned with problems that:

- clients acknowledge or accept;
- can be defined early;
- come from things that clients want to change in their lives.

 # Case study

Maria has been diagnosed as having a school phobia. She feels ill when she gets near her secondary school. She is 12 and the problem started when her best friend moved from the school at the end of the first year. Each step in the task of going to school is achieved before the next step is attempted. A possible plan could be the following:

1 Maria walks past the school with the social worker and then alone.

2 Standing outside the school at the weekend with the social worker and then alone.

3 *Being in the school with the social worker at weekends.*

4 *Being in the classroom with teacher at weekends.*

5 *In the playground with social worker on a school day.*

6 *In the school building on a school day but not in class.*

7 *In school, in class with other children.*

This approach can also be used with agoraphobic people, as we have seen on page 186.

Service design and delivery

As we have already seen in this chapter, care services need to respond to the needs of both the group and the individual service users. We will now look at ways in which care services respond to demands for independence and autonomy from service users.

Service user involvement in policy review

 ## Case study

A local Primary Care Group held a health fair in the local area. All the people attending were asked to state three things that were most important to them in GPs' surgeries. On the basis of their responses, a questionnaire was sent to all the surgeries in the area and patients were asked to fill in the questionnaire and give their views of the service provided and what could be developed. One of the services patients said they wanted developed was alternative medicine. The PCG decided to spend part of its budget on an acupuncture service in the area as a result of this exercise.

Service user involvement in day-to-day decision making

One of the key areas in promoting independence and autonomy is about giving service users a say in how care is organised.

 ## Case study

Green Gates is a small home for seven young men with learning difficulties and challenging behaviour. The client group has regular discussions, on a one-to-one basis, and also as a group, on how they want the home organised, including the menu, outings and leisure activities and all aspects of daily life. Attached to the home is a self-contained flat where a client can be prepared for living a more independent life in the community. When a client is given a trial period in the flat, every aspect of support that will be given is discussed and agreed with the care manager.

Brian was given a trial in the flat on the understanding he would get up on his own in the morning and go to his job in the town. He would keep the flat tidy and clean and do all his own shopping, cooking and cleaning. Brian agreed to this arrangement. After two weeks in the flat, Brian was not getting up and going to work. He lost his job as a result. He was rude to staff, and the flat was dirty.

Look at the case study. If you were the manager of the home, how would you deal with this?

This example shows the problems that may be faced by staff who try to promote independence. Some clients may find it difficult to adjust to being more independent, and the staff must decide what strategy to use. The manager decided that Brian had not kept to the agreement made and therefore he returned to a room in the home and another resident was given the flat. Promoting independence does not mean that people can behave how they like without considering others.

Limits to the amount of independence a person can be given can be affected by the following factors:

- **Resources:** are there enough staff to support the client? Within a limited budget, it may be necessary to decide it is better to support as many people as possible, rather than to spend most of the budget on one person with complex needs.
- **Political:** cutbacks of grants from central government funding to local councils mean that services may need to be withdrawn altogether or be charged for. Local authorities are entitled to charge for their services. The political party in control in the local area may decide on certain priorities, and this may affect which agencies provide which services.
- **Social:** if the area is very deprived and there are problems recruiting staff to the area, this may affect the level of support given. Other social factors could include demographic factors such as large numbers of older people or single parents, which could affect the level of support available and the demand for the service.

Community care

With the closure of long-stay institutions there is a range of provision available to service users to facilitate independence.

Independent living at home

Case study

John is a 35-year-old man with multiple sclerosis. He lives on his own in a council flat. He has a key worker who organises the support he needs in order to remain at home. In the morning two care workers get him up and dress him. At lunch time, a care worker comes to give him lunch and does any shopping, washing, or cleaning that he needs. In the evening two care workers come to put him to bed. It is important to John that the same care workers come each day, apart from when they have days off. Some of his old friends may drop in in the evening, but John's speech and sight are affected and he finds it very tiring seeing people. John has a panic button that is directly connected to social services in case he needs urgent help. John goes into the hospital every six months or so for respite care, assessment and therapy, which can include aromatherapy. He wants to stay at home for as long as possible.

Comment

Although John's physical needs are being cared for, he may need additional support for his intellectual, emotional and social needs. What and who could help John meet these needs?

Core and cluster housing

Case study

When a large long-stay hospital was closed, the residents were moved into bungalows in the old hospital grounds. Cliff Avenue is an area that was part of the long-stay hospital. When the residents moved into the bungalows, the staff who had looked after them in the hospital moved with them. A member of staff sleeps in overnight in case there are any problems. All the residents have severe learning disabilities. They had been in the old hospital for many years. They were accommodated in dormitories for up to 35 people.

When they moved into the bungalows, the residents had their own rooms and each room was decorated according to their wishes. Many of the residents have advocates who make sure that their clients wishes are respected. Most of the residents are in their 50s and 60s. When they were in the hospital they did various jobs such as working in the laundry. They love being in 'their house', as they call it. They discuss all the aspects of their care with their key worker. As there are only six residents in each bungalow, they have a lot of support. The homes are near the local shops and they are all getting used to using public transport and walking round the area. Because of their ages they do not work but they go to adult education classes for developing their communication and living skills such as cooking.

Supported housing units

Some client groups will never be able to become fully independent because of the extent and nature of their needs.

Case study

Philip is in his 40s. His parents are in their 80s and are divorced. Philip has been in various psychiatric hospitals since his teens and now lives alone in a council flat. Philip goes to the local shops and library. He has a social worker who specialises in mental health. Philip says he couldn't manage in the community without the support of the local Mental Health Resource Centre. This is a small group service that provides a wide range of facilities for people with mental health problems who live in the immediate area. There is a day centre open five days a week that offers meals, laundry services and various activities. There are also regular clinics, and counselling and relaxation classes. There is a Home Treatment Team that provides a 24-hour a day, seven days a week service for people with acute problems. There is also an outreach team that supports people like Philip to fulfil their potential through employment or education.

Factors restricting independence and autonomy

Throughout this chapter we have looked at how certain client groups may be supported in order to achieve independence and autonomy. However, there may be certain factors that limit how far a client can be totally independent. These factors may relate to the individual.

Physical disability

A client's physical disabilities can reduce their mobility and ability to live an independent life. The role of the care worker is to ensure that there is appropriate support in place so that the client can maximise their abilities, either through the provision of mobility and other aids, or by available transport services. Many organisations produce catalogues of items that assist people to lead independent lives. These can range from stair lifts and mobility scooters, to walking aids and other equipment that can help the person retain independence.

Activity

Contact an organisation or use a local disability information centre to obtain a catalogue of examples of disability aids that are available. Your local chemist may stock certain aids and leaflets.

Intellectual disability

We have seen that certain groups may have a limited understanding of their situation. This would include people with Alzheimer's disease and learning disabilities. It is important that care workers should use all available means to communicate effectively with these clients so that they can be involved in their own care and given choices as far as possible.

Case study

Alma has Alzheimer's disease, and she is going into respite care for two weeks to give her daughter a break. Alma's care worker explains carefully what is going to happen and why.

It is important that people who have limited intellectual ability are consulted about what is happening to them and are given choices. With someone with Alzheimer's, it is important to focus on those tasks they can still manage and enjoy. If you work with a client with Alzheimer's disease try to do the following:

1 Give them plenty of encouragement and let them do things at their own pace and in their own way.

2 Do things with the person, rather than for them, so they can preserve some independence.

3 Break activities down into small steps so that they feel a sense of achievement, even if they can only manage part of a task.

4 Encourage the person to take a pride in their appearance and give them plenty of praise.

5 Respect the privacy of the person when performing personal tasks, such as washing, and also when entering their room.

6 Give them a choice – too many choices can be confusing, so offer choices which require a 'yes' or 'no' answer.

You can see that even if someone is limited intellectually, care workers should still do all they can to encourage independence.

Social factors

Social factors limiting independence could include those client groups who have aggressive or violent behaviour, which means they have to be closely monitored as they may harm themselves or others. Risk assessments would be undertaken by the care worker – this could be the CPN or the social worker – in order to assess how far the client can be able to be independent. It may be that the client can only participate in certain activities if they are accompanied by a care worker.

Emotional factors

Some emotional factors, such as mental illness or depression, when the client could be assessed as being a danger to themselves or others, could restrict the freedom of the individual. Under the terms of the 1983 Mental Health Act for England and Wales, people can be admitted to hospital, or held in hospital against their will, if recommended by at least one doctor. There are different sections of the Act that are used related to treatment and detention.

Legal constraints affecting independence and autonomy

Civil law

Some patients become incapable of managing their own affairs because of mental or intellectual incapacity.

1) Power of attorney

This requires the client to give written authorisation for someone else to act for him or her. The client needs to understand what they are doing and to choose someone who is able to conduct their affairs.

2) Receivership

This is a more complex procedure for a person who is unable to make the judgement required in authorising a power of attorney. An application is made to the Court of Protection (in England and Wales), which decides for the patient whether to appoint someone to act on his/her behalf.

Ethical issues

Ethics are moral codes of practice which are concerned with professional practice in health and social care. There may be a conflict between ethical codes of conduct and the patient's own wishes.

Doctors and nurses have a duty to save life but they also have a duty to care. The obligation to preserve the life of the patient may conflict with the patient's own autonomy. Any health or care worker who imposes life-prolonging treatment on a patient who rejects it, is failing to respect the patient's autonomy. However, it should be noted that the right to refuse treatment is not itself a right to die, but a right to unwanted interference by others.

 ## Case study 1

Theresa was having her first baby. She had a severe post-partum haemorrhage. She needed a blood transfusion. Theresa was a Jehovah's Witness and refused to give her consent to a transfusion. The doctors explained the likely outcome if she did not have a transfusion, but she refused and died, leaving her husband to care for the new baby.

 ## Case study 2

In the same hospital, a 9-year-old boy had an emergency operation and needed a blood transfusion. His parents were Jehovah's Witnesses and refused consent. The hospital applied to the courts and the child was made a ward of court. The Official Solicitor acted in the interests of the child, who was given the transfusion. The parents disowned the child and he was taken into care.

In the first case study, the Code of Professional Ethics protected the wishes of the client. In the second case, because the patient was a minor, the hospital over-ruled the wishes of the parents.

In the future, the Human Rights Act may have an impact on certain areas of the treatment and care of certain client groups. The following case study is an example.

 ## Case study 3

In February 2001 Birmingham City Council was criticised by a group called the Residents Action Group (RAGE) for proposing to close a residential home and transfer the residents to a private organisation. Protesters quoted the Rights to Life, Protection from Degrading or Inhuman Treatment and Respect for Family Life, contained in Articles 1, 3, and 8 of the Act.

Similar actions are also occurring.

The following issues are likely to be a source of legal action under the Human Rights Act:

- Compulsory Detention Orders under the Mental Health Act.
- Sexual relationships and pregnancy for people with learning disabilities.
- 'Do not Resuscitate' orders.
- Withdrawal of artificial feeding of patients in a persistent vegetative state.
- Informed consent issues for a range of patients with limited intellectual capacity.
- Funding of expensive treatment.
- Any treatment that can be seen to infringe rights to privacy.

Throughout this chapter we have seen that health and care workers need to balance individual interests with the interests of the rest of the community.

References and resources

Annual Report 1999–2000. Advocacy Partners Sutton.

Gilleard, C. and Lobo, R. (2000) *Education and Emotional Wellbeing in Schools.* MSWHA Health Promotion Alliance.

Meggitt, C. (1997) *Special Needs: Handbook for Health and Social Care.* Hodder and Stoughton.*

'NSF for Older People' (2000) DoH.

'Pocket Guide to the NHS in London 2001–2' (2001) DoH.

Richards, J. (1999) *The Complete A–Z Health and Social Care Handbook.* Hodder and Stoughton.*

'Signposts for Success in Commissioning and Providing Services for People with Learning Difficulties' (1998) DoH.

Thomson, H. *et al* (2000) *Vocational A Level in Health and Social Care.* Hodder and Stoughton.*

'Valuing People' – White Paper (2000) DoH.

Recommended reading for Students marked with an asterisk.

Useful addresses

Many of these organisations have their own websites. It may be quicker to use these. If you contact charities, always send postage or enclose a SAE.

Age Concern England
Astral House
1268, London Road
Norbury SW16 4ER

Alzheimer's Disease Society
10, Greencoat Place
London SW1P 1PH

MIND
Granta House

15–19, Broadway
Stratford
London E15 4BQ

MENCAP
123, Golden Lane
London EC1Y 0RT

RNIB
224, Great Portland Place
London W1N 6AA

RNID
19–23, Featherstone Street
London EC1 8SL

SCOPE
12, Park Crescent
London W1N 4EQ

Shelter
88, Old Street
London EC1V 9HU

Useful websites

http://www.disabilitynet.co.uk
The British Institute of Learning Disabilities
  www.bild.org.uk

Glossary

ALs   Activities for Daily Living: everyday activities that are essential to the process of living.
Advocacy   A procedure in which a health or social care worker (or other person) speaks on the behalf of the client in order to support the client's rights and interests.
Care assessment   The process of identifying a person's need for care services.
Care management   The process that is carried out in various ways to co-ordinate and arrange services for an individual person.
Care plan   The document that records care needs, how these needs will be met and the required outcomes.
Carer   Someone who provides care and support for a person on an informal (unpaid) basis
CMHT   Community Mental Health team.
Community Care   Services and support to help someone with care needs to live as independently as possible in the community.
CPN   Community Psychiatric Nurse who works with people with mental health needs.
Disability   Limitation of personal activity as a result of an impairment.

Domiciliary care   Care provided in the person's own home.

Handicap   Resulting personal and social disadvantage that limits or prevents the fulfilment of a role that is normal for the person.

Impairment   Any loss or abnormality of psychological; physical or anatomical structure or function.

Inspection   The process through which local authorities check standards of care in residential homes, and health authorities check standards of care in nursing homes.

Learning disability   A permanent disability, usually occurring from birth, which affects learning ability.

Respite care   Provides a break for the carer, either on a regular basis or occasionally. Can also apply to the service user who may go into a hospice or other organisation to have re-assessment of needs and additional therapy.

Value base   Those values which should underpin all practice in the provision of care.

Answers

Chapter 4

Pages 178–9. Table 4.3: exercise on mental health statistics.

You might be tempted to say that the lower rate of mental health problems in rural areas is due to:

- extended family support;
- less stressful life style;

and that the higher rate in towns is due to:

- poorer housing;
- less support;
- more stress.

However, you would have to find out additional information before you could make any assumptions about the *causes* of the differences. Notice that the figures are numbers not percentages, so it could be that:

- there is a higher population in urban areas;
- there are more doctors surgeries;
- people who have mental health problems may be living near mental health units for support in the community.

You can see now how important it is never to take statistics on their own, without additional information. Statistics may show a pattern but they cannot explain why the pattern is occurring.

Chapter 5

Ethical and legal aspects of health and social care

This chapter describes

- ethical concepts and principles;
- ethical perspectives and decision-making;
- legal principles and precedents;
- major ethical issues;
- everyday ethical issues;
- ethical principles relevant to care work;
- applying ethical and legal principles.

Ethical contexts

The purpose of an ethical approach to health and social care

Ethical and legal issues are central to health and social care. Care workers are faced with ethical dilemmas in many areas of everyday and specialist professional practice. In resolving these dilemmas professionals will be guided both by specific **legal obligations and duties** and by certain agreed **ethical principles**. However, it is important to realise that although ethical and legal principles may overlap, sometimes they will not, and practitioners will need to reach judgements that seek to balance the competing requirements of law and ethics. This chapter first addresses the important ethical principles and concepts that inform health and social care, and then goes on to consider the legal framework within which practitioners must operate. Examples of potential conflict are provided, together with an opportunity to apply ethical and legal principles to typical care work situations.

What is ethics?

'Ethics' or 'morals' – the terms can be used interchangeably (Warnock 1987) – have for thousands of years been the subject of study by philosophers and others. Some of those who study ethics take a theoretical approach and try to understand what morality is about and why human beings have moral systems at all. This is known as **meta-ethics**. Others have been more concerned with what is known as **normative ethics** or the practical application of morality. Here philosophers have attempted to understand the moral rules which govern social life and to suggest how best we can live together.

One method that can help to make sense of ethical problems is the **thought experiment**, which creates an artificial situation that allows us to see clearly some of the basic rules and assumptions of our moral system.

A famous example of a thought experiment is the 'Trolley Problem' (Foot 1978):

The Trolley Problem

You are standing on a bridge overlooking a railway line and can see that an empty railway trolley (an old-fashioned one as in many old American films) has broken loose and is careering down the track. You see that the track forks: on the left, a small girl is playing on the track; on the right, there are five children playing. You realise that the trolley is going to the right and is going to kill the five children, who appear oblivious to its approach. You are too far away to warn the children but there is a lever beside you on the bridge. You cannot stop the trolley with the lever but you can switch the track so that the trolley will head for the little girl instead. This will mean that only one child is killed rather than five.

Activity

1   In small groups discuss whether it is morally permissible for you to pull the lever.

2   Now imagine that you are a doctor with six patients, five of whom will die without immediate organ transplants. The sixth has a non-life-threatening illness, and has tissue which is compatible with that of your other five patients.

   a   Decide whether it is morally permissible to kill patient number six in order to save the lives of patients one to five.

      (It is quite likely that you reached different conclusions with this and the Trolley Problem case.)

   b   In pairs try to identify the morally significant differences between them.

Comment

Our moral intuition seems to tell us that in the first case it was permissible to pull the lever in order to save lives, but that in the second case it is not permissible to kill in order to save lives. Why might this be?

The motivation in the two cases appears to be different. In the trolley example, the intention is simply to save as many lives as possible and – although you know your action will kill a child – this is not your reason for acting. In the second case, you appear to take someone's life deliberately. However, when you operate on patient number six, perhaps you do not *intend* to kill him (see the 'Doctrine of Double Effect' on page 217). Instead, your sole intention may be to *save the lives* of your other five patients. The death of patient six is an unfortunate side effect of an otherwise morally well-intentioned act.

However, you may still not be satisfied. Perhaps the real difference here is that pulling a lever is in itself a *morally neutral* act (it is only in its *consequences* that it can be good or bad). But people have a right to their own body, and whipping out someone's internal organs without their permission is clearly a violation of this moral right, so that whatever your intention, this act cannot be morally justified.

This exercise should enable you to realise a number of things about our 'ordinary morality', including the following:

- We can all recognise moral issues.
- As members of a particular society, we share (at least some) moral beliefs and intuitions.
- Disagreement seems to be an important element of morality.

Ethical perspectives

There are many ethical perspectives or theories which try both to explain what morality is and to identify how we can behave morally. Two important but very different theories are explained here:

1 Consequentialism.

2 Deontology or duty ethics.

Consequentialism

Consequentialist theories hold that the rightness or wrongness of an action depends entirely upon the effects which that action has – that is, on its consequences. One kind of consequentialism is **classical utilitarianism** which says that: 'we must always act so as to promote the greatest happiness of the greatest number.'

In any situation, the morally right action will be whatever brings about the most pleasure or happiness or most decreases suffering or unhappiness – or both. It is important to note that in this view nothing is morally wrong or morally right *in itself*. Actions can only be judged as good or bad in the light of the consequences which they bring about. Utilitarianism says that we must not give greater weight to our own happiness or that of those closest to us, but must consider the interests of all human beings equally as this promotes the greatest happiness of the greatest number. This may seem a very 'democratic' approach, but it also means that the interests of the minority will always be sacrificed to those of the majority.

Activity

What would you see as the major criticisms of the consequentialist approach to moral problems?

Deontology or duty ethics

Deontological theories hold that there are certain acts that are right in themselves and thus always morally required; or, more frequently, that there are certain acts that are always morally wrong even as the means to morally praiseworthy (good) needs. The word deontological derives from the Greek *deon* meaning duty and is frequently contrasted with the teleological (*telos* meaning goal) approach to morality of consequentialism.

One famous deontological theory was put forward by the philosopher, Immanuel Kant, as follows:

*   A moral action is one that is performed out of a sense of duty.
*   It is the motivation (the reason) for action which is important, *not* its consequences.
*   We, as rational beings, have certain duties that are absolute and unconditional, whatever the consequences, such as: we ought never to lie or commit murder.
*   To act in accordance with moral duty, we must only do things which it would be acceptable for everyone else to do. This is known as the '**universalisability principle**', and is something like the golden rule of Christian ethics: 'Treat your neighbour as yourself.'
*   Morality requires us always to respect individuals (persons) as ends in themselves ('sovereign wills') and never treat them as means to be sacrificed to some greater end. That is, we must respect their **autonomy**.

Activity

1   Explain simply, in your own words, how the consequentialist and deontological approaches differ.

2   Look at the two thought experiments.

   a) Assume that the man in box 1 is a consequentialist. Who would he save and why? Do you agree with his decision? If not, why not?

   b) In box 2 would a consequentialist go ahead with a mass vaccination programme. If so, why?

Thought experiment 1

Two people are trapped in a burning building. One is a leading cancer researcher and the other is her cleaning woman. A man comes on to the scene and attempts to rescue them. However, he finds that he can only save one because of the degree of smoke and damage to the building. He must therefore decide who to save and who to leave to die. The man is the son of the cleaner.

Thought experiment 2

After many years of research a new and effective vaccine has been developed against a major childhood illness. However, extensive testing has indicated that 1% of all children who are vaccinated will experience severe (but not fatal) side effects. It is not possible to screen all children in advance to identify those likely to be affected.

Acts and omissions

Many moral systems make a clear distinction between *acting*, on the one hand, and *omitting*, or failing to act, on the other. Deontologists, for example, would say that there is a big difference between the moral rule that says 'Do not lie,' and the requirement, 'Tell the truth.' They do not believe that the two are equivalent in moral terms or that the former entails (i.e. logically leads to) the latter. This means that if we actively lie, then we have behaved immorally, but that if we fail to tell the truth, we have not. For consequentialists, acts and omissions are equally important morally. As we saw above, if the moral worth of actions is to be judged in terms of their consequences, then the failure to prevent an act with harmful consequences is no less morally wrong than actually performing the act in question ourselves.

Activity

1 For consequentialists, lying and failing to tell the truth amount to the same thing. Do you agree?

2 Consider the thought experiments 1 and 2, and decide whether you think it is morally justifiable to distinguish between acts and omissions in these cases.

It seems likely that in these examples you found no real moral difference between the **act** of Mr Smith and the **omission** of Mr Jones, but in other, more realistic cases, you may well feel justified in distinguishing morally between the two. Look at thought experiments 3 and 4.

3 Is Nurse Jenkins equally responsible for the harm caused to the patient in each of these cases? If not, why not?

Thought experiment 1

James Smith stands to gain a large inheritance if anything should happen to his six-year-old cousin, Tom. One evening whilst Tom is taking his bath, Smith sneaks into the bathroom and drowns the child. He arranges things to look like an accident.

Thought experiment 2

John Jones stands to gain a large inheritance if anything should happen to his six-year-old cousin, David. One evening while David is taking his bath, Jones sneaks into the bathroom, planning to drown the child. However, just as he enters the bathroom, Jones sees David slip, hit his head and fall face down into the water. Jones is delighted; he stands by, ready to push the child's head back under if this is necessary, but it isn't. With only a little thrashing about, the child drowns all by himself, 'accidentally', as Jones watches – and does nothing.

(Adapted from James Rachel's article in Palmer, 1999.)

Thought experiment 3

Nurse Susan Jenkins has been requested to fit cot sides to the bed of a patient who has returned to the ward from the operating theatre, and to leave them in place for 24 hours. However, on locating the cot sides, Nurse Jenkins finds that she cannot fit them properly so, being in a hurry, she attaches them in a rather haphazard manner – although she knows this is dangerous – and leaves the ward. Later the patient falls out of bed and sustains an injury.

Thought experiment 4

Nurse Susan Jenkins checks on a patient who has recently returned from the operating theatre and finds that her cot sides have not been fitted properly by another nurse. She intends to report the matter to the ward sister but fails to do so before the patient falls out of bed and sustains an injury.

The doctrine of double effect

Deontologists can also make use of the Doctrine of Double Effect – or **non-maleficence** – which says that where there are two (or more) foreseeable outcomes to an action, the individual will not be held morally responsible for the negative outcome where this was not their *intention* (refer back to the Trolley Problem). For example, where a doctor foresees that saving the life of a mother in labour may also mean the death of her baby, the doctor will not be held morally responsible for this death because it is only a side-effect of the *intentional action* to save the mother's life.

Activity

Do you think that consequentialists would accept the Doctrine of Double effect? If not, why not?

Key ethical principles and concepts

Many people are unaware of particular ethical theories or perspectives. What they are much more familiar with, are the specific ethical rules or principles we use in everyday, ethical decision-making. It is important to realise, however, that few, if any, of these principles are moral absolutes. In each situation we face, we must decide what principle is most important. At times we may find it hard to reconcile conflicting demands, and we will find ourselves in a moral dilemma where we are faced with difficult moral choices, as the following section explains.

Rights, obligations and duties

In some ways moral rights can be understood as freedoms: the freedom to do something, or freedom from something. By contrast, as we have seen, moral duties and obligations (the terms are often used synonymously) can be understood as the opposite: as the requirement to do something. Many moral (and legal) obligations and duties arise in direct response to the rights possessed by others. For example, your right to freedom is balanced by my duty not to interfere with you; your client has a right to confidentiality, and you have a duty to respect that confidentiality. For deontologists, moral duties must be discharged whether or not there are any corresponding rights.

Legal rights and duties

Unlike moral rights, obligations and duties, legal rights are publicly acknowledged and legally enforceable, for example the right not to be discriminated against in employment. However, although an attempt has been made here to separate ethical and legal issues formally, in practice they are often difficult to distinguish, and health and social care workers will face many situations where both legal and ethical rights, duties and obligations come into conflict. The following moral principles can perhaps best be understood as the expression of certain rights, obligations and duties.

Autonomy

Autonomy means, literally, 'self-rule' and refers to the degree to which an individual can think, decide and act independently. For many, respect for the autonomy of the individual is a key goal of ethical practice. The thought behind the high regard afforded to autonomy is the uniqueness of each individual human being, and the belief that to remove from the individual the opportunity for self-determination (the ability to make their own decisions and act on them) is fundamentally to compromise their humanity. Respect for the autonomy of the individual provides some protection in cases where the needs and wishes of the majority may override those of the individual or minority.

Activity

Suggest why respect for autonomy is such an important goal.

Independence

Linked to autonomy is the concept of independence: the idea that we are most fully human when we can decide for ourselves what we want and achieve it without dependence on others. Independence is freedom to do something. For many health and social care workers, enhancing the independence of their clients is an important aim of professional practice. However, full recognition of – and respect for – the autonomy and independence of the individual patient or client is not always possible or desirable. In the case of small children, for example, we recognise that their intellectual skills are not developed fully enough for them to be able to take major decisions about their own lives. Similarly, a person with learning difficulties or a mental health problem may not be able to exercise their independence. In such situations the principles of autonomy and independence may be supplemented by the principles of **protection from harm** (see page 220).

The Independent Living Movement

The general movement by people with disabilities towards greater **integration** into mainstream society and greater **control** over their own futures has become embodied in the **Independent Living Movement**. The philosophy of the movement is based on four assumptions:

1 That all human life is of value.

2 That anyone, whatever their impairment, is capable of exerting choices.

3 That people who are disabled by society's reaction to physical, intellectual and sensory impairment and to emotional distress have the right to assert control over their lives.

4 That disabled people have the right to participate fully in society.

The concept of independent living is a broad one, involving human and civil rights. Having control over their lives does not mean that disabled people have to be able to care for themselves without assistance. Independence is created by having control over the personal assistance that is required to go about daily life, by deciding when and how one requires it.

The meaning of care when related to personal independence

Jenny Morris (1993) questions the use of the term 'carers', 'caring' and 'dependent people'. She writes:

> Those who need help with daily living activities cannot be treated with respect, their autonomy cannot be promoted, if their physical requirements are assumed to turn them into 'dependent people'. Neither can their personal relationships be respected if their partner, parent or relative is treated as a 'carer'. We need to reclaim the words 'care' and 'caring' to mean 'love', to mean 'caring *about*' someone rather than 'caring *for*', with its custodial overtones.

She also argues that:

> While impairment is seen as necessarily creating dependency, as being a problem, a welfare issue for society to deal with, policies will always be at variance with disabled people's civil rights. Impairment and old age need to be seen as part of our (i.e. the whole society's) common experience.

 ## Activity

One group of people historically denied the right to full independence are those with disabilities. Try to find out what measures physically disabled people feel would enhance their independence.

Protection from harm

All health and social care workers have an explicit moral as well as legal duty to protect vulnerable patients and clients from harm, and always to act in their best interests and in the best interests of those to whom the clients themselves may pose a threat. This is sometimes known as a **parentalist approach**, that is, the practitioner acts towards their clients or patients as any good parent would.

Potential ethical conflict

Ethical conflict can occur between the right to autonomy and independence and the duty to protect from harm. For many vulnerable people, the exercise of autonomy and the enjoyment of independence are inevitably going to lead to the risk of harm. However, the necessity, indeed the right, to take such risks is explicitly recognised by agencies that work with vulnerable people. What health and social care workers must do is to assess and manage potential risk but without unduly curtailing the freedom of the individual.

Activity

> **1** Why is it important to be allowed the freedom to take risks, even when harm may result?
>
> **2** What steps can child care workers take to balance children's need to become independent, with the need to protect them from harm?

Paternalism

In contrast to parentalism the principle of **paternalism** is more authoritarian:

- Decisions can frequently best be taken on behalf of others by those who have the best interests of those others at heart and who are in possession of all the facts.

- In a medical context this may take the form of the medical model – i.e. 'doctor knows best' view.

- This principle will result in a denial of the patient's autonomy and right to play a full part in decisions about their treatment, but will be justified by the belief that patients cannot possibly be as well informed as their doctor and can therefore make no useful contribution to decision making.

Potential ethical conflict

Some argue that paternalism is never ethically acceptable because it fundamentally violates the right to autonomy and independence, but others believe that sometimes it is necessary when working with those who are vulnerable or in danger of harming themselves or others. One way of understanding this is to say that it may be morally permissible to violate someone's autonomy in order to preserve it for the future. A consequentialist would say that paternalism is always justifiable where it increases happiness or minimises suffering.

The following extract illustrates very clearly the problems which can result when the demands of paternalism and autonomy and independence come into conflict.

Case study

Interfering mother barred by court

A youth with cerebral palsy won a unique High Court ban when a Family Division Judge granted an order restraining the 18-year-old's mother from interfering with his rights.

Matthew, the judge said, suffered from cerebral palsy, spastic quadriplegia and speech and learning difficulties, but was a mentally capable adult. Matthew's adoptive parents had had a child of their own but it had died when a few months old. 'After the death of their own baby, the joy of these parents in this adoption can easily be imagined,' he said. 'Their expectations were shattered when Matthew was about a year old and was diagnosed as having cerebral palsy ...' Their local authority became involved when Matthew was five years old because of the mother's 'fiercely over-protective attitude to Matthew'," the judge said ... 'She exercised an increasingly close and intimate control of Matthew's life ... she would keep him from school, saying he was ill, when doctors said he was not. She would make excuses, such as it was too cold, to avoid Matthew having showers that were necessary.'

She made it impossible for him to have any semblance of social life and prevented him from developing his full potential, physically, socially, emotionally and educationally. In the end, Matthew was taken into care. In June, just before the care order was due to expire on his eighteenth birthday, he went to court seeking an order preventing his mother from running his life again by interfering with his right to live where and with whom he wanted. Granting that order, the judge said that 'On the facts as I have found them ... There seems to me to be a real risk of infringement of Matthew's freedom.'

Activity

1   If you were a social worker with involvement in this case, what steps would you have taken to try to avoid the necessity of a court case?

2   In what situations do you think it might be justifiable to adopt a paternalist approach?

Respect for people

Respect for people is another very basic ethical principle, and it requires that we take into account the rights and wishes of all those affected in a particular situation. No individual, however autonomous, can demand treatment or services without reference to the needs of others or without reference to the opinions of those charged with their care. Likewise, even where the rights of one individual must clearly be given priority, respect must still be shown for others involved.

Potential ethical conflict

It is clear that respect for people is likely to conflict with other ethical principles, including those of autonomy, independence and protection from harm. There are many situations where such conflict can occur in health and social care practice, both in the community and in institutional settings, where the needs and wishes of individual clients or residents must be weighed against the needs and wishes of those around them. An example is the use of secret cameras in hospitals, described below.

Child protection

The harmful consequences of the physical and sexual abuse of children are now widely recognised, not least in the Children Act 1989, which makes the rights of children 'paramount'. Subsequent guidelines to social workers have further emphasised the importance of intervention by social services in suspected cases of child abuse. However, concern has recently been expressed both by families and by the Department of Health that the goal of protecting children from harm has been prioritised above other important principles and has, in some cases, in fact, contributed to harm.

Secret cameras in hospitals:

The use of hidden cameras in hospitals to spot child abuse by parents is legal and ethical, says a report. The technique was used most controversially at North Staffordshire hospital where researchers suggested some cot deaths were the result of child abuse. A specialist advisory committee in paediatrics was set up as a result and raised reservations and objections concerning the procedure, which is only used when abuse is suspected. But another study, published in the *Archives of Disease in Childhood*, the journal of the Royal College of Paediatrics and Child Health, says hidden cameras, monitored by nurses or other health staff, should continue 'in the absence of any viable alternative'.

The research says medical staff have a legal duty under the Children Act 1989 to intervene to protect the best interests of the child. But there are concerns about when to intervene. 'One of the main dilemmas is that the abusive action has to be allowed to continue long enough to obtain conclusive evidence, yet intervention has to occur in sufficient time to prevent harm to the child.' However, the researchers say the risk must be balanced against the danger of returning the child to an abusive situation.

Betrayal of trust

Some health staff have expressed concerns that the use of hidden cameras is a betrayal of trust and a breach of the partnership between parents and paediatricians. But the researchers say the procedure is 'no different' from current child protection investigation procedures, except that it may take longer and that police have already established 'the principle of video surveillance'. They add that a recent child death inquiry found that 'parental rights cannot be insisted upon by a parent who has abused these rights'. They also state that partnership may not be possible 'in the type of abuse where perpetrators are devious' and that, if the carer knows they are being videoed, they will change their behaviour. And they say hidden cameras could help ensure that innocent parents do not unfairly have their children taken into care.

The researchers say protocols have been developed and that staff should not be forced into taking part against their wishes. 'They must have the right to opt out,' they said. And they call for proper training of staff taking part in hidden screening, particularly given concerns that hospitals could be sued by representatives of the child if delayed intervention causes it harm. They also counsel that it is wise to involve at least two independent experts in drawing up protocols.

The Foundation for the Study of Infant Deaths said it agreed with the use of hidden cameras in cases of suspected child abuse, but only if local child protection procedures were followed. But it pointed out that they 'did not have a major relevance for cot death' since they were used to investigate 'repeated episodes of collapse', which only happened in 7% of cot death cases. 'Covert video surveillance (CVS) may reveal child abuse, though child abuse is not the only cause of repeated episodes of collapse,' said the Foundation.

The Royal College of Nursing said it had concerns about the use of hidden cameras and would only back their use if 'appropriate protocols' were agreed. It is also against staff being forced to take part in CVS if they are ethically opposed.

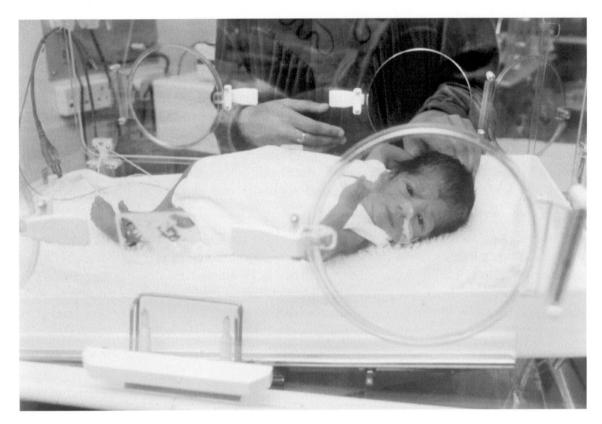

Figure 5.1 Babies in the special baby care unit are constantly monitored

Activity

1   What ethical principles are involved in the use of covert video surveillance in hospitals?

2   What general difficulties do child protection workers face in attempting to balance the needs and rights of children with those of parents and staff?

Persons and human beings

Some moral philosophers argue that the requirements of morality relate only to persons, not to human beings. This may seem confusing because we often think of 'human being and person' as synonymous. However, in the sense in which the terms are used within law and ethics, human beings are only persons if:

- they are rational and self-conscious; and
- have the ability to fully exercise **moral agency**.

Some philosophers believe that some animals, such as higher apes and dolphins, may count as 'persons' whereas some human beings may not. This is of course a very controversial claim, not least because it means that many of those we automatically think of as persons, such as severely brain-damaged adults, would seem to lose their moral status; it also implies that foetuses, which are not conscious or rational, would seem to warrant no moral consideration at all. However, others, including many of those opposed to abortion, believe that foetuses are 'potential persons' and as such must be granted full moral status.

Activity

1   Carry out some research into the status of foetuses in law. Do they count as 'persons'?

2   In small groups discuss the consequences for health care policy of making a formal distinction between persons and human beings.

The sanctity of life

The belief that life is intrinsically valuable or sacred is a widely held moral principle. Most people think it wrong to kill most of the time, and this is reflected in laws throughout the world that prohibit indiscriminate killing. However, the principle of the sanctity of life is, in fact, rather ambiguous. For example, it does not necessarily mean that killing is always wrong; many people believe that sometimes overriding moral principles such as self-defence make it right. Others say that only the life of a person is sacred, and that where someone has lost or has no consciousness or self-awareness, objections to killing do not apply. For others again, life is only sacred where a person has a desire to live, or where they have a certain quality of life.

Potential ethical conflict: euthanasia

The word 'euthanasia' comes from the Greek words *eu* and *thanatos*, which together mean 'a good death'. Today, the meaning of 'euthanasia' has widened to include how that good death is brought about. Specifically, 'euthanasia' is understood to mean a good death brought about by a doctor providing drugs or an injection to bring a peaceful end to the dying process. Other terms include:

- Active euthanasia: an active intervention by a doctor to end life.
- Passive euthanasia: deliberately withholding or withdrawing medical treatment that would help the patient to live longer, with the intention of ending life.

- Voluntary euthanasia: when euthanasia is performed following the request of the person who dies. This is against the law in the UK, and any doctor who helped a terminally ill patient to die would be open to a charge of murder.
- Involuntary euthanasia: ending the life of an able patient without their permission or against their will. This is murder.
- Non-voluntary euthanasia: ending the life of a patient who is not capable of giving their permission. The person who carries out the euthanasia may do so for the patient's 'best interest'.
- Physician-assisted suicide: this is closely related to voluntary euthanasia, but the doctor only *prescribes* rather than *gives* the patient a lethal drug.

Euthanasia is sometimes called 'mercy killing'. It illustrates clearly the potential ethical conflict between the principle of the value or sanctity of life and other ethical principles we have considered. A number of surveys have shown that doctors regularly receive requests for voluntary euthanasia, and that a sizeable number have carried it out. The recent case of Diane Pretty raises serious ethical and legal dilemmas.

 # Case study

Dianne Pretty

Background information

Diane Pretty is dying at the age of 43. She suffers from motor neurone disease (MND), which kills the nerve cells that control her muscles. She is almost completely paralysed, and can only communicate through a touch pad on the arm of her wheelchair. Diane Pretty's mind is unaffected by MND and she wants to choose the moment of her death because she feels that her quality of life is so poor that she should not be forced to continue living. Her husband Brian – they have been married for over 20 years – is prepared to help her die because she lacks the physical strength to take her own life. Rather than do this secretly, she has made known what she wants. She has asked the Director of Public Prosecutions, the official with responsibility for prosecuting criminal cases in England and Wales, to guarantee in advance that he will not put her husband on trial for assisting her to commit suicide. According to the 1961 Suicide Act, he could be sent to prison for up to 14 years for what constitutes a crime at present. The following newspaper extracts outline the case.

'Diane's Last Wish Denied'

Mrs Pretty, 43, is suffering from Motor Neurone Disease, a degenerative condition which has left her unable to do any physical task. Already paralysed and confined to a wheelchair, scarcely able to speak and fed through a tube, the prospect that lies before her is progressive suffocation as her breathing and swallowing muscles fail. Yet her mind remains crystal clear.

Mrs Pretty had hoped her husband would be able to help her take her life without the fear of prosecution.

End of battle?

The highest court in the land has ruled that terminally-ill Diane Pretty has no right to assisted suicide. But the decision in the House of Lords appears to mean the end of Mrs Petty's legal battle, and has enormous implications for other terminally-ill patients. Five Law Lords ruled unanimously that her human rights were not infringed, and that assisted suicide was against the law.

Right to life

Lord Bingham of Cornhill said no one who had heard of Mrs Pretty's illness and its consequences could be unmoved by the frightening ordeal facing her. But neither did anyone have the power to suspend or abandon laws without parliamentary consent. The right to life did not imply the right to self-determination over life and death. Mrs Pretty's lawyers argued that the law subjects her to inhuman and degrading treatment, which is in breach of the European Convention of Human Rights.

'Profoundly frightened'

Philip Havers QC, representing Mrs Pretty, said she would face death soon. "The final stages of the disease are distressing and undignified and she is profoundly frightened by the thought of the distressing and undignified death she will inevitably have to endure. She very strongly wishes to control how and when she dies."

The case split those in all camps, from the religious to the medical, because it touches on the very sanctity of human life and the right of any individual to end it. Critics said any decision to allow Mrs Pretty the right to die could be abused by others. Prime Minister Tony Blair has said he is not in favour of reforming the Suicide Act to allow ill people to take their own lives.

Activity

There are wide-ranging issues raised by Diane Pretty's fight to choose her own time of death without her husband facing prosecution.

> She might be paralysed and wheelchair-bound but she is still a person with a mind of her own; and she wishes to make choices about her own affairs, above all to say when, where and how she will leave the life which, for all the happiness it has brought in personal terms, is drawing to an end so cruelly. Natural justice says that this is her right; and so does the Convention on Human Rights. All she asks is that her rights be respected.

1   Do you agree with the statement above that Diane Pretty's rights as a human being are being violated?

2 It is not regarded as a criminal offence if someone takes his or her own life. Why should someone who is not physically able to do this themselves not be allowed to enlist the help of a friend or relative?

3 Organise a general discussion about euthanasia, which includes the following questions:

- What if the patient's illness is *not* terminal, for example, they could recover? How would we know?

- What if the patient doesn't really want to die? How do we find out whether they are serious about it or whether they are temporarily depressed?

- What if there is a close relative who is expecting to inherit a large amount of money? How would we know that there was no pressure on the patient to request euthanasia?

- What if it is suspected that relatives are fed up with caring for the patient? How would we find out if they are persuading her that it would be the 'decent thing' to request euthanasia?

- What if the patient is taking up a hospital bed in a very busy hospital which is running out of beds and financial resources?

- What if there is evidence that a cure is about to be produced?

4 Find out about the pro- and anti-euthanasia pressure groups for information on their respective positions.

The legal position on euthanasia

The legal position regarding euthanasia is clear. The law makes a distinction between acts and omissions and holds that:

- Active euthanasia must be treated as murder or manslaughter.
- The courts on a number of occasions have sanctioned passive euthanasia by means of the withdrawal of life support from patients who are in a Persistent Vegetative State (PVS). Patients who are *not* in PVS (and are therefore able to express their views) may have *therapeutic* treatment withdrawn (patients have a right to refuse treatment), but may not have palliative care (nursing care and nutrition) withdrawn.

Whilst strongly opposing active euthanasia, the British Medical Association does counsel against artificially keeping individuals alive at all costs. They recognise that there are limits to care (see page 238 for 'Rationing of care').

Supporters of euthanasia include consequentialists who do not recognise the act/omission distinction. Many feel that actively taking the life of someone who is in pain can be more humane and 'moral' than letting them die slowly. Others believe that sometimes other moral principles must take precedence over the sanctity of life, as the two following opinions make clear.

Opinion 1 Now that the law allows suicide, it is difficult to explain why it should object to assisted suicide and that is what voluntary euthanasia is. Allowing voluntary euthanasia is an increase in options and is to be welcomed by anyone who values self-determination. Of course, such an increase in options brings risks, but the way to think about it must be from the starting point of personal autonomy. We must think about the circumstances in which we want to live and the range of choices that we want to have available to us. The question is one of risk analysis.

Opinion 2 Opponents of euthanasia claim that with modern methods nearly all pain can be controlled and that euthanasia is a sign of medical failure. However, a recent survey suggests that this may be wide of the mark. It found that the main reason for expressing a wish to die was not pain but a fear of becoming dependent upon others. Requests for euthanasia may then indicate not that patients are giving up in the face of suffering but that they are positively asserting their desire to control events.

Activity

What moral principles are identified in the above opinions in support of voluntary euthanasia? Do you agree that they may override the principle of the sanctity of life?

Opponents of euthanasia include people who are opposed even to the passive euthanasia of patients who are in PVS. For them, the principle of the sanctity of life means that life must be preserved at all costs. Many such opponents, however, are more concerned about the consequences of legalising active euthanasia. Their main fear is that if the direct taking of life were to be legalised, this would lead to a relaxation of our general prohibition on killing. This would mean that it would become easier to kill disabled children who failed to reach an arbitrary 'quality of life' threshold, and that it would be easier for families to force elderly relatives to 'choose' to die.

Potential ethical conflict: abortion

Abortion is the ending of a pregnancy before the foetus is developed sufficiently to survive outside the uterus. The law in England, Scotland and Wales is based on the fact that after 24 weeks the foetus is often **viable**, in that with medical care it can survive outside the womb. The law states that an abortion can be performed before the twenty-fourth week of pregnancy:

- if two doctors agree that there is a risk to the life or the mental or physical health of the mother if the pregnancy continues;
- if there will be a risk to the mental or physical health of other children in the family.

However, there is no time limit if there is a substantial risk that the baby will be born severely disabled, or there is a grave risk of death or permanent injury (mental or physical) to the mother. In practice, this means that almost every woman who wants an abortion and is persistent in seeking one before the twenty-fourth week can obtain one. However, some women who do not realise that they are pregnant till too late (perhaps because they are very young or because they are menopausal) may not be able to have abortions though they would have qualified on other grounds.

Abortion demonstrates the difficulties of rigid rules in moral decision-making. Medical science has advanced to the point where we have options that were unthinkable even a few generations ago and where old rules cannot cope with new facts:

- Some very premature babies can now be kept alive, which has altered ideas about when foetuses become human beings with human rights – or achieve **personhood**.
- Many illnesses and disabilities can now be diagnosed long before birth.
- Some very ill or disabled babies who would probably once have died before or shortly after birth can now be kept alive.
- The sex of a foetus can be known well before birth (and some parents would like to be able to choose the sex of their child).
- Genetic research makes it increasingly likely that parents will be able to know, or even to select, other characteristics for their unborn child. A few will want to reject some foetuses.
- Abortions can be performed safely, though they can occasionally cause medical or psychological problems.

These are in themselves morally *neutral* medical facts, but they bring with them the necessity to make moral choices and to consider who should make those choices. Should the decision-makers be:

- doctors?
- politicians?
- religious leaders?
- medical ethics committees?
- individual women?
- their partners?

The debate about abortion

Some examples of contemporary rules and views about abortion will demonstrate the complexity of the problem:

- Some religious people think that all human life is sacred, that life begins at conception, and so abortion is *always* wrong (some people also believe that contraception is wrong).
- People often argue that it is not for doctors 'to play God' and that it is for God to decide matters of life and death.
- It could be said that all medical interventions are 'playing God' (even your childhood vaccinations may have kept you alive longer than God planned) so we have to decide for ourselves *how* we use medical powers.

- Some moral philosophers have argued that full consciousness begins only after birth or even later, and so foetuses and infants are not full human beings with human rights.

- Doctors have a range of opinions on abortion, but tend to give the medical interests of the mother (which may include her mental health) the most weight when making decisions.

- Some doctors and nurses dislike carrying out abortions because they feel that their job is to save life, not to destroy it.

- Some people believe that a woman has absolute rights over her own body, which override those of any unborn foetus.

Case study

A 35-year-old woman, 16 weeks pregnant, undergoes amniocentesis to determine the presence of foetal defects. The procedure, which takes about three weeks to complete, involves removing foetal cells from the amniotic fluid surrounding the foetus in the womb, growing, and then analysing the cells. The procedure carries little risk for either mother or child. Her doctor reports that the foetus shows no sign of abnormality and that the woman can expect to give birth to a girl. Several days later the woman requests an abortion. The reason she gives the doctor is that she does not want to have another daughter. She has two children, three and five years old – both girls. Her husband is opposed to abortion and would prefer to have the additional child. The marriage appears to be stable and happy, and the couple have no financial worries. The doctor did not know that the information regarding the sex of the foetus would lead to a request for an abortion.

Activity

Read the case study.

1 Assume you are the woman's doctor. What justification would you have for performing or not performing the abortion?

2 What difference, if any, would it make if the foetus were defective?

Genetic engineering: cloning for medical purposes

What is therapeutic cloning?

Scientists take the genetic material from a cell in an adult's body and fuse it with an empty egg cell. With the right trigger, this new cell can then be persuaded to develop into an embryo. It is the same basic technology that produced Dolly the sheep. Scientists have been trying to isolate and culture these special cells in the lab for many years. When the task was finally accomplished in 1998, it was hailed as one of the great breakthroughs in modern research. Scientists believe these special stem cells can provide us with a ready supply of replacement tissue. Initially, individual cells would be implanted into our bodies to repair the damage caused by degenerative illnesses such as heart disease. Ultimately, however, it may be possible to persuade stem cells to grow into *complete* organs. However, even if this is possible, it is thought to be many years away.

The value of cloning in medical research

Cloning would allow the creation of perfect-match tissue. At the moment, if you have a transplant, your body will try to reject the donated cells because it sees them as *foreign*. Doctors dampen this immune response by prescribing powerful anti-rejection drugs that patients must take for life. But the cells created through therapeutic cloning would not have this problem. They would be derived from the patient him/herself and the immune system would recognise the cells as the body's own.

This approach could end, for example, a leukaemia patient's desperate search for the right bone marrow donor. With therapeutic cloning, doctors would create perfectly matched bone marrow using, perhaps, the patient's own skin cells.

Scientists are very confident that new nerve cells can be transplanted into people with Parkinson's and Alzheimer's disease. New heart muscle could repair damaged hearts.

The Argument for human cloning By Professor Steve Jones	Argument against cloning By Kevin Dillon
Therapeutic cloning might be the breakthrough that means that transplants of kidneys or hearts become a standard treatment	*Human beings should never be treated as a means to an end*
Cloning is one of those words that delivers a lot less than it promises. Cloning is simply reproduction without sex. You are a clone, and so am I, descended in the most chaste fashion from a single fertilised egg by simple cell division. Every one of the millions of King Edward potatoes is one too, grown without sex by dividing one plant into two. There is also, of course, Dolly the sheep. That amazing animal that was cloned by inserting the genes of one sheep into the emptied egg of another, to give a perfectly normal lamb with no father but two mothers.	The public belief that science acts in the interest of society is in crisis, according to a recent report of the House of Lords committee on Science and Society. And this finding accurately reflects the publication of the report by the Donaldson committee, which sanctions the first stage of human cloning. Electing to speculate on the "quick fix" approach, the government has forgone cutting-edge research that has shown the efficiency and ethical viability of using adults as an alternative source of stem cells. Instead, they have adopted the grossly simplistic and unsubstantiated position that the ethical objections are "outweighed by the potential benefits".
All this is cloning but most people see the word only in terms of making identical copies not of sheep, but of humans. The government has given the go-ahead for a very limited form of the process, for copying cells, not people. This therapeutic cloning just might be the breakthrough that means the transplants of kidneys or hearts become a standard treatment, rather than exceptional events that depend on a matching donor becoming available. Even if that is not possible, there is already hope that such engineered stem cells could be used to make skin for burns victims, or brain cells for those suffering from Parkinson's disease.	The Donaldson committee's approach can be explained in simple terms. First, it has escaped public notice that the goverment has co-ownership of the patents required to exploit therapeutic cloning in the marketplace. Secondly, that scientists are set to export their research elsewhere if the government refuses to legalise therapeutic cloning.
Every day, thousands of early embryos are thrown away from fertility clinics because, to have any chance of success, many more eggs are fertilised than are in the end replaced to the potential mother. The new law allows these small groups of cells to be used in the hope of treating the sick, rather than simply being discarded. I would expect that parents of those tiny pieces of material would feel happier that they are used in this way than simply seeing them as gone forever. It is worth remembering that half a century ago, even transplants of the cornea of the eye from a corpse to a blind person were not allowed on ethical grounds. Organ transplants are now a standard part of medicine.	The government is being held to ransom by what the expert in genetics Dr Patrick Dixon refers to as "institutions" that "have the power to dictate terms to governments". But this approach may already have backfired. The recent announcement by the Roslin Institute that it is to abandon a £12.5m research project into the cloning of pig organs for human transplantation indicates that there is a real fear of public backlash within the corridors of power.
My guess is that 50 years from now, we will look back in as much amazement at the days when therapeutic cloning was seen as unethical, as we now do at the time when the blind stayed blind because society was not willing to follow where science was leading them.	Creating human berings as tiny stem cell generators, only to destroy them once their utility has been served, tramples on the critical ethical principle that human beings should never be treated as a means to an end. Ethics have been no more than a 3–5% consideration in the entire debate, according to the geneticist Art Caplan, commenting in his capacity as ethical advisor to the Human Genome Project. The ultimate irony is that the government has spent more time deliberating on the "stage management" of Wednesday's report than on the profound ethical implications of its findings. Public confidence in science may be at its lowest point in recent history, but public confidence in government is now running a close second.
Professor Steve Jones: University of London	**Kevin Dillon: Movement against the cloning of Humans**

Table 5.1 The arguments for and against cloning

Activity

Identify the ethical principles involved in the use of cloning in medical research and practice.

Maintaining confidentiality

Health and social care professionals have both a legal and a moral duty to maintain confidentiality – that is, to respect privileged information that has been given by, or about, patients or clients. Maintaining confidentiality is linked to autonomy and respect for persons as well as to the moral requirement of keeping promises.

Case study

Helen and Lucy are on their way home after a busy late shift on the children's ward at St Lawrence's Hospital. Both are feeling tired and stressed as the ward was understaffed and extremely busy. They settle down on the bus and begin to discuss the day's events. One of the children on their ward has recently had major surgery and has now developed post-operative complications. They are both worried about the girl and are talking about other similar cases and whether they think she'll pull through. Seated just behind them is the little girl's aunt, who is becoming increasingly agitated about the nurses' conversation. When she gets home, she phones her sister (the girl's mother) and tells her what she has heard. The next day, the nurses are called in to see their supervisor as the parent has lodged a formal complaint.

In this case study, there was no *intent* on the nurses' part to cause harm or to act in a non-ethical way. An act of thoughtlessness led to a serious breach of confidentiality where privileged information was discussed openly and names were used.

Potential ethical conflict

Sometimes, however, the duty to maintain confidence may conflict with other equally important principles, such as the duty to protect others from harm, or respect for (other) persons.

Activity

Suggest two health and social care situations that may present dilemmas between these three principles: confidentiality, protecting from harm and respect for other persons.

Consent

Consent may be defined as 'the granting to someone the permission to do something that he would not have the right to do without such permission'. In a hospital context, consent is involved in all types of contact between patients and the health care professionals. For example, consent would be required before:

- taking a blood sample;
- bed-bathing a patient;
- examining a patient physically.

As with confidentiality, the requirement to gain consent is both an ethical and a legal principle, and it too is explicitly linked to autonomy and respect for persons. To have regard for people, we must take into account their wishes and seek their permission when we need to undertake actions that may infringe their autonomy and individual rights. Sometimes there are particular problems in gaining consent, for example, where there are intellectual barriers to communication.

Consent and choices are closely linked and while the positive aspects of both are evident, the potential negative aspects must always be remembered.

 Case study

Mr James visits his GP for advice about a digestion problem. His GP discusses three different options of treatment and recommends Treatment A. Mr James does not consent to Treatment A, but opts instead for Treatment B. This is duly given but is unsuccessful. Both doctor and patient are left with feelings of guilt and anger.

The conflict in this case study is between respect for the autonomy of the patient, even if he is making what the doctor regards as a misguided decision, and the desire of the professional, governed by the principle of benevolence, to help the patient.

Truth telling

Truth telling is a basic moral principle in our culture; it is something we teach children as they grow up, and something that is widely punished if violated. If you think back to the deontological and consequentialist theories, you will perhaps guess that deontologists think that telling the truth is a moral duty which *must* be observed. Consequentialists would say that we should tell the truth whenever the consequences of doing so are more favourable than the consequences of not doing so.

Potential ethical conflict

Certainly, health and social care workers will frequently find themselves in situations where it is not immediately clear that telling the truth should take precedence over other equally important moral principles, such as respect for confidentiality or protection from harm.

Treatment of HIV and Aids

The following is an example of ethical conflict in the context of the treatment of HIV and Aids.

People who are unaware that they have HIV seem to live longer than those who know and this finding challenges the increasingly stated medical view that patients should know they are HIV positive as early as possible so that they can seek treatment. However, researchers say it is still important that people know their HIV status so they can take measures not to spread the virus. In a study of 436 patients treated for Aids, researchers found that the patients had different types of illness, with those in the 'ignorance group' having a dangerous, but treatable, form of pneumonia, while those who *knew* of their condition had more wasting Aids symptoms. Among those who knew of their infection before Aids developed, 194 patients died over the study period compared to 56 from the group who were ignorant of being HIV positive.

Activity

In the light of these findings, are health workers justified in not revealing diagnoses to their patients? What ethical principles must they consider in reaching such a decision?

Case study

John: HIV positive

John was in his mid-thirties, married and with two young children, when his company sent him to set up a new branch in Central Africa. He was nine months on his own, and during that time he worked exceptionally hard and successfully, letting himself go only on one regretted occasion when, after a convivial evening with some clients, he visited a local brothel. By the time John returned home, Jane had found a cottage in her parents village where their belongings could be stored when they returned to Africa together. To buy the cottage, John needed a small mortgage, and two questions on the form led him from Dr Browne, their family doctor, to a London consultant and back again. It was just good luck, Dr Browne told him, that Jane's gynaecological condition had temporarily prevented them from having intercourse since their return. But John now clearly had no alternative but to tell her that he was HIV-positive.

When he came back to see Dr Browne after thinking things over, John tried to explain his misgivings about telling her. Dr Browne was unimpressed. John was like a man with a loaded revolver as far as his wife was concerned, he told him. He was also more explicit about his own potential role. His duty of confidentiality towards John was not absolute. Jane was also his patient, and both the General Medical Council and the British Medical Association made it clear that in these circumstances he could breach confidence.

Reluctantly, John told Jane. As he feared, she took his confession extremely badly, becoming quite hysterical and refusing to listen further. She took the children home to her parents, saying that it was not safe for them to be in the same house as him, and shortly after she began divorce proceedings. Before he went to Africa, John revisited the consultant in London, who discussed his options, gave him some good practical advice and told him how he might know when it was time to come back. When the time came, however, unable to face his situation and the prospect of dying of AIDS, John killed himself.

Activity

> **1** Did the doctor act correctly or should he have respected his patient's confidentiality, come what may?
>
> **2** Should the fact that the wife was not at risk have affected his decision?

Equality

Equality is another frequently espoused moral principle, but it can be understood in many different ways. As it is mostly used in ethical discussions, it refers to the view that all human beings are fundamentally of equal worth: whatever our sex, race or colour, we are all of the same value. The usage of quality with which health and social care workers will be most familiar, therefore, is that of **equality of opportunity** and **equality of treatment**.

However, it is certainly not the case that such equality has been extended to the whole population. Comprehensive anti-discrimination legislation has yet to cover people with disabilities, and there are still occupations where individuals may be dismissed purely because of their sexuality. In a number of high-profile cases, lesbian and gay service personnel have challenged this discrimination as a violation of civil rights.

Case study

'Parents' pain: social services accused of discrimination'

A couple with learning difficulties who have had all their three children taken into care by social services – the most recent in dramatic circumstances after fleeing to Dublin – claim they have been discriminated against.

The parents, who cannot be identified for legal reasons, live near Manchester. They travelled to the Irish Republic shortly before the birth of their third child and were *arrested when gardai arrived at their bed and breakfast hotel, searched the room and found a camping knife.*

When the baby girl was born by caesarean section in a Dublin hospital the following day, she was removed by social workers. The couple, who are prohibited from seeing the infant, have told The Guardian: 'We have been discriminated against because we are disabled and have learning difficulties.'

Social services had wanted to take the couple's first child into care at birth in 1990, but a court ruled that he should live at home with his parents, with support. When the boy was three, however, his parents put him in care voluntarily. The father admits that he had lost his temper and assaulted him.

The second child was taken into care at birth and adopted against the couple's wishes. A complaint about their treatment was later upheld by the local government ombudsman. The couple fled to Ireland on the day a case conference was due to take part on the third pregnancy. The birth was under general anaesthetic, although the mother had wanted an epidural so she could see the baby. Denied access, the couple returned home after four days.

They had gone to Ireland in the hope they would be treated differently. But they said: 'It is just the same rules over and over again. It is heartbreaking for both of us.'

The couple, who have been together for 14 years, attended a case conference in Dublin last Thursday. The baby's father refused to stay in the room when he recognised a social worker from previous encounters. The mother stayed, but was told they could not have the children. Given the opportunity to see the baby for an hour-long supervised visit, the couple declined as they felt they had lost her already.

The case highlights the complexities of work with parents with learning disabilities. Some research has suggested that such parents run a risk of having their children taken into care on evidence that would not hold up against non-disabled parents. The social services department involved in the case denies discriminating against the couple. It says it supports a number of parents with learning disabilities and does all it can to keep their children at home.

From an article in *The Guardian*, November 28, 2001.

Activity

Find out about the latest legislation on Disability Discrimination. How do social services departments support parents with learning disabilities in the community?

Equity

It is important to distinguish equality from equity or fairness. To treat people equitably is not always to treat them equally. Whereas equal opportunities legislation requires all people to be treated in the same way, the principle of equity recognises that people have different needs and that responses may have to be tailored to the requirements and circumstances of particular individuals. For example, as many studies have shown, poor people in Britain (and elsewhere) have a greater need for health care than those who are better off. In trying to achieve equal levels of health, it may be necessary to create unequal access to health care services to ensure that those who need care the most receive it. To treat people with different needs in the same way (i.e. equally) may be to treat them unequitably.

Activity

Identify those types of health and social care provision that are delivered on an equitable, rather than an equal, basis. Is this morally justifiable?

Justice

Justice is another central ethical principle, and most people would agree that it is worth upholding. Justice can also be understood as fairness, ensuring, for example, that where people violate agreed codes of conduct and are to be punished, this is done in a fair way or in a way which is 'just'; or that where resources are allocated, this is done equitably. The problem here is that, morally and politically, not everyone can agree on what constitutes justice. This is certainly the case with, for example, criminal justice legislation. Some people believe that justice is served by rehabilitating offenders, whilst others believe that it will only be served by longer prison sentences or the reintroduction of capital punishment. Frequently, in terms of criminal law, justice will and must compromise those other moral rights that the criminal has forfeited, such as the right to freedom, independence and autonomy.

Potential ethical conflict: the rationing of health care

One area of health and social care in which concerns about equity and justice are prominent is that of the rationing of health care. This is a contentious political issue, with many people arguing that, in Britain, if public health care were better funded, the rationing of treatment would not be necessary. However, even the 'architect' of the National Health Service (NHS), Aneurin Bevin, recognised 50 years ago that there would be some mismatch between resources and the demand for care: 'We never will have all we need. Expectation will always exceed capacity. This service must always be changing, growing and improving. It must always appear inadequate.' (Davey and Popay, 1993).

Some, therefore, argue that if resources are finite, then it is important that health care be allocated in a just and equitable way. In response to this, a number of methods have been advocated, each of which makes use of different ethical principles:

- Priority ranking: This approach, first adopted in Oregon in the USA, consults the public and asks them to rank treatments in order of priority.

- Quality Adjusted Life Years (QALY): This is a formula for rationing health care. Using this method, treatments are ranked according to their costs and weighed against the projected increase in life expectancy and quality of life they will bring about. This means that patients will receive treatment only where the long-term benefit is deemed to outweigh the cost. Critics argue that this approach discriminates against people requiring continuing care and favours those needing immediate, one-off procedures. It may also fail to give sufficient priority to preventative health measures.

Other shortcomings of the QALY method of rationing health care are highlighted by the Medical Research Council:

> Since such measures are affected by average life expectancy, they may discriminate against those sectors of society that already have a lower life expectancy. If applied rigorously they would favour whites over blacks, upper social classes over lower and women over men (as well as young over old). The choice of determinants of resource allocation is not in itself simply an issue in economics; it is primarily an ethical question.

Activity

Investigate the QALY approach and assess the validity of these criticisms.

There are many ethical principles that could be used to govern the allocation of health care resources. The following are some suggestions:

- Need: those in greatest need should get help, regardless of age, cost of treatment, etc.

- Merit: those who deserve it most should get help – this would mean that those whose illness is 'self-inflicted' (for example, smokers with lung cancer) would not be treated.

- Welfare maximisation (utilitarian): resources should be allocated so that the maximum number of people benefit. This could mean that very expensive procedures such as organ-transplant surgery or kidney dialysis may be excluded altogether.

- Random allocation: some argue that as all the above principles would exclude some patients from treatment in advance, the fairest system would be a 'lottery' where all have an equal chance of 'success'.

Activity

Identify arguments for and against each of the above as principles for the allocation of health resources.

'Rationing health care: Ageism in the NHS'

There are many other more subtle ways in which the elderly seem to be discriminated against by the NHS. Research by Age Concern showed that almost two million people – one in 10 – have noticed different treatment from the NHS since their fiftieth birthdays.

One of the problems that bedevil this whole issue of rationing care is the definition of illness. If a person has a low blood count or a broken leg or a severely-infected appendix, there can be no doubt that they are ill and need treatment by the NHS. And they will get it. But is being old and frail an illness? The State says it is not, that it is part of ordinary life and that therefore the costs of care in those later years should be an individual citizen's (or his or her family's) responsibility. And that makes sense, until you remind yourself that getting pregnant and giving birth to a baby is part of normal life. And no one suggests that the NHS should opt out of maternity care. Older people, and a good many far-sighted younger ones, too, are protesting that as we move further into the new century, when the life expectancy of people in the Western world is confidently predicted to lengthen dramatically (the number of centenarians is already increasing, and more and more will reach their late eighties and nineties) it is not acceptable for the NHS to discriminate against the old.

They accept that a degree of rationing in the NHS is inevitable, as demand rises ever higher and costs spiral. But, they say reasonably enough, they want justice for all users of the NHS. It is not good enough to aim covert rationing at the elderly. It should be overt and honest, with all citizens sharing in the exercise of cost containment.

Adapted from an article 'Ageism: A national disgrace' by Claire Raynor, President of the Patients' Association (17 February 2000)

 Activity

Find out about other types of discrimination that arise from rationing care in the NHS and in the social care sector, for example, children with Down's syndrome, who may be refused heart transplants, or drug addicts who may be denied social care.

The legal framework of health and social care provision

The law refers to the set of rules by which a society regulates the behaviour of its members. In the case of health and social care, it provides a complex legislative framework which confers legal rights, duties and obligations on both service providers and users.

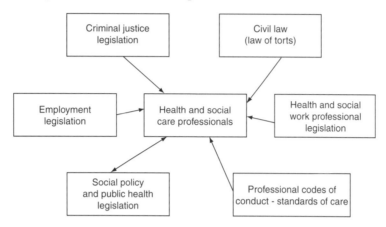

Figure 5.2 The legal framework of health and social care

Sources of law

There are three main sources of law:

1 **Custom or common law:** This is law based on accepted ways of doing things, on 'custom and practice', which go back many centuries. The Duty of Care, which is of particular concern to health and social care practitioners, has its origins in common law.

2 **Case law or judicial law:** This refers to the application and interpretation of existing laws by judges. Over time, judgements reached in certain cases have been recorded and have established examples or **precedents** for the treatment of similar subsequent cases. The law on medical negligence, for example, has been laid down largely through judicial opinion.

3 **Statute law:** This is law made by Parliament. The British constitution grants supreme legislative (law-making) power to Parliament. Each year, typically, a hundred bills go through complex procedures in the House of Commons and the House of Lords before becoming Acts of Parliament and passing on to the 'statute book'. Some laws are also made by the institutions of the European Union and are incorporated into British statute law.

Some of the statute law of concern to health and social care workers is referred to later, but it is beyond the scope of this chapter to cover anything but a small sample. Some examples include the Children Act 1989, the NSH and Community Care Act 1990, the Disability Discrimination Act 1995, the National Assistance Act 1948, the Police and Criminal Evidence Act 1984, and the Mental Health Act 1993.

Other important instances of statute law in this context include equal opportunities legislation and those acts which establish and regulate the health and welfare professions, such as the Local Authority Social Services Act (1970) and the Nurses, Midwives and Health Visitors Act of 1979 and 1992.

Activity

The most recent piece outlining the rights of people with disabilities is the Disability Discrimination Act (1995). Investigate its main provisions and identify how these differ from those of earlier disability-discrimination legislation.

The administrative machinery of the law is divided into two branches, one dealing with criminal law and the other with civil law.

Criminal law

Crimes are offences committed against the state either in the form of:

- an act that the law forbids (such as theft);
- or in the form of the omission of an act that the law requires.

If there is sufficient evidence, the offending individual may be charged by the police with the crime in question and sent for trial. Where the verdict of the jury is 'guilty', the defendant may be sent to prison. (In Scotland only, there is a possible verdict of 'not proven'.)

It may be the case that the defendant will enter a defence plea and argue that although the act or omission is normally wrong, in this case there were special mitigating circumstances – in other words, there are special facts about this case which mean that the act or omission which is *normally* wrong is not so in this case.

The concept of criminal responsibility is important. Under common law, for a crime to have been committed, there must normally be a guilty mind, or *mens rea*, and for this to be inferred there must be evidence of intention, recklessness or negligence. The following extract concerns the case of a babysitter who was jailed for three years for bringing about the death of a child in his care:

'Minder high on heroin killed baby'

A teenage babysitter shook to death a nine-month-old baby while high on heroin after becoming exasperated with his continuous crying.

Jonathan Murdoch, 18, was left to care for Jack Betts while his mother Deborah, with whom he was a lodger, was visiting her boyfriend in February.

Nottingham Crown Court was told yesterday that neighbours in Sutton-in-Ashfield reported hearing Jack wailing for around half an hour. Then, there was a sudden bump. Murdoch emerged from the house cradling Jack's body and began banging on doors. The baby was taken to hospital with severe head injuries and died from the effects of 'moderate' shaking.

Murdoch, who admitted manslaughter, was jailed for three years.

From an article in *The Daily Telegraph*, 24 July 2001

Activity

Why did the judge reach a manslaughter rather than a murder verdict in this case?

Civil law

This involves the rights and duties that individuals have towards each other. In such cases legal action is taken by one private individual against another individual or organisation. Where the verdict is guilty, the outcome is usually the award of monetary compensation, for example, in cases of libel. It is important to note that much law has both a civil and a criminal element (for example, employment or health and safety laws) and that some civil wrongs are also crimes, such as assault and battery, and gross negligence (see page 253). In such cases the wrong is considered so grave that it goes beyond compensation between citizens and amounts to a wrong against the community.

Much of the work of health and social care professionals is covered by civil law, and, in particular, that part of it known as **torts** (delicts in Scotland). A tort is a civil wrong and it results in common law action for damages. The language used in the two branches of law differs: in criminal cases, the person facing charges (the defendant) is prosecuted – usually by the State (i.e. the Crown Prosecution Service) – whereas in civil cases one private body or individual sues another.

The court system in England and Wales

The court system, staffed by law officers, is at the heart of the legal system:

- Tribunals. At the preliminary level (see Figure 5.3) are tribunals that are more informal than other courts. These deal with a large number of disputes concerning things such as rent and claims for industrial-injuries compensation. Tribunals are overseen by a chairperson with legal experience who is appointed by the Lord Chancellor.

- Magistrates' courts are overseen by magistrates or Justices of the Peace (JPs). JPs are not legally qualified (although they attend a compulsory training course), generally work part-time and are unpaid. They are assisted by a legally qualified Clerk to the Court. About two million cases a year are dealt with in magistrates' courts. Magistrates have the power to sentence an offender for up to six months in cases of minor or summary offences, but must pass on more serious offences to higher courts. Care workers may have significant contact with magistrates' courts as these deal with family disputes and applications for care orders.

- Juvenile courts deal with criminal cases involving young people under 17.

- Coroners' courts are presided over by coroners (a solicitor or doctor) and investigate all cases of unexplained death.

- County courts hear less serious civil cases and are presided over by legally trained circuit judges.

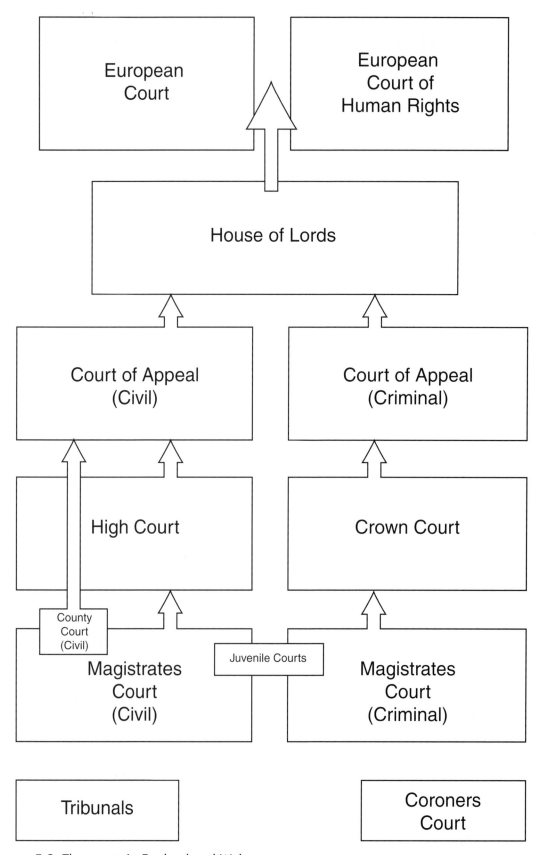

Figure 5.3 The courts in England and Wales

- Crown courts with a judge and jury try all serious crimes. The central criminal court is the Old Bailey.

- The High Court has three 'divisions': the Queen's Bench, the Family Division and the Chancery Division. These deal largely with serious civil cases.

- The Court of Appeal hears appeals against verdicts passed by lower courts and has two divisions: the civil division is headed by the Master of the Rolls, and the criminal division is headed by the Lord Chief Justice.

- The House of Lords is the highest court of appeal in Britain (and some other Commonwealth countries) and is presided over by the 'Law Lords'.

- The European Court and European Court of Human Rights. Cases may also be referred on appeal to these European courts.

Law officers

Whilst magistrates and judges oversee the judicial process, solicitors, barristers and probation officers represent and assist those bringing or defending cases.

Solicitors

Solicitors are general legal advisers accessible to the public who hire their services in a wide range of legal matters. Solicitors may be advocates (who officially speak on behalf of clients) in the lower courts but not usually in the higher courts.

Barristers

Barristers have exclusive right of audience (as advocates) in the higher courts and are known as 'counsel' for the prosecution or the defence. Barristers are only accessible via a solicitor. They usually wear wigs. Judges must be appointed from experienced barristers.

 Activity

1 Conduct some research into the socio-economic background of members of the judiciary and construct a profile of a typical judge. Give him/her a name and write a short biography. What conclusions do you reach about the nature and representativeness of British judges?

2 In which courts do you think the following cases would be heard?

  a A student at a college of further education has been accused of raping and sexually assaulting a fellow student.

  b A student has just started a course at university and is found dead in her room. Suicide is suspected.

  c Three men plan an elaborate bank raid and succeed in stealing several million pounds worth of gold bars.

> d A woman and her daughter have been repeatedly threatened and harassed by the woman's partner, and she wants to have him excluded from the family home.
>
> e A crown court judge gives a defendant found guilty of manslaughter leave to appeal.

Probation officers

The probation service is involved at every stage of the criminal justice system. Its key functions are to provide information to the courts by means of pre-sentencing reports, to supervise offenders on court orders (including those 'on probation') in the community and to work with offenders in custody and on release. In this the service is intended to contribute to the:

- protection of the public;
- prevention of re-offending;
- successful reintegration of the offender into the community.

Figure 5.4 below illustrates the position of community sentences in the 'tariff' available to judges passing sentence.

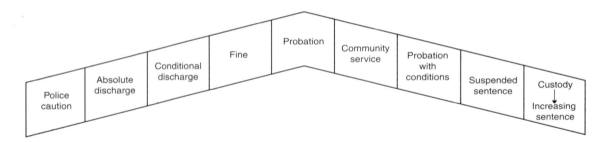

Figure 5.4 The sentencing tariff for offenders

Although the majority of the work of probation officers is in the criminal justice system, they also have a range of statutory court welfare responsibilities. These include the preparation of reports in county court divorce proceedings, conciliation work with divorcing parents, involvement in domestic and family proceedings in the magistrates' courts and wardship proceedings in the High Court. The role of the court welfare service is to help the court to resolve disputes where children are concerned and to ensure that their welfare is paramount.

Functions of the legal system

The legal system has a number of broad functions, of which the following are the most important:

- protection;

- regulation;
- compensation;
- punitive.

Protection

One function of criminal justice legislation is to protect victims and potential victims from further harm by imposing custodial sentences on those found guilty of violent offences against the person. Laws such as the Domestic Violence and Matrimonial Proceedings Act 1976 and the Children Act 1989 can be used to protect children and adults, for example, through the granting of court orders or injunctions against those who have committed acts of violence or harassment within the home. Similarly, the largely civil laws and regulations concerning the provision of goods and services have a protective function to ensure that users and consumers are not taken advantage of by unscrupulous traders and agencies.

Regulation

Linked to protection is the law's regulatory function, where it seeks to enforce mutual rights, duties and obligations. This is frequently undertaken by means of official circulars and guidelines as well as by specific Acts of Parliament. Such regulation may include the monitoring of health and safety standards in schools or factories, or the measurement of levels of industrial pollution. Within the field of health and social care, it includes the registration and inspection of residential care facilities under the Registered Homes (Amendment) Acts of 1984 and 1991.

Activity

1 Investigate the main provisions of the Child Support Pensions and Social Security Act 2000. What rights, duties and obligations does the child support law seek to enforce? Has it been successful in this?

2 Identify three laws, circulars or sets of guidelines which affect professional child care workers (you could contact the National Childminding Association for advice).

Compensation

The law may also be concerned with securing redress or compensation for the victims of harm. As we have seen, the majority of civil cases aim to achieve monetary compensation for the victim rather than the custodial sentencing of the offender. In criminal cases, on the other hand, the Criminal Injuries Compensation Board may award compensation to the victim.

Activity

1 Write to the Home Office for information on the 'tariff' of awards that may be granted to the victims of different types of crime.

2 Collect a range of broadsheet newspapers over the next two or three weeks and identify those court cases where compensation has been awarded to the victim in criminal and civil offences. Do the levels of compensation reflect the severity of the offences?

Punitive

Of course the law also has a punitive or punishment function. This serves to teach the offender that 'crime does not pay', and may also have a deterrent effect on others.

Convention on Human Rights: Article 3

No one shall be subjected to torture or to inhuman or degrading treatment of punishment. This will usually apply to the treatment of those in custody and will enable challenges to punitive restraint practices, such as keeping women prisoners in handcuffs during childbirth and the use of punitive restraint techniques. It may also lead to new laws against corporal punishment, physical punishment of children by parents or guardians and other domestic violence. It is also relevant to the treatment of refugees facing deportation to countries where they might suffer torture. If that threat exists, the Convention forbids deportation to that country.

There is disagreement amongst professionals in the legal system as to the proper balance between the punitive and rehabilitation functions of custodial sentences, as the following article demonstrates.

Jailing mums puts children at risk

In the UK over 60 per cent of women prisoners have young children. Women are nearly always the primary caregivers and are often single mothers. At least 4000 children are affected by their mothers' imprisonment. Only three per cent of women have a child in prison with them. So children have to be farmed out. Most are living with their mothers prior to the women's imprisonment and for 85 per cent it is the first time they have been separated for more than a day or two. Siblings are often separated. There is evidence that most children become withdrawn and depressed. One in four has difficulty sleeping or becomes physically ill. Seventy per cent see their mother only once a month or less. Half of all babies under one year who are in care because their mothers are in prison are moved between two and four different homes. We know that it is vital for babies in the first year of life to form a strong attachment to one person. From this grows a sense of security and trust, self-esteem and the capacity to love. The enforced separation of mothers and babies is another form of violence against women and is an abuse of our power over children.

Adapted from an article in the *Observer*, 14 March, 1999.

Activity

1   Do you agree with the writer that the law is too punitive in this case?

2   Find out about victim support organisations and also organisations concerned with the support and rehabilitation of offenders. Are there significant differences in their views on dealing with crime and possible reform of the criminal justice system?

The legal responsibilities of health and social care workers

Health and social care services are provided by a wide range of agencies and organisations, each of whom is subject to different laws and regulations in its operation. The main types of provision of health and social care are as follows:

1   **Statutory:** this relates to provision established by Acts of Parliament, and includes all health and social care provided by public bodies, including NHS hospitals and local social services departments.

2   **Private:** this refers to services offered by businesses on a profit-making basis. These providers may contract to undertake work on behalf of the public sector, or they may provide services directly to private customers.

3 **Voluntary:** this refers to services provided by voluntary organisations such as Barnardos or the NSPCC. Many of these are both registered charities and large organisations that receive grants from central and local government to run services on their behalf. Some *do* make a profit but then re-invest this into their services – such as the sheltered housing provided by the Royal British Legion.

In some parts of the country, voluntary and not-for-profit organisations have stepped in to fill gaps in statutory provision. Each of these types of organisation is governed in its operation by the framework of law as set out in Figure 5.2 above. These laws and regulations all confer legal responsibilities which can be divided into **duties** and **powers**:

1 Duties are where a law imposes a duty upon a professional, they are required to carry it out;
2 Powers are where the law gives them a power, then it may be exercised at their discretion and in accordance with their professional judgement.

Where the professional fails or is negligent in the discharge of these responsibilities, he or she will be held accountable or answerable for the consequences. In some cases this will be under (statutory) employment or contract law. Recently, concern has been expressed at the fate of 'whistleblowers' who break contracts of employment forbidding them to speak out about poor standards of care in hospitals or nursing homes. The recent case of baby deaths in Bristol highlighted the difficulties and delays experienced by the whistleblower in this case.

Whistle-blower accuses NHS

Stephen Bolsin, the consultant anaesthetist who alerted the country to the unacceptably high death rates of babies undergoing heart surgery at the Bristol Royal Infirmary, yesterday accused the medical establishment of effectively exiling him to Australia for his whistle-blowing:

'I and my family are living and working in Australia as a direct result of the treatment I received in Bristol after criticising the conduct of paediatric cardiac surgery at the infirmary. No medical or non-medical professional in the NHS should have to endure the threats and discrimination that I was subjected to in Bristol. My initial concerns were expressed confidentially to senior colleagues within the United Bristol Health Care Trust. Only when those concerns were ignored did I involve senior medical officers at the Department of Health. Even at that stage the concerns were expressed in a professional and confidential manner.'

Professor Bolsin admitted that at one point he talked to Phil Hammond, then a trainee doctor writing the 'MD' column in *Private Eye*. The story began to leak into the public domain but heart operations on babies only ceased after Joshua Loveday died in 1995, despite attempts by various people in authority, including the Department of Health, to get the operations stopped.

The medical establishment never forgave him, he said. He and his wife Maggie, a nurse at the BRI, felt forced to go to Australia. 'There was a deep mistrust of me by many of the management group and clinicians in management. I felt a bit like a Russian dissident who was being accused of psychiatric disease for not thinking the right thoughts. What helped me and my family get through was a very clear knowledge that what I had done, and was doing, was the right thing for current and future patients, as well as the past parents and relatives of patients who had been treated so appallingly,' he said. 'I have been back to Bristol and have very good friends in the city. But professionally, I would find it impossible to achieve at the level I want to in Bristol, or probably in the UK. The UK medical establishment also has a very deep mistrust of what I did in Bristol, although I have no doubt I did the right thing.'

In his statement, Professor Bolsin offered his deepest sympathy and apologies to the parents and relatives of children who died or were damaged at the BRI. He continued to work as an anaesthetist even while he was questioning the surgeons' competence. 'No actions can adequately compensate for the suffering they have endured, and I hope that the publication of the report will help to heal their wounds,' he said.

He said he hoped that today's report would result in real change. 'My earnest hope is that the report will lead to a genuine commitment on the part of the medical profession to implement policies to enable the monitoring of professional practice in all specialities. Such policies and procedures should be capable of identifying excellence, endorsing acceptable practice and raising the standards of practice before any patient harm occurs.'

BBC Health report 18 July, 2001

Since the Bristol scandal, the Department of Health, the General Medical Council and the doctors' professional bodies have attempted to put in place a framework that will prevent such a tragedy from happening again as follows:

- **The Commission for Health Improvement (CHI)** – a kind of Ofsted for hospitals, which will regularly inspect Britain's hospitals.
- **The National Clinical Assessment Authority (NCAA)** – a sort of 'hit squad', it is designed to go in and investigate any brewing crisis.
- **The National Patient Safety Agency (NPSA)**, which will collate information on medical errors.
- **Annual appraisals** for hospital consultants and a new 'MOT' for doctors – a revalidation system every five years, in which they have to prove they are still fit to practice.

The Bristol Royal Infirmary made two radical proposals:

- that the system of clinical negligence litigation should be abolished;
- that any member of staff who reports an unexplained death within 48 hours should receive immunity from disciplinary action.

As there is still no single organisation whose responsibility it will be to make sure that a doctor's performance is satisfactory, the inquiry is recommending two umbrella organisations:

1 The proposed Council for the Regulation of Health Professionals would oversee the General Medical Council and the new Nursing and Midwifery Council.

2 A Council for the Quality of Healthcare would take in organisations like CHI and the NPSA.

Activity

What ethical and legal principles must care workers consider in deciding whether to speak out *against* what they see as harmful or damaging practices in their place of work?

Where workers are found guilty of professional misconduct (defined as behaviour that is unworthy of the profession), they are liable for discipline or even dismissal. In serious cases such individuals will be struck off their professional register. The most common reasons for removal from the United Kingdom Central Council (UKCC) Register include:

- insensitivity or unkindness to patient's relatives;
- reckless or unskilful practice;
- obscene or indecent language in patient areas;
- concealing untoward incidents;
- misleading vulnerable patients;
- neglecting duties;
- failure to keep essential records;
- failure to summon emergency aid;
- falsifying records;
- failure to protect or promote patients' interests;
- failure to act when knowing that a colleague is improperly treating or abusing patients.

Unfortunately, there will also be cases where health and social care professionals engage in activities that not only constitute gross professional misconduct but also clearly breach criminal law. In the UK members of the public are becoming increasingly aware of their rights, and there is a growing trend for patients and clients to take legal action against those who have acted in unprofessional or incompetent ways. However, we have not yet reached the situation in the USA where fear of litigation and 'ambulance chasers' often dictates the way health and social care is provided in practice.

The following section considers three broad areas of legal responsibility for health and social care workers: **duty of care, confidentiality** and **consent**.

Duty of care

In its broadest sense we can all be said to have a duty of care towards other members of society; it is a part of common law. In a judgement in 1932, Lord Atkin laid down this duty of care as it is owed by ordinary members of the public to each other:

Figure 5.5 The public are more willing to take legal action against unprofessional care workers

In law a person must take reasonable care to avoid acts or omissions which he can reasonably foresee as being likely to injure his neighbour [defined as] 'a person who is so closely and directly affected by one's act that one ought reasonably to have them in contemplation as being so affected when one is directing one's mind to the acts or omissions being called in question'.

Activity

List six situations in which you would expect others to exercise a duty of care towards you.

Health and social care workers also have a statutory duty of care to their clients and patients, as do their employers, as well as a duty of care to colleagues, relatives and visitors, albeit to a lesser extent. Similarly, nurses may not refuse to care for patients, nor social workers to assist clients, except in very rare circumstances. For example, both the Royal College of Nursing (RCN) and the General Medical Council (GMC) have made it clear that failure to care for patients with HIV/Aids constitutes a disciplinary offence. For nurses, midwives and health visitors, the professional behaviour expected of them is laid out in the United Kingdom Central Council Code of Professional Conduct. For social workers, the Central Council for Education and Training in Social Work and the British Association of Social Workers publish codes of conduct. The law does not accept that when a nurse or doctor is off duty they no longer have a duty of care, or that such a duty of care extends no further than that of a lay person. Indeed, if a nurse goes to assist someone in the street involved in an accident when they are off duty, they could be sued for **negligence** if harm results from a failure to provide the standard of care expected of a nurse.

Negligence

Negligence means carelessness, and is one of the most important torts. Negligence occurs where there is harm resulting from a failure in the duty of care, and can be the consequence of an act or an omission. It is through the concept of negligence that the relationship between professional accountability and the duty of care becomes clear. The legal definition of negligence was laid down in a judgement of 1891: 'Negligence is the omission to do something which a reasonable man, guided upon these considerations which ordinarily regulate the conduct of human affairs, would do, or to do something which a prudent and reasonable man would not do.' In order to prove negligence, there must be evidence that:

1 The defendant owed the plaintiff a legal duty of care.

2 There has been a breach of the standard of care.

3 Harm was suffered as a result of negligence (consequential damage occurred).

    1. **Duty of care.** We have already seen that 'duty of care' can be widely interpreted, and certainly in the case of a social worker and their clients, or a nurse and their patients, such a duty is owed.

2. **Breach of the standard of care.** Negligence can only be claimed where it can be shown that the individual concerned failed to provide the standard of care that is consistent with the duty of care in that occupation. In the case of nursing, the UKCC's code of practice would provide a guide. The standard of care used as a measure will change over time as guidelines and professional expectations change (for example, guidelines for the nursing of sick children were revised by the RCN after the Allitt Inquiry, when Nurse Beverley Allitt was found guilty of murdering four children in her care). For a claim of negligence to be brought by an employer (under the law of contract) or by a professional body, only the first two elements need to be proved. However, for a patient or client to sue for negligence, the third criterion, consequential damage, must also be fulfilled.

3. **Proof of consequential damage.** The burden of proof lies with the plaintiff (the person who brings the complaint) to show that the harm they have suffered is a *consequence* of the negligent act. The formal legal rule is that the plaintiff must prove negligence on the balance of probabilities – that is, that negligence is the most likely explanation for the harm caused. In a criminal court, the proof must be of a higher standard: it must indicate guilt *beyond reasonable doubt*. It might be that there are no witnesses to the scalding of a patient in the bath, but if negligence by a nurse is the most likely explanation, the case may be successful.

The following case study illustrates these three points concerning proof of negligence.

Case study

Coundett v Northampton Health Authority (1985)

A woman was admitted to hospital having taken an overdose. Her stomach was pumped and she was transferred to a mental-illness ward where she was diagnosed as depressive. She experienced delusions about Christ, snakes and fire. The registrar gave instructions that she was to continue to be nursed on that ward but that constant supervision was not necessary. Some days later, at the end of a visit, her husband handed the charge nurse a box of matches that his wife had said she intended to use on herself. The charge nurse did not record this in the patient's case notes. A few days later the patient went into the toilets with another box of matches and set fire to her skirt.

The trial judge in the case ruled that both the doctor and the nurse owed a duty of care. In the case of the doctor, the standard of care had not been breached, but in the case of the nurse this standard had been breached because any reasonably competent nurse would have recorded the incident with the matches.

The plaintiff in a negligence case does not have to show that the negligent act was wholly to blame. If, for example, the offender is felt to have at least contributed towards the harm suffered, the case will then be one of **contributory negligence**, and any compensation awarded will be accordingly reduced.

It is important to note that claims for negligence may be successful in cases not where actions have been omitted but simply where they have not been recorded. In one such case, a staff nurse was officially disciplined for failing to record the outcome of half-hourly post-operative observations. For nurses, midwives and health visitors, the importance of good record-keeping is made explicit in the UKCC guidelines, which state that:

> The important activity of making and keeping records is an essential and integral part of care and not a distraction from its provision. There is, however, substantial evidence to indicate that inadequate and inappropriate record keeping concerning the care of patients and clients *neglects* their interests through:

- impairing continuity of care;
- introducing discontinuity of communication between staff;
- creating the risk of medication or other treatment being duplicated or omitted;
- failing to focus attention on early signs of deviation from the norm and;
- failing to place on record significant observations and conclusions.

Degrees of negligence

The law says that all those who are (even indirectly) responsible for providing care can be found negligent, should harm result. However, there will be degrees of culpability. This means, for example, that although a student nurse may be found to have given inappropriate care, her staff nurse or charge nurse may be found negligent by delegation. Having said that, learner nurses do have a clear responsibility to ask for help: 'Acknowledge any limitations in your knowledge and competence and decline any duties or responsibilities unless able to perform them in a safe and skilled manner' (UKCC 1992). Primary nurses (who have a greater degree of autonomy in the exercise of their duties) will consequently be required to accept a greater degree of accountability than those who work as part of a team. Similarly, the health authority or trust may itself be deemed negligent by **vicarious liability**. This means that in law the employer is held accountable for the torts of their employees and can be punished on their behalf. This was made clear in the following case, Roe and Woolly (1954):

> Hospital authorities are responsible for the whole of their staff, not only nurses and doctors, but also for anaesthetists and surgeons. It does not matter whether they are permanent or temporary, resident or visiting, whole time or part time. The reason is because … they are the agents of the hospital to give the treatment.

Confidentiality

The legal obligation to maintain confidentiality applies to everything that is not public knowledge. A simple test to determine whether you must maintain confidentiality is to ask yourself the following two questions:

1 Do I only know this information because of my professional role?

2 Does my client/patient trust me to keep this information secret?

If the answer to both questions is 'yes', then you have a duty to maintain confidentiality. Breaching confidence could lead to legal action by a patient or client only in those cases where it contributes to a negligent breach of duty, but it could easily provide grounds for official disciplinary action or even dismissal on the part of a professional body or employer. For example:

- A nurse was found guilty of professional misconduct by the UKCC Professional Conduct Committee for allowing her sister to read patient case notes.
- A doctor was held negligent, in law, for revealing to his patient that her husband thought she was 'paranoid'. The husband had discussed his fears in confidence with the doctor and had expressly not told his wife because he feared it might jeopardise their marriage.

Breach-of-confidence defences

Sometimes in law, (if not always morally), it will be possible, or indeed necessary, to breach the confidence of a patient or client, for example, in the following situations:

- Where the information concerned is in the public domain and is common knowledge, there is no duty to maintain confidence.
- Where the patient or client consents – clearly if a practitioner does have to violate a confidence, it is always better to gain the patient's or client's consent first.
- Where it is in the interest of the subject – it is permissible to breach confidentiality where the interests of the individual are at risk in terms of their health or well-being.

But even so, only the minimum information necessary should be disclosed:

- Where the law requires or permits disclosure. There are legal requirements for the disclosure of certain information such as:
  - information that may identify those involved in motor accidents must be passed on to the police;
  - all gunshot wounds must be reported to the police;
  - all notifiable diseases must be reported (the Public Health Act 1984 and Public Health Regulations 1988);
  - court orders to disclose information: the police may seek a court order forcing health or social care workers to disclose confidential information.
- Where the public interest outweighs the obligation to secrecy: this may include cases where there are serious threats to others (including staff) or where there is a knowledge of child abuse, drug trafficking or other criminal, offence.
- In the case of the disclosure of HIV/Aids infection to a partner: 'There are grounds for such a disclosure to spouse or sexual partner, only where there is a serious and identifiable risk to a specific individual, who, if not informed, would be exposed to infection.' (General Medical Council 1989)

Consent

Consent may be defined as the granting to someone the permission to do something he would not have the right to do without such permission. There is a legal requirement to receive consent from a patient or client before attempting any invasive procedure, including surgery. A key defence in the law of tort against negligence is *volenti non fit injuria* (no legal wrong can be committed against a consenting person). Therefore, if consent is obtained, a tort has not been committed.

In health and social care practice, types of consent include:

- implied;
- informed;
- voluntary;
- competent.

1 Implied consent. When a patient visits a doctor or dentist it is assumed (implicit) that confidential information can be shared and physical examinations carried out without formally asking for consent. Consent to treatment may also be *inferred*.

Examples are as follows:

- A patient in the community allows a district nurse into her home. In such a case, where the nurse may need to dress bedsores, there is clearly no further need for formal consent, although the intimacy of contact will necessitate sensitivity on the part of the nurse.
- In a hospital situation it will be respectful to seek oral permission to undertake an enema or pubic shave, for example, but where the patient rolls over in anticipation of a pre-med injection it is safe to say that consent can be *inferred*.

However, hospitals usually require express **written consent** for procedures or treatments that involve some marked risk to the patient. In such cases, a **consent form** must give details of the operation in question. In a number of cases, patients have sued where a surgeon has undertaken a different or more serious operation than that to which consent was formally given. Where the surgeon suspects that they may need to undertake more radical surgery, this must be made clear when the consent form is signed. The patient retains the right to refuse further treatment or to change their mind at all times.

2 Informed consent. The patient must always be given sufficient information to enable them to make a fully-informed decision. Such information will usually be given in broad terms, and those risks and side-effects that are reasonably probable will be highlighted. A number of factors will determine the amount of information provided, including the extent to which the patient wishes to be informed and the likely effect of such information on them. Many questions have been raised about this aspect of consent, for example, is it possible for a 'lay' person to be fully informed and how much information should be provided?

3 Voluntary consent. The patient consents of his or her own free will and is not pressured to agree. Difficulties arise when a patient is too vulnerable to refuse, for example, if a patient knows she has a terminal illness she might agree to any aspect of research or treatment as she is in a vulnerable state.

4 Capacity to consent. Wherever an individual has the ability or capacity to understand the information given to them, and are deemed to be able to make a rational decision, no one else may give or withhold consent on their behalf. Where there is opposition to treatment from relatives, for example, on religious grounds, the courts are unlikely to be sympathetic and frequently side with clinical advice. In cases where a spouse is opposed to a course of action on the part of their husband or wife, the courts take the view that this can have no bearing on a decision even in cases of the termination of pregnancy or sterilisation. In other cases, consent may be given, or withheld, on the individual's behalf by someone else. This is known as **consent by proxy**. In this context, difficulties arise with consent from children, adults with learning disabilities or mental illness and unconscious patients (see below).

Activity

Obtain a copy of a hospital consent form. Redesign it so that safeguards are built in to prevent patients giving consent to treatment without a full appreciation of the consequences.

Consent: children (minors)

In the case of young children, consent must be sought from parents or guardians. However, where parents refuse treatment for their children, this is often overruled, because counterbalancing the parents' or guardians' legal custody and control of their children is their **duty of care** to their offspring, which requires them to provide necessary medical attention. In some cases the health authority will itself obtain a **care and protection order** to enable it to exercise parental authority, or the child can be made a **ward of court**. In other cases parents or guardians have themselves sought wardship.

Case study

Jeannette, a 17-year-old with a learning disability, was made a ward of court because her parents wanted her to be sterilised but they did not have the legal power to give permission for this. Wardship was granted and permission for sterilisation was given by the court (Carson and Montgomery 1989).

In the case of 16- and 17-year-olds, the law seems a rather grey area. Although young people of this age can give consent themselves, where doctors break the confidence of their young patients they appear to incur no legal penalties. However, in a case in 1986 (Gillick v West Norfolk and Wisbech Area Health Authority), it was established that 15-year-old girls may be prescribed contraception by a doctor without their parents being informed. This was a very important judgement in terms of the age at which minors may consent to treatment without the agreement or knowledge of their parents, and in a number of subsequent cases courts have taken into account the maturity of individuals rather than strict chronological age.

Consent: adults with learning disabilities and mental illness

For some adults with severe learning disabilities, consent may be given on their behalf by a guardian or advocate. For adults with mental health problems, **consent by proxy** may also be necessary. However, it is important to note that this is not the same as treatment without consent, and because someone has a severe mental health problem it should not be assumed that they are unable to give consent. For example, in 1994 Mr Justice Thorpe upheld the right of a 68-year-old man with **paranoid schizophrenia** to refuse to give permission for the amputation of his foot which had developed gangrene. The judge held that the operation could not be performed without the express written consent of the patient. In his ruling the judge suggested a test for capacity to give consent:

- Does the patient comprehend the information given to them? Do they believe it?
- Have they weighed up needs and risks before reaching their decision?

If the answer in each case is 'yes', the patient is deemed capable of giving and withholding consent.

Exceptions to the need to gain consent

The Mental Health Act (1983) allows for people to be admitted to hospital, or held in hospital, and treated against their will where they are deemed to be suffering from a mental disorder. Different sections of the Act make provisions for the detection of different groups, which is why compulsory admission to mental hospital is known as 'being sectioned':

- In most cases (for example, under Section 2) a person can be admitted to hospital for assessment for up to 28 days. This can then be extended. The application is made by an approved social worker or nearest relative and supported by two doctors.
- Under Section 5(4) of the Act, recognise nurses have the power to detain patients for up to six hours.
- Section 7 of the Act also allows for people to be taken under the protection of approved guardians in the community. The guardian must be acceptable to the local social services department. This part of the Act requires the sectioned individual to:
  - live at a certain place;
  - attend for treatment, occupation, education or training;
  - allow access to a doctor.

The Mental Health (Patients in the Community) Act 1995 allows those responsible for the care of mentally-ill people to take and convey patients to a hospital against their will.

Alliance to fight mental health plans

Proposals to extend compulsory treatment of mentally-ill people could increase violence and damage race relations, a group of charities is warning.

Fifteen leading mental health, carers, nursing, legal and disability groups have formed an alliance to counter moves to introduce **compulsory treatment orders** (CTOs). A government review recommended the imposition of CTOs for people who are deemed at high risk of endangering themselves or the public. This would mean if they failed to take their medication while in the community, they could be returned to hospital. The review follows concerns about a number of killings by community care patients, some of which were due to the patients failing to take their medication.

Some mental health groups, such as SANE, believe the public needs more protection, although they also have concerns about CTOs.

The alliance, which includes Mind, the Carers National Association and the Mental Health Foundation, say they have 'serious reservations about whether compulsory treatment in the community, and the way in which it will be implemented, will deliver the benefits alleged'.

Mind says its research shows the importance of non-compliance with medication in killings by community care patients has been overstated and other factors, such as lack of support for patients, are more important.

The alliance believes few community care patients are a risk to the public. It is concerned CTOs might deter people from accessing services which could lead to a deterioration in their condition, increasing the risk of violence. It believes legislation should reduce the emphasis on compulsion in mental health treatment, ensuring it is used as a last resort, and ensuring patients have more rights rather than less. Groups are also concerned about the focus on medication, rather than support, and about how the CTOs will be enforced. In addition, they want assurances they will not be used in a racist way, given research showing black people are more likely to be detained in hospital and less likely to receive alternatives to medication than whites.

From BBC News online 9 November, 1999

Activity

1 What has prompted the proposals to introduce compulsory treatment orders and who will be subject to them?

2 What objections does the alliance have to the introduction of compulsory treatment orders?

3 Do you think the objections by the alliance are well founded?

Failure to gain consent

Where practitioners fail to gain consent for a procedure, or where a patient's or client's wishes are overridden, the individual may sue under the tort of **trespass**.

Trespass can be committed against a person, goods or land, for example a social worker may leave him or herself open to the charge of trespass to *property*, perhaps, through letting themselves into a client's home with a key which they have been given. Nurses are more likely to be concerned with the law of trespass against the *person*, which is also known as **assault** and **battery**.

Assault is an attempt or threat to apply unlawful force to another person, whereby that other person is put in fear of immediate violence or at least bodily contact. Words alone do not constitute assault, although they may form a part of another illegal act such as that of threatening behaviour.

Battery is the actual application of force to the person of another against their will.

There are, of course, many situations in which a nurse or doctor is involved in actions which, if undertaken by anyone else, may be deemed to constitute assault or battery (or both) but in the vast majority of cases they will have adequate defence.

Activity

You are a social worker, and a client who is not very mobile offers you the key to his flat so that you may let yourself in when you visit. What do you do and why?

Public health legislation

The Public Health (Control of Disease) Act 1984 and the Public Health (Infection) Regulations 1988 allow action to be taken without consent, in the interests of public health, where individuals are suffering from **notifiable diseases**. These include tetanus, leprosy, anthrax and measles. Anyone suffering from these illnesses must be reported to the local authority.

The liberty of such individuals is restricted by the criminal offences of either knowingly passing on the disease or exposing others to the risk. People with notifiable diseases are forbidden to use public libraries or public transport. Furthermore, a magistrate can order:

- compulsory testing;
- forcible removal to hospital;
- detainment in hospital.

However, there is no right under statute to treat people against their will (except in the case of mental illness). HIV is *not* notifiable (despite calls to make it so) but certain provisions of the Public Health Act do apply to Aids so that, with the approval of a magistrate, compulsory testing is possible, as is removal to, and detention in, hospital.

Activity

Public health legislation violates a number of important ethical principles. Identify these principles and suggest why, in the light of over-riding moral principles, this may be acceptable.

In some states in the USA, pregnant women who are known to be drug addicts face imprisonment and the possible loss of their babies if they refuse to attend detoxification centres. The women's behaviour is treated as deliberate intention to cause harm to, or as gross negligence towards, another person (in this case, the foetus is granted personhood).

Activity

Is this treatment morally justified? Explain your answer and identify any morally significant differences between the treatment of these women and the measures outlined in UK public health legislation.

National Assistance Act (1948)

Section 47 of this Act aims to secure:

> the necessary care and attention for people who:
> a) are suffering from grave chronic disease, or, being aged, infirm or physically incapacitated, are living in insanitary conditions; and
> b) are unable to devote to themselves, and are not receiving from other persons, proper care and attention.

In such cases, with the certification of a GP and the agreement of a magistrate, the individual concerned may be removed from their home to hospital, local authority or private residential accommodation (to the cost of which the individual would have to contribute).

Although use of this Act is not uncommon, cases of people compulsorily removed from their homes are not widely publicised.

Rehabilitation of Offenders Act (1974)

The basic function of this Act is to allow people who have been sentenced to imprisonment of not more than two-and-a-half years, or who have received some lesser sentence, to disregard their convictions after a period of time if they have not been re-convicted. Their conviction is then said to be 'spent', and they are under no general obligation to disclose it.

Furthermore, the Act makes it an offence for social workers and others to reveal any information other than that which is required for the conduct of 'official duties'. However, there are some circumstances in which **confidentiality** can be breached. These include cases of:

- disclosure to local authorities accessing the suitability of a person to have the care of children and young persons;
- criminal proceedings;
- reports compiled for courts for proceedings involving the adoption, guardianship or wardship of children.

Probation officers have a particular responsibility to present any avoidable risk to the life and well-being of children. In this case, those who have responsibility for clients who have abused children are required to disclose to potential employers or others any facts about offences, personality or character that may affect the offender's suitability for a specific job. Probation officers in prisons are also required to notify local social services departments of the release from custody of those who have offended against children in the family.

Access to information

Closely linked to the issues of consent and confidentiality is the right of access to information, which is enshrined in both statutory provisions and official guidelines and which stresses the importance of openness and access to information for patients and clients. These include:

- The Access to Medical Reports Act (1988);
- The Access to Health Records Act (1990);
- The Patients' Charter.

However, there is much evidence to suggest that, frequently, health and social care professionals fail to provide sufficient information.

A study reported in the *British Medical Journal* (23 February, 2001) asked 824 patients in the waiting room of three doctors' surgeries to complete a pre-consultation questionnaire about what they wanted the doctor to do in the consultation. Three areas of patient preferences were identified: "communication", including listening to the patient and exploring their concerns; "partnership", including discussion and a consensus about treatment options; and "health promotion", including how to stay healthy and reduce the risks of future illness.

A majority of people (85 per cent) in the study said that they wanted the doctor to be interested in what they, as the patient, thought was wrong with them. Even more people said they wanted to be given advice on how to reduce the risk of future illness. Only 25 per cent said they wanted a prescription.

Figure 5.6 Good communication improves patients' health and well-being

Bad communication hurts cancer patients

Doctors who fail to communicate effectively with cancer patients are damaging the physical and emotional well being of both patients and themselves, according to research. A survey by the Cancer Research Campaign found widespread flaws in the way doctors talk to cancer patients about their diagnosis and treatment. When speaking to patients, doctors held back information which they thought would cause distress. But the report shows that this lack of openness fuels patients' anxiety about the seriousness of their disease.

Poor communication is also having a negative effect on doctors and nurses. The researchers found that inadequate training in communication and management skills is a major factor contributing to their stress and lack of job satisfaction. The report also showed that doctors need not only good communication skills, but also a personal awareness of the barriers to effective communication. The environment in which doctors talk to cancer patients was cited as another major problem. Interruptions by people entering the room and the telephone ringing during consultations were common.

The paper also revealed that doctors are failing to find out how much cancer patients know about their disease and expectations of treatment before consultations. As a consequence, doctors are rarely fully understood by patients. Hospital patients only manage to remember just over 50% of the information they receive from doctors about their diagnosis and treatment.

But this figure drops to only 25% in cancer patients, as information of a distressing nature raises patients' anxiety levels and reduces their ability to remember detail. Few doctors and nurses receive adequate communication training, often to the detriment of patients. The report underlines the urgent need to introduce a system which ensures all our cancer specialists get an adequate level of training in this area, otherwise our patients will continue to lose out.

Adapted from BBC News 23 December, 1999

Activity

1 Why is good communication so important to patients?

2 What barriers to communication are mentioned in the article?

3 A general rule of health and social care practice is that the right of access to information must not over-ride the right of others to privacy and confidentiality. How far would you agree with this?

Applying ethical and legal principles to care work

Legal and ethical justification

Central to the resolution of problems in health and social care is the ability to reach ethically and legally justifiable decisions – that is, to be able to identify the relevant legal requirements of the situation and to demonstrate sound ethical reasoning. This means that:

- the principles governing your decisions are clearly stated;
- that you have fully taken into account possible alternative views and courses of action;
- that you demonstrate consistency; that is, in similar cases you apply the same principles and standards of judgement – it is not acceptable to arrive at different conclusions in similar situations, out of prejudice, personal dislike or sloppy thinking.

The following section provides the opportunity to apply and test your knowledge of ethical and legal issues, and to reach justifiable conclusions in typical care work situations. Frequently this might be difficult, and you will need to strike a balance between competing and perhaps conflicting obligations and duties. You might find it useful to use role play in some of these examples.

Case studies in health care

1 Sarah Cohen

Sarah Cohen is 45. She is a teacher, and has two young children. She was admitted to a surgical ward, where you are the charge nurse, to undergo a biopsy, which has confirmed that she has breast cancer. However, her prognosis is good because the growth has been detected early. You have built up a good rapport with her, and she seems convinced that with a mastectomy followed by radiotherapy she will have a good chance of survival. She signs an operation consent form. However, on the evening of the following day, as you are leaving after a late shift, you see Sarah getting dressed and she tells you that, after talking it over with her partner, she has decided that she does not want to go ahead with the treatment.

Questions

a Can you legally prevent Sarah from leaving the ward?

b What moral principles are at issue in this case?

c If you were a consequentialist, what would you do and why?

2 Brian Mitchell

You are a staff nurse on a psychiatric ward and have just admitted Brian Mitchell who is 35 and has a long-term history of schizophrenia. On this occasion he has been admitted to the hospital as a voluntary patient. Over the next 24 hours he becomes increasingly aggressive and disturbed. In the past, Brian's episodes of aggression have only been verbal and have always been short-lived. However, on this occasion he grabs a nurse around the throat and threatens to strangle her.

Questions

a What action can legally be taken by you at this stage?

b What action are medical staff likely to take later?

c What moral principles come into conflict in this case?

3 Gail White

You are a community psychiatric nurse caring for Gail White, who is 25, and has recently been released from psychiatric hospital after six weeks as a patient 'under section'. Her mother who is caring for her has become increasingly worried about Gail's delusional state, and believes that she is no longer taking her medication. She asks you to ensure that Gail takes her medication by supervising this activity yourself.

Questions

a Will you accede to this request?

b What ethical and legal rights does Gail have in this situation?

4 Seema Ahmed

Seema Ahmed has been admitted to hospital and has signed a consent form for surgery on a malignant tumour that has been found in her colon. As a staff nurse on the ward you are preparing Seema for surgery and you remark that she seems very composed. She tells you that she knows there is nothing to worry about – the doctor has told her she has a 'blockage'. It is clear that she does not understand the extent of her condition.

Questions

a Do you continue preparing Seema for surgery? If not, why not?

b What legal and ethical factors can be identified in this case?

5 Joseph Mbuti

You are a district nurse caring for Joseph Mbuti who is 76. His twin sister visits him every day but she is unable to undertake a major caring role. Mr Mbuti believes that he will recover from his illness but his sister has told you in confidence that Joseph has inoperable liver cancer. One day Joseph asks you directly what you know of his condition.

Question

What action would you take, and what ethical principles would you weigh up in reaching your decision?

6 Simon Stevens

Simon Stevens, aged 30, is admitted to Accident and Emergency after a road accident. As the admitting nurse, you find a card in his wallet which says that for religious reasons he cannot accept a blood transfusion. You know that without a transfusion he will die, so you decide to destroy the card.

Questions

a Could you ethically justify your action?

b What legal action could Mr Stevens take if he recovers?

7 Baby M

You are a paediatric nurse who has taken a special interest in the case of Baby M. She was born three months prematurely with severe congenital abnormalities. On the advice of the paediatrician, Baby M's parents gave permission for her to undergo two major operations. Both have been unsuccessful and without a third attempt it is certain that the baby will die. The past three months have been very painful and distressing for both the parents and the nursing staff. Baby M's mother now feels that all therapeutic treatment should be withdrawn and nature be left to take its course (palliative care will not be withdrawn). However, the baby's father and the consultant are convinced that a further operation must be attempted.

Questions

What are the ethical and legal principles at stake in this case? What advice would you give to the parents?

Case studies in social care

1 Elderly woman

The 80-year-old woman is a chronic shoplifter. Her targets are some of London's best-known stores and on one occasion she was found with more than £1000 of goods. Her shoplifting does not appear to be for personal gain. She is known to give the goods away on the journey home to Hackney, probably in an attempt to win friends. As a result she has been mugged several times.

Police are concerned about her, while security staff in department stores have been given her photograph and told to stop her entering. In one month Hackney social services had two referrals from Marylebone Police after her arrest.

The flat where she lives alone is in a poor state and food was found that was months past its sell-by date. She turns down offers of home care and meals-on-wheels, and refuses access to the district nurse. She talks of suicide and loneliness, and is depressed about the death of her husband and sister, but she refuses bereavement counselling.

A case conference is held and she agrees to allow access to health and social services. At a second conference Part III residential care is pursued and a place is found. She agrees but then changes her mind.

A third emergency case conference is held after she is arrested again and the Crown Prosecution Service decides to take action. Conference decides, reluctantly, to seek a Guardianship Order, under which she would be directed to move into residential care, although the application is postponed while alternative action is taken. Once more she agrees voluntarily to go into a residential home but again changes her mind.

She is now being offered Part III accommodation again but if she refuses or fails to stay there, a Guardianship Order will be sought (under the Mental Health Act 1983), initially for three months.

(Part III accommodation refers to the Housing Act 1985 (Part III) which places a duty on local authorities to house certain categories of people.)

Arguments against seeking a Guardianship Order

- Her wish to stay in her own home counsels against seeking a Guardianship Order. She is a very independent woman who has declined most forms of help, both physical and financial.
- Concern that moral judgements on her shoplifting activities should not influence decisions about her care. Social workers have been at pains to avoid being judgemental despite some pressure from other agencies to do something.
- Her rejection of Part III accommodation on two occasions has underlined her desire to remain in her own home, even to the point of barring visitors.
- A hope that she may be persuaded to see what was needed voluntarily and co-operate without the need to resort to further action.
- Concern that a Guardianship Order and Part III accommodation would mean the end of independent living for her.

Arguments in favour of seeking a Guardianship Order

- The safety and long-term needs of the woman are of paramount importance, particularly in view of her lifestyle.

- History of depression, loneliness, self-neglect, threatened suicide and the deterioration in her ability to look after herself were an issue of concern to social workers.

- Her feelings of loneliness may be helped by a residential setting with the availability of companionship.

- As she has been mugged several times, there are increasing fears for her physical safety in Hackney, particularly after dark. She is known to carry money with her.

- Concern about the effect on her life of the continued shoplifting and the likelihood the police will pursue a prosecution against her.

- Her rejection of home care support and of statutory financial aid.

- Some evidence of a decline in mental health has also been recorded with the possibility of early signs of dementia.

 Activity

> **1** In your own words, identify the arguments for and against seeking a Guardianship Order.
>
> **2** Explain what action you would take and why.
>
> **3** What other Acts can be used to remove elderly people from their homes in their own interest?

2 Sunnybank

You have recently accepted a post as a care worker at Sunnybank residential home. Your contract of employment prohibits disclosure to a third party of any information concerning the business. There is a clear-cut internal procedure which you must follow should you wish to raise a grievance.

It soon becomes clear to you that the home is severely short-staffed and that the safety of residents is at risk. You raise the problem with the manager of the care home, but nothing is done about it.

Question

What do you do next and why?

3 Mary and Kevin

Mary is 16 and has just given birth to a premature baby daughter, Sharon. Mary did not know that she was pregnant and does not want to keep her baby. As her social worker, you have talked to Mary and have explained to her that there is support available to her whatever she decides. You ask about the father of the baby, Kevin. At first, Mary says she does not want him to know, but you encourage them to meet and to talk about the baby before making a final decision about whether to keep the baby or put her up for adoption. After seeing Kevin, Mary tells you that she has changed her mind. Kevin has told her he would love to be a 'proper' father and he wants the three of them to settle down as a family.

However, it soon becomes apparent that Kevin is well known to the local social services department. He has a previous conviction for aggravated assault during a burglary, and he has received a caution for possession of drugs (cannabis).

Questions

1 Do you reveal to Mary what you know about Kevin's past?
2 Can you justify your decision ethically and legally?

4 Suzanne

You are the tutor of Suzanne, who is 17 and has a moderate learning disability. Her parents, and in particular her mother, have found caring for Suzanne very demanding, and they have received very little support. It is likely that Suzanne will live at home for much of the rest of her life. She attended a special school from the age of five, which her mother took her to and collected her from every day for 12 years. Suzanne made some female friends at school but had no social life and has never had a boyfriend. However, she recently started a pre-vocational life-skills course at the local further education college. She enjoys the freedom of college very much and has now found a boyfriend, Simon.

Suzanne's mother has found out that Suzanne and Simon have started a sexual relationship, and she is very angry and upset. She feels that it is wrong for Suzanne to have sex because she believes that Suzanne is not sexually mature (in fact she believes that Suzanne will never be able to have a 'proper' sexual relationship) and, furthermore, that she has been taken advantage of. She also feels that the college has failed to adequately supervise her daughter by allowing this to happen. At a meeting between Suzanne, her mother and you, her tutor, Suzanne's mother threatens to withdraw Suzanne from college. For her part, Suzanne says she loves Simon and wants to stay at college.

Questions

1 What is your response?
2 What suggestions can you make to resolve this conflict whilst recognising and respecting the autonomy and rights of all the people involved?

5 John and June

You work in a residential home for young people with learning difficulties. All of the residents are encouraged to celebrate birthdays and the staff use these occasions as an opportunity to reinforce life skills such as decision-making, shopping, sharing, etc. John will be 17 next week and is eagerly awaiting his party. However, for the past few weeks he has been very disruptive and the usual sanctions the staff use have failed to encourage him to co-operate. As on previous occasions, you threaten not to let him have a birthday party, but on the day itself you relent. Some weeks later another resident, June, is equally disruptive and unco-operative at the time of her birthday. On this occasion you decide that you must exercise your authority, so you refuse to give in and her party is cancelled.

Questions

1 Why is this not a consistent or justifiable decision?

2 What are the likely consequences of your action?

6 Benjamin

Benjamin is a widower of 76. He has recently come to the attention of social services because a neighbour reported that he was looking increasingly dishevelled. You are a social worker and you visit him. He has six cats and his house is very dirty. He cannot manage to wash his clothes very well and he eats mostly from tins. He is rather forgetful and he tells you that on one occasion he left the cooker on all night.

Activity

In pairs, each write down an approach to this client: one will stress autonomy, the other paternalism. Which will bring about the best outcome for the client?

7 Joshua

You are a registered nurse who manages a day centre for young people with learning disabilities. You have about 16 members who attend regularly. They benefit from the activities provided and a number have developed useful work-related skills. One, John, recently left and has just started working for Remploy, a sheltered workshop. However, another member, Joshua, is very disruptive and unco-operative, and you have asked that his parents find an alternative placement for him. They plead with you; they need the respite provided and know of no alternative. You have sympathy for them but are also concerned for the other members of the day centre, a number of whom are very troubled by Joshua's behaviour. Joshua's mother suggests that she sedate him before bringing him to the centre until he gets over his 'difficult period'.

Questions

1 Whose needs are important in this case? Do those of the majority outweigh the needs of Joshua or those of his family?

2 What will you do and why?

8 Child protection

You are a social worker involved in child protection. As part of her training, a student social worker must analyse a number of studies and consider alternative approaches to them. She asks you to suggest two explanations for each of the following:

1 A 12-year-old girl from an ethnic minority family writes in an essay that she sleeps in the same bed as her father.

2 A three-year-old child clings to her health visitor during a home visit. She wants to be held and is reluctant to return to her stepmother.

3 A six-week-old baby of middle-class parents, the third child after a gap of six years, has not regained his baby weight. His mother insists he is content and feeds well.

4 A girl aged six arrives in school with a bruise on the side of her face. She says she bumped into a table.

9 Violet Hayes

As a social worker you have been asked to assess the needs of Violet Hayes and put together a care package for her. Mrs Hayes is 83 and has been a widow for 20 years. For the past eight years she has been cared for full-time by her unmarried daughter, Margaret.

On your first visit you speak to Mrs Hayes alone. She says she is very happy living at home and does not wish even to visit a luncheon club, let alone go into residential accommodation. On leaving, you notice a bruise on Mrs Hayes's neck. On your next visit, you speak to Margaret and hear a very different story. She says she cannot cope with providing full-time care for her mother any more. She also claims that the only reason her mother refuses to visit a day centre is that she wants to maintain constant control over her (i.e. Margaret). At this point you ask about the bruise on Mrs Hayes's neck, and Margaret breaks down and confesses that she and her mother regularly have physical fights. She tells you that if you do not ensure that her mother attends a day centre at least three times a week, she is frightened of the consequences.

Activity

Explain what you would do in this case and which ethical and legal principles seem most important to you.

Index

Further Studies for Social Care